DARK HORSE

John Bartlett

www.chequeredjustice.com
www.AmazingJourneys.co.uk

twitter @ChequeredJ

Amazing Journeys Publishing
Kent, England

Amazing Journeys Publishing England

First published in Great Britain in 2012 by
Amazing Journeys Ltd

Cover design by Avalon Graphics.
Cover artiste: Jonathan Bartlett

Printed, bound & typeset in Baskerville

A catalogue record for this book is available from The British Library

Hardback format ISBN 978-0-9569104-1-7
Paperback format ISBN 978-0-9569104-2-4
eBook format ISBN 978-0-9569104-3-1

An environmentally friendly book printed and bound in England
by www.printondemand-worldwide.com

Mixed Sources
Product group from well-managed
forests, and other controlled sources
www.fsc.org Cert no. TT-COC-002641
© 1996 Forest Stewardship Council
FSC

PEFC Certified
This product is
from sustainably
managed forests
and controlled
sources
PEFC
PEFC/16-33-415
www.pefc.org

This book is made entirely of chain-of-custody materials

To my wife Mary, my sons George and Jonathan.

Though much is taken, much abides; and though
We are not now that strength which in old days
Moved earth and heaven; that which we are, we are;
One equal temper of heroic hearts,
Made weak by time and fate, but strong in will
To strive, to seek, to find, and not to yield.

Alfred, Lord Tennyson (1809-1892)

Thank you

ONLY AFTER PUBLICATION did it become fully clear what I wanted to achieve with the release of *Chequered Justice*. Yes, I had wanted the truth to be known, albeit in the only guise "the system" would permit, but it was far more than that... Seeing *Chequered Justice* on the shelf at my local bookshop was like removing a massive weight from my shoulders – *at last my story was out there*. It had taken over a decade to produce and based on more than twenty years of my life. A story told with some trepidation – *How would friends react? – Would it sell? – Would anyone even turn up to the launch party? What about the papers? – What sort of spin would the holier-than-thou media attach to a story exposing the British justice system's darkest Masonic secrets?*

Fortunately, as it turned out, the media were at that precise moment preoccupied with a little phone hacking scandal of their own! Some friends, unaware of the past, were shocked and politely vanished; many more however were supportive. *Chequered Justice* went onto become a Number 1 best seller with more than ten reprints to date. In one week alone, more than six thousand copies were down loaded in eBook format!

Following the publication of my story, I think I'm a slightly different person... I can't say if I'm a better person, but I am working on that. And any improvement on that front could only be credited to my best friend, soul mate and wife of twenty eight years, Mary. It was only with her love, support and encouragement that *Chequered Justice* and *Dark Horse* saw the light of day.

I would like to thank sincerely all those that gave their time, help and support, test reading this prequel: My wife, Mary, whose first comment on reading my original dyslexic draft, was to paraphrase the late Eric Morecambe: *"Darling, you've got all the right words... but not necessarily all in the right place!"* And the subsequent test readers: Hilary Wilkes, Tim Vicary and Sue Rush, for providing further invaluable feedback. My other major thanks go to Dirk Schoysman, Andy Powell and Chris Taylor at Mithril Racing for reminding me of my correct race lines when the grey matter began fading. Also Henry Hope Frost at *AutoSport,* Chris Parsons and Mark Cole for digging into race archives, to find the obscure track detail necessary to recreate this twenty six years of "pure fiction"...

They can't chain my spirit!
My spirit runs free!
Walls can't contain it!
Laws can't restrain it!
Authority has no power over it!"

Wolfdyke Bill Watterson (American Author)

Author's Note

Officially the events portrayed in *Dark Horse* can never have happened, for the simple reason that it's a prequel to *Chequered Justice*. And if you've already read *Chequered Justice*, you'll know that I wasn't permitted to publish a full and factual account of the strange events that overtook our lives... *but I was allowed to write a novel or a fiction based on them.* So I wrote *Chequered Justice* as a novel, based purely on personal experience. Unfortunately, this locks any prequel into the same genre, and therefore *Dark Horse* is officially classified as fiction, more figments of my overactive imagination. So, before we begin, I'm therefore obliged to point out that what follows is a work of complete fiction: names, characters, race teams, race car manufacturers, places and incidents are *again* the product of my overactive imagination. Any resemblance to actual persons living or dead; events, races, race teams, race car manufacturers, and legal activities or locations are entirely coincidental. Please take this as fact. *I should know... I was there!*

Chequered Justice began with the profoundly dyslexic seven year old Will Middleton meeting his childhood hero, Graham Hill, deciding there and then that he too would become a famous racing driver. The story then jumped twenty-six years to the eighties, the time when a toxic cocktail was developing: our country controlled by political spin, strangled by corruption, sinking beneath a sea of debt, controlled by fear, a fear stoked by media. It was a point in time when our police were increasingly intertwined with dishonesty, bribery and sleaze, much of which would not be exposed for decades.

Inevitably, being a prequel to *Chequered Justice*, *Dark Horse* is a very different story, for the obvious reason that the events happened prior to the account in *Chequered Justice*.

In essence, *Dark Horse* is the story of the missing twenty-six years. It's a story of a boy growing up in 1960s boarding schools, profoundly dyslexic at a time when dyslexia was misunderstood. It's a story of single-minded determination, drive, naïvety and ambition. As with *Chequered Justice*, I'm allowed to say *Dark Horse* is *inspired by true events*, although others may speculate that it's an autobiographical account of events that were a part of my life... but as I conclude this prequel, recreating life back in the sixties, seventies and eighties, perhaps it's just as well *Dark Horse* is officially classified as fiction!

John Bartlett

Preface

Wednesday 19th January 1955

WILL MIDDLETON drew his first breath on a cold snow clad night in January 1955. Nazi Germany had surrendered less than ten years earlier, Great Britain was still heavily in debt and struggling with record unemployment, but to Will's mother life couldn't get any better. Outside, the winter snow had brought the country to a near standstill. Betty Middleton lay back peacefully in her hospital bed. Outside, gentle flakes of snow shimmered in the orange glow of the street lamps. Today just happened to be her forty-first birthday and the treasure she was cradling in her arms was the greatest gift she could have received; a son and heir...

Prologue

---

*A dark horse which had never been thought of, and which
the careless St. James had never even observed in the list,
rushed past the grandstand in sweeping triumph*

Benjamin Disraeli (The Young Duke)

O N THE WALL of the Main Hall, next to the glass display
cabinet filled with shiny cups and rugby trophies, hangs a
fading collection of prints portraying images of former
boys; all smartly dressed in school uniform; red and white ties, red
flannel blazers proudly displaying the school crest and motto
'altiora peto', *striving, always, to seek higher things*.

An inscription beneath each frame depicts the school year on
tarnished brass plaques. Each picture is formally posed, boys lined
up in tiers; the older, taller boys at the back in their long grey
flannels, the younger ones sitting cross-legged at the front in grey
shorts and grey woollen stockings. Arms crossed, eyes focused
directly ahead to a flag pole upon which flutters a Union Jack.
Each boy's hair has been carefully trimmed beneath peaked red
caps, each with the same crest just above the peak. In the centre
of each group, looking sternly ahead, sits the headmaster, Mr
Wickham.

You would have to look very closely to notice just one boy on
the front row of the 1962 picture who's ignoring the posed posture
of his peers. With a quizzical look on his face, Will Middleton
gazes intently into the lens of the camera as its clockwork
mechanism pans inexorably towards him. Will was just seven years

of age, profoundly dyslexic, destined to live out his school years at the back of the class, where he dared to dream...

CONTENTS

The 60s
Part 1 Schooldays

The 70s
Part 2 Adolescence,
Life, Love & Liberation

The 80s
Part 3 Legal Wrangles
& Races

Free-Fall! (sample)
Chequered Justice

1

"The only source of knowledge is experience"

Albert Einstein

London, England – 20ᵗʰ December 1985

Royal Courts of Justice Court 17 – Chancery Court
Devron Racing Cars Limited v William Middleton

THE ROOM WAS SILENT, everyone listening. Humphrey Fotheringham-Brown raised a quizzical brow as my learned barrister, the Honourable Sebastian Whitcomb, rose from his seat offering a small and congenial bow. He cleared his throat and adjusted his dark polyester gown. He was a slim man of thirty six years, clean-shaven, and despite years at the bar, still retained his boyish good looks. On his head he wore his trade mark 'peaked wig' of tight curls, stylishly crafted by Ede & Ravenscroft, giving him the intense look of an eagle. To his left sat the fuller figure of Percival Drummond, similarly attired but crested with a 'friz top' creation by the same outfitter.

My brief lifted his eyes to the bench, 'My Lord will appreciate,' he began smoothly, 'that my client is being prosecuted in-person by a corporation with limited liability'. He placed particular emphasis on the word limited, glancing momentarily in the direction of his opponent, the Honourable Percival Drummond, who was meticulously stroking his greying goatee whilst listening attentively. 'Prior to commencement of these proceedings,' my brief continued, 'litigation had been rumbling along for some six months. The first appearance before your Lordship was way back in June this year after my client was served with an injunction attempting to prevent him from running the Devron at Le Mans. I suspect costs will have already accumulated to some fifty thousand pounds or more and my esteemed colleague has only now provided us with his estimate of a further three days of evidence.'

Percival Drummond's complexion registered vacant contempt. It was true the time estimate had been requested some days back, but he was a busy man with far weightier matters of law requiring his attention. This case was merely a quarrel over an unimportant race car. My barrister continued, 'We shall of course then require a further two days ourselves to rebut the claim. Our concern is that in the event of a favourable outcome for my client, the plaintiff may simply prove to be insolvent and be unable to meet even its own costs, let alone any award this court may consider granting Mr Middleton, or indeed his legal costs.'

The Honourable Percival was already rising from his seat, exuding the natural bonhomie of a man having already billed some twelve thousand pounds for his last six days in court. His head was shaking in bewilderment, 'My Lord, may I reassure my learned colleague that in the extremely unlikely event of a favourable outcome for Mr Middleton, my clients are a well established racing team with an excellent reputation....'

'My understanding,' interrupted the judge impatiently, 'is that they only purchased the assets of the formerly bankrupt company very recently. The question is: do they have the wherewithal to stump up some hundred thousand pounds, if called upon to do so? That I believe is the nub of the matter, Mr Drummond!'

'This may assist my lord...' replied my noble brief helpfully, rising again from his bench, a cluster of papers held aloft in his right hand like a trophy. '...It's the plaintiff's first year accounts along with an in depth analysis commissioned by my client.' The usher, an attractive dark-haired lady in her early thirties stepped forward, relaying copies to both his Lordship and the prosecution. Sebastian Whitcomb paused for few moments allowing the appalling analysis to be absorbed. 'Based on this submission my lord, we would respectively request that the plaintiffs pay an agreed sum into court as security against costs, before proceedings continue further.'

Humphrey Fotheringham-Brown ran a quick eye over the analysis. Percival Drummond was clearly outraged; he indignantly flicked pages of figures. For him this was a tricky situation. Judging by the accounts, his client Devron already appeared insolvent, on the verge of collapse – should he encourage some sort of settlement and hopefully still collect his outstanding fees or push on, bill a further twelve grand and risk seeing the lot sink beneath an ocean of debt? It was clearly a decision to be taken at a later stage, over a very large glass of Dow's 77 Ruby. First however, the wretched submission must be opposed! He rose smiling, 'My lord, we strongly oppose my learned colleague's application for security against costs. Your lordship will be aware that such accounts, produced for tax purposes, may not necessarily convey... '

'Are you suggesting that these *audited* accounts are in some way inaccurate, Mr Drummond?' enquired his lordship impatiently, brows raised in disbelief.

'Most certainly not my lord...' replied the honourable Percival, somewhat flustered, his wig having listed slightly to the right since his last address, now looking set to part company with its owner. Giving a small swift bow of submission, he planted a steadying hand on the tenuous curls as he quickly lowered himself to his bench.

'In that case,' concluded his Lordship, 'if we are all in agreement that these accounts *do* accurately reflect the state of the plaintive company, I shall adjourn briefly.'

The court resumed following its short recess. Humphrey Fotheringham-Brown gazed down from his high bench. 'Having given careful consideration to the submission placed before this court,' he began, 'and following examination of the plaintiff's audited accounts for the 1984 tax year, I order that a sum of ten thousand pounds is to be paid into court prior to proceedings continuing further, as security against the defendants costs.'

There was a sudden shuffling of papers by the plaintiffs, accompanied by some urgent harsh murmuring. Robert Arnold, the managing director of Devron, a tall man with penetrating eyes, turned his head slowly in my direction. He gave a long hostile glare, eyes wide, thinning oily strands of hair slick against his scalp, which gleamed beneath the stark florescent lights. His expression resembled a cartoon character accidently stepping off a cliff, momentarily suspended in space, the realisation of its imminent demise dawning. I was tempted to give a little wave and a *Beep! Beep!* but resisted, and simply returned his gaze blankly.

His lordship studied his wristwatch and discovering the working day was at an end added, 'As we are approaching 3.30, I consider this may well be a convenient point to adjourn.' He paused, studying his diary, 'and with Christmas growing remorselessly closer, I would like to reconvene next year following the break on Wednesday the 9th January 1986, by which time the security must have been paid into court by the plaintiff.'

Drummond's assistant was waving a hastily scribbled note. 'If I could take just a brief moment my lord,' requested the honourable barrister. He leaned across and took the paper, quickly scanning its contents before whispering something to his colleague. Turning back to the judge he continued smoothly, 'My lord, before adjourning, the plaintiffs would request that the defendant surrender his filofax diary for examination over the holiday period.'

'Any particular reason for this application?' enquired the judge.

'Well, as your lordship is aware, we maintain Mr Middleton had always intended withdrawing the race car from my client's workshops, having no intention of allowing them to prepare and run it in the World Championship. We do not accept his argument that its removal was a last minute decision brought on by any alleged delay in completing the car's construction. We consider it highly likely that his diary therefore contains evidence to support our submission. That is, that meetings took place with another team, run by a certain Angus Maciver, well prior to any alleged delays, which may or may not have been caused by my client in relation to the car's completion.'

His lordship turned to my barrister, 'A fairly reasonable request Mr Whitcomb, wouldn't you agree? Does your client have any objection?'

Sebastian Whitcomb raised himself from his bench, 'My lord, if I may just confer with my client?'

I could feel my heart accelerating, 'Absolutely not,' I blurted. 'It's my *personal* diary, with all my *personal* stuff in it! They have no right to see it.' I could hear my voice was tight and rose in irritation but I no longer cared.

Sebastian turned his head to one side, silently questioningly – Why? *What's up?* – He gestured to me to relax. 'Okay, Will,' he said soothingly. Turning back to his lordship, 'My Lord, this does seem to be something of a fishing exercise,' he faltered slightly, his voice had a defensive edge. 'My client insists that his filofax is a private, personal document, containing private information which has no bearing on this case and therefore he objects...'

The judge raised a hand as though warding off further debate, 'But *I* do consider this to be a perfectly reasonable request, Mr Whitcomb,' he concluded matter-of-factly. 'Any personal references will be of no relevance and will I'm sure, be ignored.'

I looked over at Toby my solicitor, hoping for support but he just shook his head. 'You've got to hand it over, Will,' he said, glancing at my barrister. Something wordless passed between them. Dumbfounded, I opened my briefcase and took out my filofax. It was an expensive, heavily grained leather bound organizer, a gift from Beth, my wife, divided into sections for contacts, notes, calendar and diary itself. It contained the details of all my sponsors and business acquaintances, including some home phone numbers for directors of major corporations. I opened the jaws of the ring binder and carefully drew out the diary section, reluctantly handing it to my brief. He flicked a few pages before passing it to Percival Drummond.

Drummond forced a smile, quickly scanning the pages, 'We'd actually quite like the *full* document, my lord,' he said without lifting his eyes from the pages. 'That would include any note and contact sections and the calendar itself.' His lordship gestured in my direction.

I handed over the complete filofax. Robert Arnold couldn't suppress his delight, his eyes glittering with glee, like a hunter whose target had just been snared.

We left Court 17 and made our way down the stone central stairway to the main hall and out beneath the elaborately carved archway of eminent judges, into the thunder of London traffic. It was cold, the December snow drifting downward out of a colourless sky. I pulled the collar of my leather bomber jacket around my neck and headed into the street, the snow crunching beneath our feet.

Standing on the pavement I hailed a black cab, 'Victoria Station,' I said, stepping into the back with Toby.

At the station we boarded the 16:36 train to Ford in West Sussex. I sat gazing absent-mindedly out of the window as it pulled out and gathered speed. 'So, what do you think? Do you reckon they'll find ten grand and push on?' I finally asked.

Toby shrugged, 'It's a big gamble for them. They started this battle, you simply ordered the race car from them, and paid up front... that was a bit of a mistake, Will. You should never have paid them in advance, especially when the car hadn't even been built.'

'I trusted them and anyway, if they'd completed the damn thing on time, I wouldn't have needed to take it away to get it finished.' I replied ruefully.

'That's understandable with them having already missed the first races,' he sighed. 'The next one was the biggy wasn't it? The Le Mans 24 hours? If you hadn't got another team to finish it Will, you'd have missed that as well and been sued by your sponsors for breach of contract!'

'Yeah, tell me about it. Great choices – sued by my sponsors or sued by Devron! I don't need all this crap... it's not what I imagined when I set off down this path.' For a few moments neither of us spoke.

I looked up to find Toby's sharp blue eyes boring into me, 'Will, I have to ask you...' he hesitated. 'This *filofax*, is there anything detrimental in it?'

I shrugged, reluctant to talk about it.

He raised an eyebrow and continued more urgently, 'We need to know, Will. If there's anything in there, you should tell me so we can be prepared.'

I turned to face him. 'Toby!' I whispered. 'I can't spell!'

'*You can't spell?*' he repeated slowly, 'I don't quite follow...'

'I mean, I *really, really* can't spell' I continued sotto voce, glancing about the crowded carriage. 'And my handwriting's barely legible... it's like a kid's writing. Half the time I don't even join up letters. Toby, *nobody* knows, except for Beth and obviously my parents. I've always kept it secret... from everyone...' I let my words trail away in frustration.

Relief flickered across his face. 'Will, is that *all* you're concerned about?'

'*All*!' I blurted, 'Isn't it enough?' I hated the idea of showing any weakness.

'It's no big deal, Will. I have an eleven year old boy who's dyslexic... I do understand.'

'But I'm thirty, Toby! And a lot of people still *don't* understand. They think you're thick if you can't spell! Devron will tell everyone. If my backers find out... it could be the end of everything. Who'd want to work with me?'

'They work with you because they like you Will and trust you ...believe in you,' he retorted. 'This has obviously affected you deeply – but people *do* understand now.'

He was smiling, which I found vaguely irritating, 'It wasn't like that in my day,' I muttered. 'My school life was hell,' I said, almost shuddering as memories surfaced in my mind.

An attendant arrived, pushing a towering trolley of disposable cups, sandwiches and fossilizing sausage rolls. I ordered a couple of coffees and watched Toby stirring sugar into his. 'So, do you reckon they'll cave in and give up?' I asked.

Toby sipped his coffee, removed a cigarette from its pack and lit it. 'As there was never anything formally agreed with Devron about preparation or running the car in the world championship, I still feel our position is strong, and I actually think the judge likes you. The trouble is, nothing is ever certain Will. If it goes against you, you and your family could end up losing everything!' It was a typical lawyer's answer – no answer. I crumpled my empty paper cup and in the absence of a bin, consigned it to the floor amidst the rest of the day's abandoned trash.

The train slowed as we approached Croydon station, and for a moment I sat gazing out of the window thinking. *Why was my life such a battleground? Why was it that for as long as I could recall, I'd had to fight for everything? Why so many ups and downs when others appeared to sail blithely ahead without a cloud in their sky?*

'Just promise one thing, Will,' Toby added.

'What's that?' I asked.

'When this is all over, learn from the experience and for the future, put in place some protection for yourself and your family.'

'Like what?'

'You currently race and operate as a sole proprietor. Let me set you up as a limited company like Devron – *"Middleton Racing Limited"* – or something else – *"Worldwide racing ...* or *"Team something or other"* – whatever you like, and operate only through that company.'

'What's the point?'

'Well...it'll be more tax efficient for a start, but more importantly, it will give you and Beth some degree of protection, a sort of fence between your racing and your home life. This racing world seems brutal and litigious, a bunch of thieves, bullies and sharks, just waiting to take a bite out of you... I suspect you'd never have been sued if Devron didn't think you had personal money.'

'All I have is a big overdraft!'

'You also have a house and a racing team... ' He paused smiling. 'And a helicopter! That tends to give one an impression of wealth.'

'Toby, the helicopter didn't cost me a penny. In fact I made a grand getting it!'

'How...' Toby stopped mid question.

'It was a typically complicated racing type deal,' I said, 'but all perfectly straightforward.'

'Well, all I'm saying is you should consider a fallback plan to allow for anything happening in the future.'

'I'll think it over,' I said, turning back to the window.

'You should,' Toby replied firmly. 'As a sole proprietor all you need is some frivolous judgement stuck to you and you could lose the lot. Your career could be over in a trice.'

'Okay, point made. I'll think about it, okay!'

'One other thing, Will...' Toby paused, as if unsure how far to go. 'How are things with you and Beth?'

'Fine,' I said, 'other than the poor kid trying to cope with motherhood, sleepless nights, colic and a very over stressed husband, fighting pointless legal battles in London, days before Christmas!'

'What I mean is, do you trust her... totally?'

'Absolutely... with my life... She's the only one in this shitty world that I totally trust. Well, other than you, that is.' Turning back to Toby, I smiled. 'But you're not quite as cute... Why?'

'Well, if you are intent on following this dream of yours, you may want to divest yourself of major assets. Sign over everything; gift it all to Beth... including the helicopter and that new home of yours, The Old Granary. People simply see it as a potential pot of gold and try to sue you into submission. I'm convinced Devron wouldn't be in court if they didn't think you had money.'

'Toby, the Granary is barely a shell,' I replied. 'We've hardly started converting it yet.'

'It still looks impressive, and people imagine you have money if you own something like that... and a helicopter!'

Over the next half hour we discussed Toby's suggestion. We also talked about the various possible outcomes of the case. In the end we concluded there were three very important facts – one: the judge had agreed our request for security against costs, two: Devron appeared to be out of cash and was likely to struggle finding the ten grand, and three: after today, the prosecution team probably wouldn't want to continue without being paid. We *appeared* to have gained the upper hand, but with Christmas coming, it would be weeks before we'd know for sure. Whatever the outcome of the case, it had cost us a fortune and was seriously derailing my career. It was even possible I'd have to put a 'rent-a-driver' in my place for next season, to recoup funds wasted on lawyers and legal fees.

Toby frowned, a crease appearing in his brow, 'Personally,' he said, 'I have never understood why you guys want to do what you do.'

I forced a smile, 'Because there's nothing to compare with it,' I replied. 'It's shaped much of my life. It's the most exhilarating buzz in the world, like being able to fly... It's like a drug, once it's in your blood you can never get it out.'

The snow was settling heavily when I stepped from the train onto the tiny platform at Ford Station in Sussex. I set off to the car park to find Beth. The door of the old Audi opened and she stepped out holding our son, George. At two and a half years old he was dressed in a thick blue duffel coat with bright red shiny boots, his golden hair a cascade of curls. He stumbled over to greet me, leaving behind a trail of tiny footprints in the thick snow. I reached down, scooped him up and spun him round, giving him a big hug; flecks of snow speckled his hair and eyelashes, merging with his freckles. 'Hi Daddy,' he beamed excitedly.

At home everything would be ready for Christmas. Beth had been working to make it that way for weeks – a perfect family Christmas for the three of us, with decorations hanging from the exposed beams and presents wrapped. But to most people our home, The Old Granary, was barely habitable, its damp passages and partly constructed rooms totally exposed to the howling elements, with no running water, no heating, just enormous openings where one day we hoped there would be windows and doors. It was our dream house. Beth's arms wrapped around me and for a moment the three of us locked together in an embrace. She gave me a long kiss.

Breaking away, she asked, 'So...how did it go?'

I gave a noncommittal shrug. 'It went well... a piece of cake... I think.' I said lightly, stepping into the passenger side of the car. We set off home to the village of Clymping.

I welcomed the Christmas break; the winter cold, the deep drifting snow and the isolation it would bring. It brought with it time to reflect.

'You're quiet, darling,' commented Beth. 'What are you thinking about?'

'How we got here,' I replied thoughtfully.

Sometime during the short journey, the snowflakes stopped falling, a full moon emerged and I continued thinking – how did this all start? I'd been dreaming of racing professionally since a kid but I'd never imagined it to be the crazy litigious world I now inhabited....

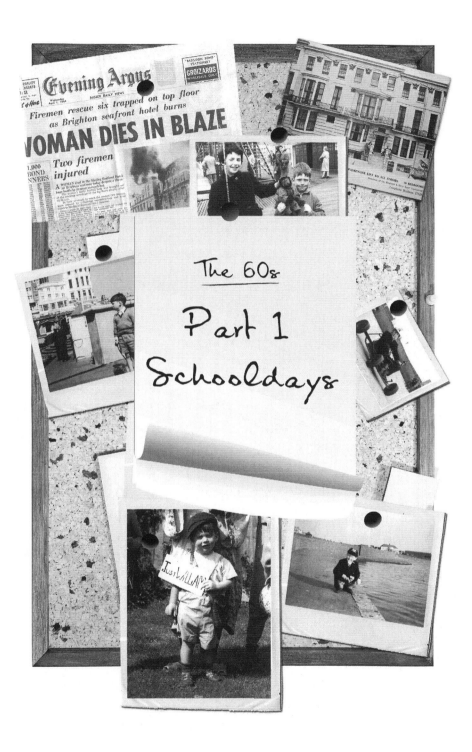

The 60s

Part 1

Schooldays

2

"School is like a lollipop. It sucks until it's gone."

Unknown author

Sussex, England.

Spring 1962 (23 years earlier)

CHILDHOOD WAS A VERY happy time; that is, if I completely disregarded my school years. My parents ran a seaside hotel and I always remember my dad having a profound love of the theatre. My mother was a big lady with a great sense of fun. She came from a long line of rather posh bankers and was forty-one on the day she gave birth to me. Through my childhood they surrounded me with love, affection and security. Their hotel, *The Claremont,* was in the seaside town of Brighton. It had been in my father's family for almost 40 years and was the oldest established family hotel in town. I remember it as a Regency property, made up of three buildings all knocked together to form one vast structure, with more than 50 bedrooms spread over four floors, an old Otis lift, two immense basements, a ballroom and all manner of staff. There were two chefs, one receptionist, several waiters and waitresses, five chambermaids, two porters, and two scullery maids. My parents worked unbearable hours in those days, typically starting at around 5am when my father would wake to prepare the kitchens for almost a hundred breakfasts, and he wouldn't finish until after midnight, when the last guest had downed their final pint in the hotel bar.

As a result, by the age of seven, I'd been raised by no less than six different nannies.

I was the third child, the long awaited son and heir to the Middleton name. I had two sisters; Jane who was four years older and still at school and Sue who'd already left home, working her way round the world as a fashion model.

Growing up in a hotel in the swinging '60s was bliss. My home was an enormous playground filled with ever changing, and occasionally, very famous faces. What little boy doesn't dream of growing up as an engine driver, a footballer or a racing driver? My first years passed happily and securely, surrounded by love, in an adventure land of Meccano, comics and x-ray specs. It was an imaginary world where anything was possible, a place inhabited by television characters; *Torchy the Battery Boy,* Steve Zodiac and Mike Mercury, the dashing pilots of *Fireball XL5* and *Supercar* and also my favourite bear, *Winnie the Pooh*.

I'd had six extremely happy years, but then everything suddenly changed and my childhood dreams of becoming a racing driver and soaring through the skies like Mike Mercury simply evaporated.

I had been at kindergarten for over two years, when my mother sat me down and with a big smile on her face told me, 'Next term you will be starting at the big boys' school!' I'd seen the big boys, just along the road from the kindergarten, in their smart red uniforms, grey shorts and stockings with red turnovers and peaked caps. I was desperate to start and so excited, that for the next few weeks, I could hardly sleep and as time passed, my excitement peaked with the arrival of my first ever school uniform. Except for the blazer, there were two sets of everything and late at night, after long days working in the hotel, my mother painstakingly sewed name tags onto every item. Even more exciting were the long white cricket trousers and special jumper. I also had my own pads and batting gloves with weird green knobbly finger protectors.

The Headmaster of my new school at Hove, was Mr Maurice Wickham, a former RAF drill sergeant with a penchant for boxing, a pastime he liked to share. His main aim in life appeared to centre on recreating the ambiance of his former military world. Each morning, lines of boys would march, military style, around the playground like clockwork soldiers as Mr Wickham barked his commands. 'Shoulders straight! Eyes front! ... Wipe the smirk off your faces!'

From the first moment I set eyes on him, I was terrified.

Discipline was strict, forces style and I quickly realised that if you were not physical and sporty by nature, you were in for a rough and painful time.

From the outset I was mildly unpopular, except with the bullies – to them I was a target. Rife was just one of many such bullies that frequented the school, the boxing ring on Wednesday mornings doubling as his extended playground.

To no one's surprise, it was my turn again this week as Rife cockily entered the ring and looking down on me, gave a derisory snort. Despite being just one class higher, he was almost twice my height and towered over me like a giant. Egged on by his cronies, he was already playing to his admirers; twisting his head from side to side, loosening up, throwing punches at imaginary shadows, each jab accompanied by a series of short exaggerated grunts.

Mr Wickham seemed delighted at the mismatch, calling us both into the centre. I didn't want to be there but I had no choice. Sir made a point of carefully checking our gloves. 'A clean fight boys, no hitting below the belt,' he said. The hall fell silent.

Rife began dancing about the ring like an orangutan, swinging wildly. For the first few minutes I ducked his blows easily but as time went on, I began to tire. Suddenly, he aimed a desperate right cross. The punch landed, connecting with a sickening crack to my jaw and for a moment I was stunned. It was the first time in my life I'd been hit like that. I could feel the sting of tears behind my eyes. Everything seemed to slow down; lights flickered around me and the cheers of the spectating boys distorted in my ears.

In those days, no form of head protection was worn, and we were considered far too young to merit any form of 'lower body protection', despite Mr Wickham's earlier warning.

I had discovered by chance, only the previous week, just how vulnerable a guy is, following an incident with a mis-aimed football! To my shock, dad collapsed on the floor in agony. My mother had tried to explain what had happened, whilst holding an ice pack to his groin. As Rife danced fearlessly in front of me, my mother's words returned – *Never hit a man down there.* Rife was tantalising close, egged on by both Mr Wickham and his cronies to finish me off. The bouncing continued, and the unrestrained target in his shorts wiggled about with every bounce, as though beckoning to me.

Without a second thought, I exploded my left glove into his groin – thud! Rife went down like a collapsing tower block... if his balls *had* by chance dropped, they were now relocated somewhere in his upper chest cavity! As he fell, my follow up right cross, instinctively connected with the bridge of his nose causing an impressive eruption of blood. The cheering stopped. The school giant lay foetally, whimpering, both hands cradling his groin, blood pumping from his nose. Mr Wickham peered down on his fallen prodigy, then turning to me, said sharply – 'My study, 10.30 Friday!'

Fridays were the only 'stimulating' part of the school week, the day the headmaster reserved specifically for caning! Three conduct minuses (or a knock out!) during the week would find you joining the line, awaiting your fate. Having to wait two days before receiving my sentence only increased the torture. I joined the group of waiting boys on the first floor landing, nobody daring to talk.

As we each entered there was a short delay, followed by a swish and a series of thwacks. Sometimes three thwacks, other times six. Then it was my turn. I shakily entered the dimly lit lair. The room stunk of tobacco and old books. Mr Wickham was sitting behind a desk that rested on carved feet resembling the clawed talons of some mystical beast. He was filling his pipe from a tub of Players Digger mixture, carefully stuffing wayward strands of tobacco into the bowl, and packing it down with a stained thumb. He rose menacingly, gripping the stem between his teeth, struck a match and held the flickering flame over the bowl. Drawing the noxious smoke into his mouth, he began a brief lecture on Queensberry Rules. I stood to attention, listening. 'Why may I ask, did you hit Rife when he was already down?' he asked finally, engulfing me in a small cloud of blue smoke.

'I didn't want him to get back up, Sir, he was hurting me!' I replied honestly, trying hard to keep my voice from cracking.

Mr Wickham couldn't help disguise the grin threatening to invade his composure. 'Hmm...' he went on dispassionately, '...and your initial punch was in direct contradiction to my instructions to *not* hit below the belt! What do you say to that?' I remained silent, looking at the ground, not trusting myself to speak.

He took a few moments to consider my defence before finding me guilty. 'You and I,' he concluded, 'are likely to be having more talks, which you may well find rather painful.'

Three thwacks later, totally incensed by the injustice of what had happened, I returned to my class. Pushing open the door I saw all the class standing before the teacher, Mrs Grimshaw, performing the morning mantra. In unison the boys continued chanting: *"An island is a piece of land surrounded by water"*... *"An isthmus is a narrow strip of land with water on each side, connecting two land areas"... "A peninsula is a piece of land jutting into the sea"...*

I walked quickly to my desk, turned and joined the incantation with the rest of my class: *"A continent is a land mass separated by an expanse of water"...*

Well before the end of my first term it became very clear that I would never be selected for the school football, cricket, or rugby team. But then I had little desire to be involved in anything the school had to offer. By now I hated school and just wanted to stay home and work on my Meccano set. However, Miss Bird, the music mistress had other ideas.

'I can't sing Miss. Honestly I can't,' I said desperately. 'Anyway, singing is for girls and cissies, Miss.'

'What about Elvis Presley?' enquired Miss Bird. 'Is he a cissie? And what about this new skiffle group, the Beatles? I suppose they are a bunch of cissies as well, are they, William?'

'My dad says they're a bunch of girls with long hair, Miss!'

'That is as may be,' replied Miss Bird, fixing me with a stern look. 'Singing is good for you. You'll take a vocal test for the school choir with the rest of your class this afternoon at 3.00 in the assembly hall,' she announced,

I stared back defiantly, 'I can't sing, Miss!'

'Then you decide William; a vocal test with me at 3.00, or a visit with Mr Wickham at 3.05. I'm quite sure he'll be able to whip a few notes out of you!'

I nodded reluctantly, 'Yes, Miss.'

Later that afternoon I stood sullenly in line with the rest of the boys and waited my turn. Miss Bird was perched at the school piano, pecking away at keys whilst a small boy attempted to keep pace, singing along with words from a hymn book. Abruptly she stopped playing, 'That was positively painful, Timothy,' she said with disdain. Looking in my direction, she called 'Next!'

A few boys behind me muttered as I stepped forward nervously and took the hymn book from Timothy.

'What piece are you going to sing, William?' she asked.

'I don't know, Miss. I can't sing!'

Ignoring me, she took the book, opened it and handed it back. 'All things bright and beautiful, William. Okay? Delight us!' She returned to her music, flicked a few pages and began to play some familiar notes.

Everyone fell silent. I had little choice other than to go through with it – anything to avoid being caned again. With my palms sweating and my anxiety reaching its maximum, I opened my mouth and a collection of strangled sounds tumbled out, 'All things bright and beautiful,' I gargled, mangling the notes. 'All creatures great and small, All things ...'

Miss Bird had begun grimacing the moment I opened my mouth, but I kept going, '...wise and wonderful, The Lord God ....'

Seeing her pained expression I let the last notes trail off. Abruptly she stopped playing. The hall was silent, except for the occasional distant squeak of shoe leather on the polished woodblock floor. Turning to me Miss Bird laughed mockingly, 'That was a near perfect impression of a cheese grater, William! I don't think I've ever heard anything quite so awful, since my cat was run over!'

A few boys sniggered. Embarrassed I looked down at my shoes, 'I told you I can't sing, Miss,' I replied forlornly.

'Well, that's clearly true!' said Miss Bird. 'Go back to your class, William... Next!'

I bit my lip and thoroughly humiliated, stomped out of the hall vowing never to sing another note, regardless of threats, as long as

I lived. All I could think was – *it's so unfair* –I'd told her I couldn't sing, so why *make* me sing, and in front of everyone?

In the afternoon, my nanny Jill collected me from school for the daunting two mile trudge home. The long way back was very familiar and probably intended to wear me out ready for bed. We'd set off along our usual route, past the museum and art gallery, then down to the sea front. The journey was always the same and each day we'd pass Candy's sweet shop. As long as Jill was in a good mood, we'd stop to choose a few pennyworth of this or that.

Candy's was an Aladdin's cave, filled with big glass jars of kaleidoscopic sugary delights like glistening stripy humbugs, fluorescent gob-stoppers and pitted lemon drops. One of my favourites was sherbet dabs, small yellow paper pouches filled with sugary white powder. Sucking, then dipping the hard toffee lolly into the soft white powder produced a magical explosion of effervescent froth. By filling your mouth with the *whole* pack, you could pretend you were having a fit as the froth exploded from your mouth and out through your nose, a skill subsequently banned when my distressed mother discovered me *writhing* on the hotel reception floor, one busy Sunday morning!

It was late afternoon when we turned up Cavendish Place towards the hotel.

'Wow! Look at that!' I exclaimed, pulling away from Jill and sprinting the last hundred yards up the road. I stood hypnotized by the stunning cream sports car that had just parked. The door swung open and a distinguished-looking man in his early thirties with a moustache and long side burns stepped out. Collecting a small case from the boot, he smiled at me before making his way up the steps to the hotel. He was wearing a white shirt open at the neck and his dark hair was brushed straight back from his face. 'Mister.' I called, motioning back at the car, 'What car's this?'

Whack! Jill's hand administered an open handed slap. 'Never run off like that, Will, you'll get yourself squashed!'

'Who's that man?' I asked, turning in the direction of the blow, a red welt already rising up on my cheek.

'That's Mr Hill. He's a famous racing driver,' Jill hissed, still angry. 'He's staying at your parents' place.'

I'd heard of Graham Hill and knew how famous he was. We often had celebrities staying, so I didn't feel awkward chatting with any of them. Already that year we'd had the pop star Joe Brown and the legendary daredevil Bluebird pilot, Donald Campbell. Each week it was like having another character step from the pages of my *Boys' World Annual* and check in for a few days' bed and breakfast.

'I'm going to be a famous racing driver when I grow up!' I called out, sticking the thumb of my hand against my nose and waggling my outstretched fingers. He turned back, smiling and in an instant, raised his thumb to his own nose and with a broad grin, returned the salute.

Jill shrugged dismissively, 'I doubt you'll survive long enough at this rate to get a licence, Master Middleton!'

3

M Y FATHER SLID OPEN the manila envelope using a pearl handled letter opener and extracted two pages of folded paper. Slowly he studied the school report, flipping back and forth whilst considering the contents, his face turning from anticipation to a disappointed frown. I shifted uncomfortably in the interminable silence. After a few moments he looked up at me dejectedly and said, 'Mental Arithmetic, "E".' He took a fleeting look back at my report, 'Mathematics, "D" and Reading English "E".' He continued reading out my teachers' remarks, *'Somewhat disappointing first year. Master Middleton needs to apply himself. Must try harder!'*

There was a moment's silence, before my mother added encouragingly, 'Well, at least he wasn't last darling; he could have got an "F".'

The next morning I woke with mixed emotions. I was still worrying about my bad report, but excited that we were leaving today for a two week holiday. It was just four weeks before Christmas and as the hotel was so busy over the festive period, we were taking a break before the season got under way. My mother stepped into my room. 'Good morning, darling. Did you sleep well?'

'Okay.' I said, still thinking about the school report.

'Have you looked under your pillow?' she asked, smiling.

I lifted my pillow, and on the sheet lay a silver half crown.

'That's for your holiday, darling,' my mother said, 'and for trying so hard last term. I'm very proud of you.'

Our holiday of 1963 was spent in Brockenhurst in the glorious and ancient woodland known as the New Forest. Two weeks of wandering the bracken covered moors, climbing heather-clad hills where beach, birch and oak turn golden brown and fallow deer roam in dark chestnut coats covered in white spots. Each day we'd paddle through icy streams, watch native ponies munching at the coarse grass and see woodsmen packing their drums to produce charcoal.

We usually stayed at the same hotel, Careys Manor, an old rambling former hunting lodge, with creaky old floors and massive log fires. I'd loved the place from my very first visit.

Each night exhausted, we'd snuggle down beneath thick, fluffy eiderdowns in a bedroom I shared with my sister Jane, whilst the wind howled outside, whistling through cracks in the windows, the lashing wintery rain rattling the panes. Every evening before drifting off to sleep, she'd read me Enid Blyton's *Famous Five* stories. My favourite was the one about an adventure on a mysterious moor, where two children, George and Anne, are on holiday with Timmy their Border-Collie.

Every morning we'd be up early collecting wild mushrooms from the frosty moor, taking them to the kitchen for our breakfast. Today was extra special, we were going horse riding, and to my sister's annoyance, I'd been awake since the crack of dawn, desperate to get started. I peeked over my blankets at Jane. She was asleep again, curled up on her side, her face pressed up against her fluffy panda. I pushed myself up on one elbow. On the end of her bed still fast asleep but always ready to act was

Bingo her pet poodle, guarding her against me. He didn't like me, or at least he distrusted me. He'd been that way ever since he was a puppy, when I'd accidently dropped him.

'Are you awake?' I asked excitedly.

No reply. She turned over, waking Bingo who grunted his disapproval before jumping to the floor.

I threw aside the covers, swung my legs out of bed and pulled on my trousers, shirt and jumper. Padding over to the window I pulled back the curtain. Outside, an early morning mist was drifting over the forest floor, mingling in a pungent potpourri of leaf mould, fungi and pony droppings. 'Look,' I said, 'it's almost daylight!'

Although I loved watching the ponies roaming the moor, I'd never ridden one before, so today was a special treat. We set off in our new Austin Cambridge for the short drive to Sway Road and turned into a large concrete yard surrounded by stables. A big sign announced "Mrs Turner's Riding Stables."

'It's just like Captain Johnson's Riding School in *Five go to Mystery Moor*!' I said excitedly, jumping from the car the instant the engine stopped.

All around, horses' heads were protruding from stable doors. We made our way over to one of the stalls and peered over the top.

Inside, the pony flicked his ears, snorting an alert. He watched us intently but, deciding we were of no immediate danger, poked his head over to say hallo.

'He's fantastic!' I said, looking up into his dark, shiny eyes. He was a bit rounded with a coat of coffee and cream splodges, his mane sprouting out in unruly directions not unlike my own, a sprig of forelock hanging in a tangle on his forehead. The little pony lifted his head, snorting again, scenting the air through flared nostrils.

'His name's Coco,' a horsey voice announced from behind. 'I'm Mrs Turner,' she added enthusiastically, offering a hand to my parents.

I watched as the lady entered the stable and fitted a bridle, saddle and halter, all the time explaining what she was doing. Coco took little notice and in between interruptions returned his head happily to his bucket of feed. Snapping a leading reign onto the halter she led the little pony into the yard.

'Right, up onto the mounting block!' she said sharply turning to me.

'Is it ok if I give him a sugar lump first?' I asked. At the mention of his favourite treat, purloined from the morning's breakfast table, his ears twitched forward. Mrs Turner nodded and I held out a cube on the palm of my hand. Coco lowered his head, snuffling my hand with his soft leathery mouth. I could smell the warm scent of his body. Gently he took the sugar lump, leaving me a handful of slobber which I smeared down the front of my woolly jumper.

We spent the first ten minutes circling the yard whilst Mrs. Turner issued various instructions, then out into the paddock where we gently trotted, and my love affair with this intuitive four legged friend was cemented for life.

After my lesson, we jumped back in the car and my father quickly drove off down Brookley Road, through the village and over the water splash. Turning left to the moor, we caught up with Mrs Turner, who'd taken a more experienced group of riders. I sat in the car watching as the horses cantered past. It looked so exciting, exhilarating. What a feeling of freedom it must be, I thought, to be able to ride off like that into the wild forest and explore. Not a building in sight, just an occasional gorse bush and nobody to tell you off or hit you. 'I wish all lessons could be like today,' I said wistfully, watching as the riders disappeared into the distance.

Life at my parents' hotel was always exciting, especially at Christmas. It was December 1963 and the whole place was alive, decked with multi-coloured paper garlands and bright shiny glass baubles. Bunches of holly and mistletoe hung in bunches from the ceilings. Paper chains I had spent weeks licking and sticking together with Jane criss-crossed everywhere and in the reception was a massive snow-covered Christmas tree with twinkly lights. Everyone was laughing and smiling and in the evening before dinner, carol singers would gather around the tree.

Each night there was a dance with a live band and long lines of guests would snake through the hallways and reception, kicking their legs to the "conga" or forming circles in the dance hall doing the "hokey cokey". There were special dinners in the restaurant with limitless helpings of everything, and through it all, my parents worked even longer hours, making certain everyone, including all the staff, were having the best holiday ever.

'Christmas Eve!' my mother exclaimed as she entered my bedroom, with a beaming smile on her face. I knew what was coming next, she always recited the same poem to us every year, and we knew the words by heart. 'Hang up your stocking and jump into bed,' she continued. 'Close your eyes tightly, and under the bed clothes hide your head...' She kneeled down beside me, snuggling me up under the blankets, continuing in a whisper, 'For if you take just one little peep, or so they say, Father Christmas will take his sack and quietly creep away!'

Christmas morning dawned, and with it a stocking bursting with toys and treats. My sister Jane was already fully dressed and two-thirds of the way through an entire Cadbury's chocolate selection when I burst excitedly into her room holding up a bright red Mamod model steam engine. 'Look at this,' I exclaimed loudly, leaping onto her bed, 'it's a real working steam engine!' She seemed unimpressed and continued munching away at her chocolates. 'You fill it up with methylated spirits and oil and stuff and set light to it and everything!' I continued enthralled.

With the aid of my Meccano set, I quickly set about modifying the static engine by attaching four wheels and a drive system to its flywheel. To my mother's horror, the supposedly stationary device was suddenly hurtling across the Axminster, leaving an acrid trail of oily vapour, steam and electric blue flames in its wake!

The rest of my presents were just as exciting, my own Cadbury's chocolate stocking, pink and blue sugar mice, a bag of gold chocolate coins and best of all a Scalextric racing track with all manner of racing cars and accessories.

But all too soon Christmas was over and before I could dream up a master plan to avoid it, I was back for yet another term.

My visits to the headmaster's study had become legendary amongst the boys. Practically every week would find me waiting in line on the first floor landing. Just three minuses in the week would guarantee my place in the queue, and being dyslexic, I found little difficulty in meeting the necessary criteria. Mr Wickham had no idea what dyslexia was, chances were the condition hadn't even been given a name yet, but whatever my affliction, he didn't want it infecting the rest of his boys and set about eradicating it with hefty whacks with his cane.

As time went by, I started to make friends. In part this was due to my extensive experience in the study and my ability to dispense sage advice on reducing the stinging effects of Mr Wickham's cane. 'Always wear your baggiest shorts', I advised wisely, 'and at least three pairs of underpants, preferably woollen. Try not to bend over too tightly!' I'd add.

On one occasion, based on research from the *Beano*, I suggested yelling out half way through, 'I'm going to be sick!' To our surprise, the first boy attempting this ruse was dragged from the study halfway through his punishment to the toilet, where, dry mouthed, he could barely manage a mouthful of spit. Returning to the study, Mr Wickham simply started over! The boy, barely able to restrain his disappointment, left the study clutching his buttocks, having received a record nine strokes! I ruefully shrugged as he passed... as I was to discover, sometimes in life, things don't go to plan.

4

"Bravery is being the only one who knows you're afraid."

Franklin P. Jones

T HANK GOD, you're safe!' My mother cried, barely able to contain herself. She rushed over, knelt down and enveloped me in her arms.

It was Wednesday the 1st April 1964 and I was off school for Easter. Throughout the holiday, groups of Mods and Rockers had been gathering along the promenade by nearby Palace Pier, the mood threatening to spoil the Bank Holiday break for everyone. Skirmishes had already broken out along the beach and when police using horses and dogs had been unable to move them on, I'd been told not to leave the hotel, and was playing happily in the back yard. I had no idea why my mother was so upset.

I stood, wrapped in her embrace, noticing for the first time the brush of flakes on my face and neck. Looking up, the blue sky was filled with moving grey. Like ashen snowflakes they were tumbling down and in the distance, rose the jarring sound of bells. 'Come with me darling,' she urged, 'the hotel's on fire!'

My parents had first been alerted to the blaze by one of the chambermaids screaming, 'The top floor is on fire and your son's up there!' In an instant my father had charged up the stairs, shouting to my mother to get everyone out. In fact it wasn't our building that was burning, at least not yet, it was the adjoining Bedford Hotel.

Now standing in the street, reunited with my wide eyed sister, my mother firmly instructed her, 'Keep hold of his hand. Do *not* let go of him at *any* cost!' And she dashed back into the hotel.

Looking up, I could see the fire rolling slowly across the roof, consuming everything in its path and in its midst was my father, with a ladder balanced precariously across his back, working his way relentlessly towards the edge. Directly below him, a woman was leaning out of a window with smoke bellowing over her head. She looked down, as though preparing to jump. 'Hold on!' somebody screamed, 'They're coming to get you!' My mother reappeared with two of the kitchen porters and a large blanket which they preceded to unfold beneath her window, calling for her to jump. But the Victorian spiked railings prevented them getting close enough and moments later she slumped mercifully unconscious over the ledge as the smoke turned to flame, the flames licking relentlessly over her now motionless body.

Fire engines and ambulances began arriving, their contents pouring out like ants. Ladders were erected and hoses reeled out, snaking in all directions. Firemen pointed the brass nozzles at the rampaging inferno as flames leapt thirty feet into the air, taking grip of the hundred and thirty year old structure. A small turntable ladder inched closer and closer to the woman at the ledge but was too short to reach.

Up on the roof, realising it was impossible to reach the woman at the window, my father had managed to gather a small group from the Bedford's top floor and was leading them back in their night clothes to our roof. I breathed a sigh of relief as they disappeared into the safety of our upper floor.

Another longer ladder arrived and two firemen inched closer to the lady, and lifted her unmoving body from the window. As they reached the ground, others lifted her gently to a waiting stretcher but as they did so, her blackened flesh disintegrated in their hands, sections peeling back, hanging from her motionless arms like long shredded gloves.

I stood, barely able to comprehend, the images of the fire etching into my subconscious. Suddenly, my mother was there, urgently leading us away...

The following day, banner headlines reported: *WOMAN DIES IN BLAZE*. There was no mention of my fathers' bravery, but we all knew what he'd done, as did the people he'd saved.

The rest of the spring term turned to summer, the time drifting slowly and painfully into autumn and with each passing day I lived in constant fear of that long spindly cane that rested on the top of Sir's cupboard. But my days at the Hove school were drawing to an end. The past two years had been the foundation of my education. Before starting, I had been so excited with the prospect of learning and desperate to begin my school life. Finally, after two long years I was leaving, and looking back over those years, I couldn't remember a single day that hadn't been filled with dread and despair.

5

"Compassion will cure more sins than condemnation."

Henry Ward Beecher

September 1964

I WAS NINE YEARS OLD when, with great apprehension, I started my new school life as a boarder. It had been five months since the big fire and the former Bedford was now a colossal demolition site.

We'd driven the short journey to Shoreham in my parents' Austin Cambridge. I nervously sat in the back with Jane, watching the shops on either side of the small coastal town as they drifted by. Packed in the boot was an enormous trunk, containing everything required for the term ahead. More excitingly, there was also my big new tuck box fitted with its huge brass padlock! It had been built out of plywood by the hotel handyman and stocked with all manner of goodies including a big fruit cake baked specially by the sympathetic hotel chef. The box lid even had my name stencilled on it in big black letters. It was late afternoon as we made our way up the winding side street and parked on the school driveway.

We stepped from the car and into a maelstrom of luggage, tuck boxes, small boys and parents. Mr Brewer, the headmaster strode over, 'Mr and Mrs Middleton,' he began, 'how nice to see you again.' He shook my parents firmly by the hand, before offering me a welcoming smile, reminiscent of the grin a lion might reserve for its prey. He was a tall portly man in his late 50s with grey receding hair and in his hand he held a clipboard which he studied momentarily. Finding my name he added a small neat mark. Then turning back to my parents, he added briskly, 'Luggage will find its way to the correct dorm. Probably best not to prolong the goodbyes, we'll take good care of him.' My sister sat in the back of the car, pulling faces at me through the side window. My feelings of foreboding deepened as my parents leaned down to kiss me good bye. It was all happening far too fast! They turned to leave.

'Make your way up to the first floor and report to Matron,' Mr Brewer instructed me brusquely, with an ambiguous wave of one hand. He turned and set off to greet another group of parents with a practiced smile.

I nervously looked around, and seeing a line of small boys snaking their way through a Gothic stone archway, went over to join them. A few moments later, we passed through huge heavy wooden doors into a dimly lit, polished oak hallway. At the far end I could see an open door, beams of sunlight beckoning encouragingly but just ahead, a prefect was directing the new boys up the dark, curved wooden staircase. I didn't know what awaited us; however I had no intention of finding out! 'Up the stairs and report to Matron's office,' the prefect bellowed, pointing at the carved oak stairs. I glanced over as my peers automatically obeyed the instruction, making their way to whatever fate awaited them.

'I'm supposed to go out the back first,' I said, pointing in the direction of the beams of sunlight, trying hard to control my wavering voice.

He shrugged, then busily turning to the next boy, directed him up the menacing looking stairs.

I quickly made my way to the far end of the hall and out through the open door into a sunlit playground. Instinctively turning left, I furtively skirted around the school and back out onto the roadway. Glancing briefly around, I could just see the head master, still standing outside the imposing façade, welcoming parents and new boys. I hesitated for just a moment, then bolted.

Ten minutes later I flagged down the number 13 coastal bus service and with the sixpence pocket money given to me by my mother, bought a one-way ticket to Brighton. I had absolutely no plans of returning and was home before my parents even knew I was missing.

It was not until several hours later that I was discovered by a hotel porter, curled up asleep in my secret base under my bed. Some hours earlier, following a school roll call, my absence had been discovered and the panicked school had alerted my parents who had instigated a search of the entire hotel by all the staff. I'd naïvely imagined survival in my base would be indefinite, albeit with regular clandestine sorties to the hotel kitchens for supplies.

Later that night, my mother cuddled me up in my own bed and explained. 'Nothing nasty is going to happen there, darling. You'll love it once you get used to it and it'll make you into a real man, just like Daddy.'

Sadly, my reprieve lasted just that one night. The following day I was returned to school, this time delivered into the personal care of my housemaster, the Reverend Kennet.

Over the next few days I had little choice other than to try and settle into my new surroundings, but I remained intensely homesick. Overnight I felt I'd lost everything; my parents and my home, everything I knew and was familiar with. I felt like an orphan.

My new school was much larger than the last, and it took time to find my way about. It was made up of buildings forming an E-shape. Behind it was the large asphalt playground with a cluster of prefab buildings which included my class; the first form. There was also a music room and science lab. A lean-to housed a small tuck shop, where sweets and soft drinks were sold during breaks. To the south of the playground was an old underground air-raid shelter, which was strictly out of bounds. The school even had its own chapel, with pews, choir stall and an organ!

Being the head of school, it was Mr Brewer's job, or so the story went, to deliver the most vicious beatings of any of the masters. We'd been told all about it by the older boys and we believed it. Mr Brewer's reputation was reinforced by the fact that boys would occasionally be flogged publicly during school assemblies, to act as an example to the rest of us, demonstrating what awaited us, should we dare step out of line. My initial experience of this ceremony took place during my first week there.

Assembly began much as it had on the four days prior, although curiously this morning a table had been placed in the centre of the stage. At 8.30am we all filed into the great hall and sat quietly facing the stage, a few junior teachers and prefects spacing themselves around the hall. Moments passed before the signal was given, and on cue we all stood as the procession of six masters, led by Mr Brewer, gracefully glided down the centre aisle in long black robes like a funeral cortège. In his right hand he held what appeared to be a quarterstaff. The cortège made their way up the stairs to their appointed seats. To the left sat Reverend Kennet, Mr McCallister and Mr Bridger, my new Latin, RE, English and maths masters. On the right, Mr Essex , Mr Kirk and Miss Green who took French, Science and Geography. A hush fell over the assembly. Mr Brewer, a man clearly accustomed to wielding authority, stepped forward to the lectern and stood for a moment, studying us through heavy dark framed spectacles. On his command, Mr Cousins the Music master began pounding the walnut Clifford upright as we awkwardly mouthed the words of Lord of all *Hopelessness*.

As the last notes faded, Mr Brewer signalled us to sit before commencing the morning lecture, a stern address on felony, misconduct and the harm to local community. The speech on the evils of wrongdoing droned on and on as we sat on the hard gym benches, trying desperately not to fidget. 'The shopkeepers of this town,' the headmaster finally concluded, 'work long hours to secure their livelihood, so it was with much sorrow that I received news that a boy from my school had been caught shoplifting from a local sweetshop!'

A collective gasp left our lips. It wasn't so much the shock that a boy had shoplifted, but that he'd been *caught*! We all knew something terrible was about to happen. Mr Brewer turned to Miss Green, the only female teacher in attendance, gesturing for her to leave. What was about to take place was *not* deemed suitable for a lady to witness! She rose timidly from her seat and walked carefully to the exit. At the same time, a small boy of about 12 years slowly rose to his feet on cue, making his way reluctantly up the stage stairs to the table, removing his blazer, bending over to await his fate.

Mr Brewer made a show of holding up the quarterstaff, giving it two or three sharp flicks. He took a few moments to carefully position himself and his target, before delivering a single terrific crack to the boy's backside. Turning to the shocked faces spread below him, Mr Brewer continued his lecture before turning back to punctuate each sentence with another terrifying whack to the waiting buttocks. More than ten minutes elapsed, during which time ten hard strokes were administered. The boy, trying hard not to cry, rose painfully on command, replaced his blazer and returning to his place, lowered himself very gingerly to the unyielding bench, head bowed in shock and humiliation.

Whilst I'd considered myself an expert on caning at my last school, the barbaric spectacle I'd just witnessed was on an entirely new level and I decided there and then that I would be departing this place at the first opportunity!

Not only was I terrified by the spectacle of the public flogging, I was still acutely homesick. It was the first time I'd been away from the hotel without my family and I'd been homesick from the moment I arrived.

I quickly set about formulating a plan to be reunited with my parents. My idea was as simple as it was dramatic, and I swiftly persuaded two new mates, Todd and Scott to get onboard.

They stared back at me, grinning in sheer wonder as I outlined my plan. The idea was simple; the three of us would be stalked by a phantom 'dirty old man' and we'd have to run for our lives! 'Sheer genius,' Scott remarked. 'Let's do it tomorrow!'

Of course, we had absolutely no idea what a dirty old man would want from a group of nine year old boys, but my parents had repeatedly warned me to stay away from them. 'Never go with them or take sweets from them!' they'd say. It seemed perfectly reasonable therefore, that if they thought I was being spied on or chased by one, or maybe even a *group* of them, I'd be out of school and returned home in a jiffy, particularly if all three of us had the same story!

The following day's final lesson was games, everything was set... The school sports field and gymnasium were situated about half a mile away, in Connaught Avenue and after sports we were expected to walk the short distance back to the main school for tea, a journey of no more than ten minutes.

We three took a different route, sprinting, running, crossing streets, jumping fences, making our way through villages. Only my desperate will to escape school kept me going. Finally, exhaustion took over and we jumped on a bus for the remaining journey to Brighton.

The next bit of my plan was to alert our parents to the 'dilemma'. We located a telephone box, pushed a penny into the slot and dialled the five digit hotel number. On the third ring I heard my mother's flustered voice, 'Claremont Hotel, can I help you?' I later discovered she'd been in the middle of booking in a group of 50 guests that had just arrived on a pair of Robinson coaches. I pressed button "A" on the front of the box.

'Mum, it's Will,' I began breathlessly, 'we need help! We're being chased by five dirty old men!' I never knew quite what would come out of my mouth, but whatever did, usually worked, and this time was no different. I should emphasise this was 1964, and the word *paedophile* hadn't even been invented, let alone trumpeted 24 hours a day by the media. In my mind, a dirty old man was nothing more dangerous than an old man with grimy hands, dirty fingernails and a few dried gravy stains down his shirt. However, the vision that snapped into my mother's mind was clearly quite different – she suddenly sounded terrified. 'It's okay, we've got away,' I added quickly, sensing her alarm, 'but they're still following us. I've got to go, but I'll call as soon as I can.' And with Todd shouting helpfully in the background, 'Quick Will, they're coming!' I replaced the handset.

As we'd planned, we moved on to the Curzon Cinema to sit out the next few hours. The film was a new Burt Lancaster war epic: *The Train*. We sat engrossed in the story of The French Resistance, who had to stop a German train filled with art treasures without damaging its valuable cargo. In our wildest dreams we could never have imagined how our own drama was gaining momentum only yards away, just outside!

In those days you could sit and watch a film several times over, providing you retained your ticket – our first mistake! We sat and watched the film through twice. It was around 9pm when we finally stepped out onto a dark, wet unfriendly night, wearing our school blazers – our second and most fatal error. Looking out over the wet moonlit street, homesickness took hold again and I longed to be with my parents. 'I think I'll give them another call.' I said.

Suddenly a hand grabbed me roughly from behind. 'Well boys, what have you been up to then?' Turning, I peered up into a severe face beneath a police helmet, a slow trickle of rain dripping from its brim. The officer drew himself up to his full height 'Led us a right jolly dance!' He studied us through a misting pair of wire-framed spectacles.

'We were chased by some dirty old men' I began, 'we had to run away... there was no choice!' Two more officers joined us. 'No choice?' one repeated, eyeing the remains of a large bag of popcorn in my hand. 'So, where have you been all this time?'

I was beginning to feel a little uncomfortable. 'Errr...trying to get away?...' I stuttered, but even to me my words sounded suspicious, and neither Todd nor Scott was prepared to offer an explanation. Alarm bells were beginning to ring. We were led away by two of the officers to a now waiting police car and driven the short distance back to school.

Mr Kirk, the duty master, was waiting for us. He taught science, chemistry and PE and was universally feared by the boys. Unfortunately, it had been his PE class that we'd last attended, prior to disappearing on our little escapade.

He was in his late forties, stood five foot four inches and was powerfully built. It was rumoured among the boys, that he was an ex paratrooper and the leather strap, his weapon of choice and for which *he* was so famous, had been liberated from a Nazi's parachute. According to school gossip he'd killed the man with his bare hands before cutting away the strap as a keepsake! All I knew was that I was standing before him, and the famous leather strap clearly existed as it was clenched firmly in his right hand. Just as worryingly, in his left hand he was holding a mauve cinema ticket stub which he slowly examined in exaggerated detail. One look at the leather strap set my heart thumping. I was terrified. There was nothing I could do, and there was nowhere to run.

On arrival back at school, we three boys had been separated, told to change for bed, and sent to our respective dormitories with no time to prepare our collective alibi.

I shared a dorm on the first floor overlooking the chapel with eleven other boys. Standing self-consciously in the centre of the room facing Mr Kirk, I could see eleven sets of riveted eyes peering over sheets, hypnotised by the show that was unfolding...

'So,' Mr Kirk began, his eyes boring into me as he bristled with indignation, the threat in his voice undisguised. 'You were being chased by a group of men I understand. Is that correct?' He turned his gaze back to the ticket, leisurely studying it again. I kept silent. 'This was all one big sham, wasn't it, Middleton?'

'What's going to happen?' I asked shakily, in a small voice.

Pulling off his jacket he replied solemnly, 'Remove your dressing gown, bend over and lower your pyjama bottoms.' Out of the corner of my eye, I saw the raised strap, a moment later I felt the leather bite into my flesh. I heard a cry of pain leave my lips and tried to jump up. 'Move and you'll get more!' he growled. 'Bend back down, until your hands touch the floor!' I remained bending as five further lashes rained down relentlessly.

Embarrassed and humiliated, I choked down the sobs that threatened to release from my throat and painfully climbed into the cold, uncomfortable hard bed, trying with all my strength to control my emotions; it was a point of honour amongst boys to show no reaction – any tears would be seen as a weakness and I'd be marked forever as an easy target for bullies. My plan had failed badly and I was more homesick than ever. I wanted my parents. I wanted to be home. I wanted my mother to snuggle me up under the blankets, tuck me in and kiss me good night. But that was all in the past. At least, I thought, I'm not going to be the main feature in tomorrow's assembly. I curled up, buried my face in the pillow and fell into a dreamless sleep.

The following day I was sitting at my wooden desk with its sloping top and porcelain ink-well, dipping the nib of my pen and scratching Latin verbs as neatly as I could manage into the blank pages of my exercise book.

A prefect entered the classroom holding a piece of paper. Proceeding directly to the front, he handed the communication to the master, Reverend Kennet.

He was a tall yet slender man of about forty or so, with protruding teeth, and was married with two sons. One of the kindest teachers I ever came across, Reverend Kennet took a personal interest in the wellbeing of all the boys in his care and to my great fortune, he was also my Housemaster. 'Will,' he said, studying the note gravely, 'you're to report to the Headmaster's study at once.' The words were like a death sentence.

With my heart pounding, I made my way over to the dreaded study and knocked on the door.

'Enter!'

My leather soles squeaked gently on the polished woodblock floor as I stepped into his study and cast a wary eye around. The room was cloaked in semi-darkness, reminiscent of Mr Wickham's, smelling of old books, leather and tobacco, the walls covered in dusty portraits of former headmasters, and on the mantelpiece a clock ticked tirelessly. A large claw-footed desk dominated the room and to the right, an old brown Chesterfield button-back sofa. I'd been warned that the roll top arm of the sofa served to keep miscreants in check whilst administering disciplinary correction! I was on the verge of tears at the thought of what was about to happen and prayed that my mother or father would rush in and rescue me at any moment. It all seemed so unfair.

Mr Brewer sat behind his desk, fixing me with a shrewd stare. 'Sit yourself down, Will,' he said sombrely.

'Thank you sir,' I replied shakily, lowering myself onto a hard chair, my eyes alternating between the woodblock floor and the old sofa.

'I've been talking with Mr Kirk about last night's little escapade.' I felt as if I was about to throw up. The ticking clock was now competing rhythmically with the heart beat pounding in my ears. 'I expect you're feeling homesick,' he added unexpectedly.

Looking up, I nodded in surprise, 'Yes, sir.'

'It's normal to feel homesick, Will. All boys feel that way to start with.' he said, smiling. 'Just stick it out. I've spoken with your parents and they both send their love.'

'Thank you, sir.' I replied.

He studied me thoughtfully through his dark framed spectacles, 'Are you making friends?' he asked, 'aside from Todd and Scott?'

'Yes, sir, a few sir,' I said.

'And how are you getting on with your housemaster, Reverend Kennet?'

'Very well sir, thank you sir.'

'What about games?' Mr Brewer enquired, 'Have you had a tryout for the football or rugby teams yet?'

'Not yet sir,' I said, still unsure where all this was all heading, but thankful it didn't appear to be in the direction of the brown Chesterfield.

'Well, if you are ever unhappy or need to speak to anyone, we can always have a little chat,' he smiled encouragingly. As I began to rise he added. 'Or if you prefer, speak with your housemaster, Reverend Kennet. I suspect you may consider him a little less of an ogre than me.'

'Yes, sir... I mean no sir, thank you sir.' I replied as I backed my way out as quickly as possible.

The long weeks turned into months, home sick school terms merging with all too brief holidays; bittersweet in the knowledge and dread that I'd soon be returned to boarding school. Some of my teachers, like my headmaster, were a little more compassionate, but most were brutally strict, appearing to enjoy the fear and pain they inflicted on the boys in their care. I despised every terrifying moment of my education and, despite fear of reprisals, would run away regularly, only to be returned in trepidation and despair the next day for another brutal beating. I felt abandoned, set adrift in an unknown place, removed from the carefree happiness of my former world.

Then, at the age of ten, having endured eighteen months of hateful enforced hell, my parents broke the most amazing unexpected news. It was like receiving all my past Christmases packaged into one gift of instant joy... at the end of term I would be leaving boarding school forever. And more than that, our hotel was being sold; we were all moving to live in the wonderful New Forest!

6

"There is a garden in every childhood, an enchanted place where colours are brighter, the air softer, and the morning more fragrant than ever again."

Elizabeth Lawrence

WE'D BEEN LIVING in Hampshire for almost six months, ever since my parents had been forced to abandon our hotel in Brighton following the fire. The uncertainty and financial strain, particularly on my father, had been immense and his health had started to suffer. For almost a year the hotel's access road had been blockaded whilst the adjoining Bedford was demolished. Guests arriving for a week's holiday by the seaside were prevented from even dropping off luggage and any that did brave the war zone of tipper trucks, potholes and detritus, would normally terminate their stay within hours of the pneumatic hammering that could start at any time day or night.

Our new home was now a restaurant in the tiny village of Brockenhurst in the glorious New Forest, the place we'd spent so many family holidays, a part of the country I loved.

The restaurant was called *The Watersplash* and it was situated just up the road from a ford which lazily crossed the bottom of the High Street, where the gentle forest ponies stopped to drink from the cool clear water.

Perhaps it was just the stark contrast from life at boarding school, or maybe it was the time we now had helping our parents run the new, smaller family business, but it was the most idyllic, glorious time of my life. For the first time ever I even loved the small country school, just opposite Mrs Turner's Riding Stables.

At five each morning I'd wake to the buzzing of my alarm radio and the room would fill with the sounds of Sandie Shaw singing *Puppet on a String*. Before six I'd be off on my bike for my paper round and each afternoon, following school, I'd help with the mucking out of the stables or sweeping the cobbled courtyard.

As my experience grew, Mrs Turner allowed me to help more with the ponies and during the long warm lazy summer evenings I'd lead them out to graze in the lush sweetly scented paddock. On the weekends, in return for my help, I was even now allowed to exercise the less frisky ones, cantering them out across the pungent, bracken covered moors on my own and each time we'd go further and faster, crossing streams, jumping fallen trees and over ditches with the wind buffeting my hair, breathing sweet air of the woodland. I was now eleven and after life in boarding school, the feeling of freedom was intoxicating.

Before returning to the stable we'd stop exhausted, in some lush deserted meadow with a clear, pebbly stream from which we'd drink. There we'd rest, listening to the gentle rise and fall of the wind.

The forest was so different to my former life in Brighton and at boarding school. There was no hustle and bustle of traffic, no exhaust fumes and no stuffy school uniform, just the sound of birds singing and wind whistling through the trees. It was a perfect place, somewhere we were always meant to live. But our paradise all depended on the family business and especially my father.

* * *

We knew that something was wrong long before our mother told us. For more than a year my father had been finding it increasingly difficult to eat. Over the past months he'd been undergoing various tests both locally and more recently in London at the Westminster Hospital. Sometimes he'd been away for days at a time and as the months went by, he was losing more and more weight. It was late afternoon and I'd just returned from helping out at the stables when my mother sat my sister and me down in the flat above the restaurant. 'Dad has been admitted to the London hospital,' she said, trying to smile, her face drawn and filled with sadness. 'He's having an operation tomorrow,' she added, wiping tears from her eyes. 'It's a big operation. The doctor says Dad's got cancer. They are going to do their very best and he's a very good doctor...' she paused, not knowing quite what to say, '...but they don't hold out too much hope,' she finally said. 'We're going up to see him tomorrow before the operation and we'll stay overnight.' I nodded that I understood but the meaning of her words were somehow lost. She reached over and put her arms around us, her tears flowing more swiftly. 'My darlings,' she said, 'do you understand what I'm saying?'

The sign on the door said: Intensive Care. Two porters wheeling a trolley with a patient came out through the double doors. A nurse walked silently and swiftly. Equally silent, we followed.

The ward was warm with perhaps twelve or fourteen beds, all occupied. Tubes and pipes spiralled out of impaled body parts, medical devices bleeped and whirred rhythmically. A man in one of the beds was moaning, another deliriously calling for help. We trailed our mother, silently passing the nurses' station to a curtained off cubicle. My father was propped up on pillows, his face ashen; a clear tube dripped a fluid into his arm, his body beaten-down, but he was a fighter and he was now fighting the biggest battle of his life, for his life. Seeing our wide eyes peeking through the curtain, he smiled. 'Hi kids,' he said, his breathing shallow, 'come in.' We entered. My mother took his hand and kissed him gently.

Weeks later the restaurant was sold. Although my father had survived, he was a shadow of his former self, far too ill to work, so we had to move. Our idyll came to an abrupt end, everything happening so quickly. The school holidays were finishing and there was no opportunity or time to say goodbye to the teachers or the school I'd come to love and just the briefest stroke of each hairy muzzle at the stable. Our new home was now a bungalow in the grimy hustle and bustle of Southampton, a city with a population approaching a quarter of a million, and my new school the biggest Secondary Modern in Hampshire.

7

"Authority is quite degrading"

Oscar Wilde

Summer 1967

FOR A FEW MOMENTS I stood taking in the scene. It was terrifying – the largest secondary school in Hampshire, surrounded by housing estates, providing schooling for more than two thousand local children. It couldn't have been more different to my last school.

It was located at the end of Hill Road, on a campus covering several hundred acres, with separate entrances for the boys and girls. The boys' side where I stood, housed a hulking concrete fifties style main block surrounded by a ramshackle collection of post war timber outbuildings.

A driveway turned left past the huge main structure, where a constant stream of cars rolled into a parking area, disgorging boys of all ages. As more and more arrived, I noticed a few pointing in my direction – if my demeanour hadn't given me away, my new school uniform obviously had: *new kid!*

An older boy wearing a prefect's badge approached me, 'First day?' he asked. He had to be more than four years older and stood at least six inches taller, broad shouldered with dark hair and a fuzzy dark outline on his top lip. To me he looked almost adult. He must have been watching me standing there.

'Yes,' I replied, barely audible.

'What's your name?' he asked.

'Will Middleton,' I said as firmly as I could manage.

'How old are you Will?'

'Eleven.'

I was directed to the school office with two other new boys where formalities were dealt with by a tall, grey-haired lady, Mrs. Bennet. The school was split into five different houses – I'd been assigned to "Rickham house" and as I was starting part way through a term, would initially be placed in sets three for English and three for maths. Any adjustment could be made later.

It was past ten when I was shown into Mr Carvel's algebra class. I counted around forty boys sitting behind desks as I entered the room, one boy standing to attention behind his desk. Interrupting whatever was going on, Mrs Bennet announced loudly, 'This is William Middleton,' directing me to a vacant place at the front of the class. She handed over a paper to Mr Carvel, turned and left.

Feeling vulnerable and exposed, I quickly lowered myself into the seat and stared up at the blackboard in sheer disbelief – *An Introduction to Algebra!*

Beneath the heading in white chalk were a series of incomprehensible numbers and letters.

'Okay, William,' said Mr Carvel, strolling over to the blackboard 'we were just trying to get through to young Andrew Turner here, that $3a+2b$...' he underlined the equation with a shrill swipe of his chalk, '...can't be reduced to five anything, as I'm sure you will know. It's rather like three apples and two oranges... wouldn't you agree?'

Feeling inferior and totally bewildered at what was going on, I hesitantly replied. 'Well, Sir, they *are* all fruit.' There were a few stifled sniggers from behind me.

I had entered a new nightmare from which it appeared there was no release. Over the next few days I was assessed and reassigned into sets five, five – the lowest the school had to offer, but each class found a greater terror awaiting me. Almost every class had over thirty boys, some more than forty. All the fear and pain from my earlier school days was back, including the bullying from the bigger boys and the cruelty and injustice of constant beatings inflicted by the teachers. Each night I escaped into sleep, and as morning dawned, woke thinking about my school in the forest and dreading what the day ahead would bring. I had to bury my pain – no one could help. My father, weaker each day, was fading away before our eyes, my mother constantly by his side.

Days blended into weeks, time lost all meaning. Just surviving each school day without a beating consumed my thoughts. I hated the place but as the summer term of 1967 drew to an end, I eventually began to accept it for what it was... but then a chance observation changed everything.

In the corner of the playground, a small group of boys were excitedly discussing a deal which appeared to involve swapping small colourful paper cards. I'd never seen anything like them before and was intrigued. I moved in closely, listening carefully. The cards were apparently given free inside packs of Topps chewing gum but I didn't like chewing gum. Each boy was holding his own small stack of the things whilst contentedly chomping, arguing that his selection of cards was the most gruesome.

The pictures were all civil war scenes from America; men impaled on bayonets, blown apart by military hardware , tangled up in barbed wire or shot. I had no interest whatsoever in the gum or the gruesome pictures themselves, I couldn't see the point, but the dealing itself was fascinating. What was immediately clear was the most shocking cards were highly prized and exchanged for two, sometimes three or more of tamer images. Pocket money was always tight and the whole idea of swapping or bartering was intriguing – it was something that would hold me in good stead later in life.

Later that day I visited the local sweet shop, investing two shillings of precious savings into a stock of Topps chewing gum. Separating out the repulsive gum from the lucrative cards, I promptly recouped my investment and returned a small profit by repackaging the single slivers of gum as a delicious special bulk package deal. Over the months that followed, the popularity of the cards grew around the playground and with their demand I became a major player, the card dealing enabling me to leave behind the sadness of losing my old school and the misery at home with my father's illness. It was something I could lose myself in.

It became instinctive to convince boys to exchange stacks of cards for a somewhat smaller but 'superior' stack of my cards at a slightly higher price. I loved trying to outsmart the competition and haggling for the best deal. But I always made sure I left my customers satisfied and happy. That way they'd hopefully return for more! It was around this time I also started to notice trends... when boys were confronted with limited cash, they valued their stash of cards far lower, and when they were flush with cash, having just received pocket money, card values were considered higher... I always waited for the appropriate moment, buying low and selling as high as the 'market' could stand, and so as my stacks of cards grew, my 'card wealth' grew with it.

Over time, the cards took on a currency of their own, being traded for everything from sweets and comics to old bikes and chemistry sets. Before the winter term concluded, my reputation was firmly established as the boy willing to do a deal on just about anything.

* * *

The tiny engine spluttered into life, propelling me forward over the dusty ground, the acceleration taking me by surprise, gravel and grit instantly peppering my visor. Attempting to brace myself against the increasing velocity, I pressed down harder with my right foot without realising I was hitting the accelerator.

The little go-kart had been a very special surprise present, and was undoubtedly intended to distract me from our home troubles and settle me more into life at secondary school. 'The school motorcycle club have agreed that you can join a year early!' my mother explained as excitedly as she could manage, 'And they have said you can use the go-kart after school in the playground on club nights.'

The speed increased dramatically, taking hold of me and I flew over the tarmac, the engine buzzing like an angry hornet. Directly ahead of me, a group of watching boys leapt aside as I shot past leaving an acrid trail of oily fumes. I turned the steering at the last moment, just missing the perimeter fencing.

Ahead, a single motorcycle was carefully circling the playground, its rider concentrating intently on his hand signals. Suddenly a powerful and alien sensation hit me... *I had to pass him for no other reason than I had to be in front!* The noise and smell held me at a pitch of excitement I had never before felt. At that moment it was the most important thing in my brief life, there was no way *he* was going to stay ahead of *me*!

Now realising what the brake and throttle actually did, I worked my way alongside my 'opponent'. He appeared to hesitate momentarily but clearly didn't want to be passed. With no further thought of hand signals or careful braking, we charged side by side over the playground, my kart inching ahead as we approached the boundary wire. I lifted momentarily on the throttle and turned right, the rear wheels instantly breaking away. On impulse, I turned the steering against the direction of the slide and floored the throttle, leaning into the direction of the turn. My opponent lifted but as he turned, the bike slid from beneath him, the handlebar and footrest gouging into the asphalt surface. My kart straightened up, propelling me victoriously down the length of the playground, its engine buzzing wildly.

Directly ahead, Jack Hovel, the teacher in charge of the club was waving frantically, he didn't look amused. I coasted to a halt, grinning wildly and lifted my visor. He strode purposefully towards me, clearly unimpressed at my club debut.

* * *

Mr Jenkins was my housemaster. He was also my English teacher. He was a tall savage man in his fifties, wiry with dark hair, ill fitting dentures and a short temper and for some reason he'd taken an instant dislike to me from my first day. In truth, he seemed to treat all the boys with equal loathing and disgust. When he wasn't teaching English or reading the riot act to some small wretched boy, he'd release the day's frustrations by running circuits of the football field in his long baggy red running shorts. I'd managed to avoid his wrath during most of my first term but I knew it was only a matter of time before he got me. It finally happened two weeks into the summer term, when I'd forgotten my homework.

My father had been determined that whatever time he had left, it would be spent together as a family packing in as many memories as possible. It was a strange time, filled with exciting spur-of-the-moment trips, but with the ever present dark cloud – soon he would be gone. He loved the theatre and we'd regularly take weekends in London staying at the Cumberland by Marble Arch, seeing shows like *The King and I, Hello Dolly* and *My Fair Lady*.

The uncertainty of life at home, coupled with impulsive weekends away finally led to the inevitable confrontation with Mr Jenkins. I was twelve years old when it happened.

I sat at the back of the class at my usual wooden desk with its hinged sloping top, my head lowered in my work. Mr Jenkins was sitting at his desk at the front, eyes scanning the class of boys for any excuse to pounce. There was just ten minutes to go before lunch break. 'Right,' announced Mr Jenkins with a click of his dentures, 'take out your last week's homework and hand it to Hubbard.' All around the class, boys quickly extracted papers from satchels, holding them aloft for collection. At the mention of his name, a small boy on the front row had risen and began gathering the papers from outstretched arms. I frantically searched in vain for my homework, a feeling of dread rising in my stomach. I had spent hours on the wretched essay, but it simply wasn't in my satchel. This was the second time I'd left my work at home!

By the time Mickey Hubbard reached my desk, I'd emptied the satchel and was sitting in panic, a small pile of books and papers piled on the sloping surface. 'I can't find it!' I whispered to Mickey.

'What are you talking for?' demanded Mr Jenkins.

'I'm sorry Sir,' I timidly replied, 'I can't find my homework'.

'You mean you haven't *done* your homework,' replied Mr Jenkins, rising and striding purposefully in my direction. At that moment the leaning pile of papers and books slid from my desk clattering to the floor. Everyone stopped what they were doing and turned in my direction. I stood up in terror as Mr Jenkins approached. 'This is the second time you have failed to complete and hand in your homework, Middleton.'

'I *have* done it Sir. I've just left it at home.' I whispered.

'You are *lying*, Middleton!'

'I'm not Sir, I *have* done it.' I insisted.

'You are contradicting me, Middleton,' thundered Mr Jenkins, his dentures clicking wildly. 'Are you also now calling me a *liar*?'

'No Sir, definitely not Sir.' I backpedalled, well aware of the implications to come.

'And what may I ask is this?' asked Mr Jenkins, recovering a small grey and pink paperback from the floor. *'The Awful Spellers' Dictionary...'*

'It's mine, Sir,' I whispered.

'I wouldn't imagine it to be anyone else's,' replied Mr Jenkins with disdain. He flicked a few pages of text, eyebrows rising alarmingly. 'For what possible purpose would you require a list of misspelled words? The objective of a dictionary is to look up the *correct* spelling and definition!'

'If I knew how to spell a word, I wouldn't need to look it up, Sir,' I innocently replied but as I spoke the words they sounded all wrong – defiant. 'In a normal dictionary you can only find a word with its correct spelling.' I added, hoping to explain more clearly but only managing to dig an even bigger hole for myself.

'Do you consider yourself in a position to lecture me upon the use of dictionaries, Middleton?'

'No Sir, definitely not Sir...' I stuttered, '...it was a present from my father, Sir.'

'Your father is not your English master! I am your English master! This book will not be used in my class in future.' With that, he twisted the book back against its spine and ripped it into two pieces, throwing the remnants onto my desk. Loose pages fluttered to the floor.

Taking his time, he strolled back to his desk and collected a thin bamboo cane. Returning to me he added, 'This is the second time you have failed to complete your homework. Furthermore you contradict me, your teacher, and have the audacity to call me a liar!'

'No, Sir, I'm not Sir!' I pleaded in panic-stricken desperation.

'You're doing it again, Middleton!' exploded Mr Jenkins. 'I suggest you shut up or you'll receive a few extra strokes for good measure. Now, bend over your desk.'

Slowly I bent over and braced myself.

There was a slight delay, followed by a mighty *crack!* – a few more seconds delay before the excruciating burning sensation began – then a whoosh followed by a second *crack*! I shut my eyes – then the third, fourth, fifth and at last, the final whoosh and *crack*.

The bell rang. 'You may go,' said Mr Jenkins from behind.

I gathered up my papers and the remains of my cherished dictionary and left.

8

"Mothers of Teenagers Know Why Animals Eat Their Young".

Unknown

A T THE AGE OF TWELVE something very strange happened – I discovered girls. It was as if a couple of engines had burst into life, propelling me into an orbit of turbulent emotions, anxiety and strange physical ministrations. In the battleground that was my childhood, becoming a teenager would be a vastly more difficult time. All of a sudden, the merest flick of the Silvikrin girl's hair on television would have me imprisoned in my chair, a pillow clutched discreetly to my lap for hours.

Something else happened; my voice became deeper, I became broader, taller, more independent, self-confident and argumentative. I began communicating in little more than grunts and I categorically refused to allow the masters to cane me. This caused much displeasure, particularly with Mr Jenkins, who'd come to rely on my backside as a means of relieving his daily tension!

My parents had previously only had to contend with a couple of occasionally moody daughters, who only appeared to want to be taller, slimmer or shapelier in life. A pubescent boy was an altogether different animal. On my parents lay the responsibility of getting me through these difficult teenage years. Until now, I'd painfully endured six years of so called education, and as a result had developed a profound distrust of authority. During the next few years, my shocked parents would be catapulted into challenges they had never before conceived. It all began with the episode of the girl's shower block...

Mr Jenkins welcomed my parents with a practiced smile, his lips sliding back over polished dentures, 'Very nice to see you, Mr and Mrs Middleton,' he clicked. 'We'll be conducting the meeting in the headmaster's chambers, if you'd like to follow me.'

We set off in the direction of the study, with me trailing just a few feet behind, uncertain of what the next hour would hold. *Was I about to be expelled?* I wondered. If I was, would it be so bad? After all, I hated school! We entered the study, like every headmaster's study I'd ever visited, dimly lit with shelves stacked full of musty books and a large desk dominating one wall. A small group of armchairs were placed around a coffee table where the headmaster was seated in deep conversation with a middle-aged lady. He rose, offering my parents his hand, 'Thank you so much for coming in Mr and Mrs Middleton, this is Miss Bolton from the girl's school.' He gestured in the direction of the middle-aged lady, who frowned and didn't bother rising from her seat. 'I felt it best, given the severity of the circumstances, for Miss Bolton to join us,' he added. 'Please do take a seat.'

I was directed to one of the hard upright chairs opposite.

The headmaster opened a big filing cabinet and extracted my confiscated creation – a rather large black and white closed circuit television camera. The camera was the size of a very small suitcase with a series of switches and lamps and a lens protruding from the front. It had taken all my pocket money and was the result of almost a year's hard work. Turning to me he asked, 'What I'd first like to know,' he enquired, 'is what on earth drove you to attempt this?'

The truth was, it all began quite innocently almost a year earlier when I was just twelve...

Des Green was my best mate and together we were curious to explore whatever there was in the area, especially any dark shadowy bits. He was around the same age as me and in the same school house, even the same sets. We sat next to each other at assemblies, played together and ate our sandwiches together at lunch time in the school playground.

He lived in a children's home, St Christopher's, only ten minutes' walk from the bungalow. My parents were very unsure about Des and me mixing. They considered him a bad influence and strident efforts had been made to separate us. This had ultimately resulted in him being moved into a different school house, all of which had little, if any, effect on us. Each day we still rode our bikes the short distance to and from school together and spent break times and weekends exploring together. We confided in each other in everything, except why he lived in a children's home, but I somehow gathered it was something to do with being in trouble with the police which only gave him a certain kudos.

Des could easily have passed for my brother except for the way he spoke – straight sandy coloured hair, freckled skin, the same blue eyes and raging hormones. We'd bonded from day one, united by our tireless pursuit of the unknown. Possibly the bond also had something to do with him living in the children's home – a sort of "home" that wasn't a home, like my boarding school time. But his "home" and our lives were very different.

As we were mates it was quite natural that our discussions included the intricacies of the opposite sex. After all, my parents had never explained anything, and back then there was no such thing as sex education in schools. It would be two decades before the arrival of the information superhighway, fount of all knowledge, the internet. To me, in 1967, Des was the nearest thing to an expert on the subject of just about anything.

It was a glorious sunny day, with blue sky and gentle breeze. We were riding back from school and had just passed a group of giggling school girls when he turned and yelled back to me, matter-of-factly, 'They don't have willies you know!'

Now, you may consider that a bit of an odd thing to say, just out of the blue like that, but Des often came out with strange stuff. He was cycling just ahead of me, so I shouted back, 'I know they don't, but what do they have... and how do they pee?'

He twisted round on his saddle, munching his way through a *Curly Wurly* toffee bar in the shape of intertwined strands. 'They got nuffing down there,' he replied slightly quieter. 'It's just a sort of hole thing.'

'A hole...?' I repeated intrigued. 'Is it a big hole?'

'Some big, others small...' he explained with a shrug. '...depends on the girl.'

The traffic was light so I pulled out and cycling harder, drew alongside him, asking naïvely. 'Is it the same hole they pooh out of?'

This seemed to stump him for just a moment but he quickly recovered. 'Of course it is,' he replied. 'How many holes d'you think they have?'

I shrugged. Until recently I'd never given the matter much thought, but somehow it all now seemed quite fascinating. 'Really... so babies come out of the same hole?' I asked.

'Where else would you expect them to come from?' he replied sarcastically

'Yuuuuck! The same hole as pooh?'

'You didn't still think the stork brought them, did you! Shit Will, you don't know *nuffing!*'

For a while we didn't talk, a few cars and a bus rumbled past, some honking horns. 'How d'you know all this?' I asked.

'Found out years ago when I was just a kid. Anyway, you see it all the time at the home. The girls show 'em to me,' he announced proudly. We turned off the main road and cycled single file along a narrow ribbon track of scruffy waste ground strewn with litter, occasional trees, bushes and old rusting refrigerators, piled in heaps by the side of the track. Bulldozers had already begun work clearing the ground that was soon to become a new housing estate, but now it remained a warzone of the detritus of human habitation leading up to his home.

I glanced urgently about, my eyes landing on a couple of pretty girls making their way along the track. 'Do you think you could get them to show me...?' I asked hopefully as we cycled side by side up the driveway.

'Doubt it; you'd need to be living here,' said Des flatly as he dismounted and parked his bike in the rack.

'Oh well...,' I replied with a disappointed shrug. A bee buzzed by, tickling my ear and I swiped it away. 'Anyway, does this hole have a name?' I asked, watching as he secured his bike with a padlock and chain.

Des paused for just a moment, as if trying to recall something. Then finally he answered, 'I think they call them *vaganals, or* sum'mat like that.'

For the next few weeks nothing more was said on the subject until one day Des arrived at school with a magazine concealed under his jumper. We made our way to the back of the playground, well away from the teacher. 'It's called *Parade.*' Des said, pulling the magazine from his jumper and flicking it open. We sat down on the damp tarmac surface, legs pulled up, engrossed. Suddenly there they were – the mysteries that had confounded me all my life, girls in various states of undress, posing provocatively. I eagerly flicked through the pages of black and white pictures, eager to advance my education.

'Trouble is,' I finally said with frustration, 'there are no pictures of them below the waist and there are all these little stars over their boobs... they've covered them up or left out all the bits you want to see!'

'We could always spy on your sister,' suggested Des, his eyes alive with mischief.

'Yuck,' I exclaimed, 'you've got to be kidding?'

'We could break into the girl's school and sneak into their changing room.' Des suggested matter-of-factly.

A faint smile spread across my face. 'Do you reckon we'd get away with it?'

Des raised his eyebrows, 'I could get us in,' he said, 'no problem.'

This idea somehow had merit and we both beamed at the thought of it. 'They must have showers like in our changing rooms.' I added.

'We could take some *real* pictures and flog them, we'd make a fortune!' added Des.

Despite a few reservations, I couldn't deny this was incredibly daring and a potentially profitable idea, and so over the next few days the plan was hatched. In the weeks that followed, the idea gathered momentum when my monthly magazine *Practical Electronics* published the design for a black and white television camera. The idea was now to build the device and then install it overnight in the girls' showers, utilising Des's apparent skills on breaking and entering, then to relay the video signal via one of my modified walkie-talkies as a television signal.

9

"Mother Nature is providential. She gives us twelve years to develop a love for our children before turning them into teenagers."

William Galvin

THE PLAN ALL STARTED to go wrong when I couldn't fathom out how to make the transmitter work.

I hadn't considered joining an after school activity group before, tending to sprint from the confines of the place at the first clang of the end of school bell, but 'project booby' as it had now become, was changing everything.

Des led the way into the science block. The building was on two levels on the edge of a large green which served to separate the boys from the girls' school. This structure was the only building shared by both sexes, which for any second year boy, made visits there almost as scary as a trip to the dentist.

Ignoring the jibes of sixth formers milling about the stairwell trying to impress girls, we made our way up the stairs to the first floor and pushed open a door marked 2SB. The air was thick with the odour of chemicals, craft glue and acrylic modelling paint. Boys clustered in groups around the classroom. On one bench, two were adding the final touches to an *Airfix* kit of a 1905 Rolls Royce. On another, a boy carefully painted an 1815 British 10th Hussar. Another boy was engrossed with the task of cementing wheels to a model locomotive.

At the front of the class some older boys were working on *Triang* electronics kits. I made my way over the electronics bench and removed my creation from a bag. Immediately they stopped what they were doing and gathered round. A couple of sixth formers at the back of the class, noticing the sudden movement, wandered over and began whispering with Des. Every now and then they'd burst into fits of sniggering. I tried to ignore them.

The activity class was run by Mr Ascot, the only teacher in the school I liked.

'This is fascinating Will. I must ask...where did this interest in electronics come from?'

I shrugged.

'Well... did you build this entirely by yourself?' he queried.

I nodded, 'Yes.' He looked doubtful, knowing I couldn't even spell the word camera; logically, how could I ever build one? How could any child assemble together the hundreds of electronic components needed, into a working television camera, and from scratch? The fact was, I was still hopeless at spelling and never read anything other than electronics magazines, the detail, intricacy and precision of the circuitry fascinating me. I appeared to learn by osmosis. Weirdly, I could somehow accurately recall piles of useless detail from way back in my grammar school years, Latin verb conjugations, tenses, persons and moods, yet my writing remained appalling, the scrawl now carefully cultivated to such an extent that it was impossible for teachers to see I was misspelling the words. Unfortunately, this also made it impossible for them to read them.

Mr Ascot waved his hand in front of the camera lens and watched in awe as the image flickered ghostlike across the screen.

'The camera works just fine,' I said, 'but I can't work out how to transmit the video signal properly.' I held up a section of *Vera Board* dotted with transistors, resistors, condensers and an RF coil. A small nine volt battery hung pendulum like from a pair of wires. 'I designed this RF modulator,' I added with frustration. 'I've linked the amplified video signal from the camera's videon tube and modulated it with the carrier signal from the walkie-talkie but I still can't get the picture to transmit wirelessly to a TV.'

'Fascinating... absolutely fascinating,' said Mr Ascot, as more and more of the class gathered around, 'but why do you want to do that?' he asked. 'You could simply plug the RF signal directly into your set or connect the image output into the TV's video amplifier.'

'We'd need a rather long cable to do that,' Des mumbled unhelpfully.

I signalled to Des: *Shut up!* Ignoring Des's idiotic attempt at humour, I shrugged, adding quickly, 'I'm just interested.'

'Well, you'll never manage to transmit a video signal using those walkie-talkies,' said Mr Ascot. 'They could never handle the bandwidth.' He went over to the blackboard and drew a few diagrams sketching pipes and water flow to explain the problem graphically. 'The difficulty is the amount of information and detail that you're trying to send.'

'You bet!' sniggered Des... 'Ow!' he yelped as my trainer collided with his shin, 'that hurt!'

I nodded, now beginning to understand the problem. Ignoring Des's strange comments, Mr Ascot continued, 'So, how far do you want to send the signal?'

'About as far as the games field,' said Des with a grin as the two sixth formers struggled to restrain a fresh bout of sniggering.

'Well, apart from anything else,' Mr Ascot went on, 'it's not strictly legal to transmit anything without a licence. That said, you may find a suitably high bandwidth transmitter down at the army surplus store in town, but don't mention that I suggested it. Whatever you transmit could well appear on half the televisions in Southampton... you're likely to find yourself competing with *Coronation Street* for viewers!'

'I doubt there'll be much competition,' Des retorted, still sniggering.

10

"When you go in search of honey you must expect to be stung by bees."

Joseph Joubert

FOR A TWELVE YEAR OLD BOY, the whole predicament was deeply embarrassing – like being caught by your parents whilst engrossed in a dirty magazine. To me the most worrying bit was they probably all considered me to be some sort of pervert. At the very least, everyone in the room including my parents, now knew I was interested in girls, particularly naked ones and that thought alone made me squirm.

I sat with my head down, studying ink stains on the polished parquet flooring, legs swinging back and forth agitatedly, as the interrogation continued. Every now and then I'd look up to see Mr Jenkins jaw drop in horror as another indictment would be hurled at me.

The headmaster worked his way through his questions in an orderly manner. Occasionally Miss Bolton would query something more accusingly. 'But you did...' she insisted, '...manage to enter the girls changing room, didn't you!'

'No, Miss Bolton, we didn't,' I maintained, squirming under her scrutiny. 'Honestly we didn't... it was all just talk,' I said. 'I've never been anywhere near the girls school. I promise!'

And that had been the trouble. All the talk and gossip. Our plan had been destined for disaster the minute Des had opened his big mouth in the science block. From that moment, rumour and speculation had spread through the school like wildfire, word quickly reaching the girls, courtesy of older brothers. Suddenly, girls were refusing to enter their changing room or use the showers, insisting that they were being spied on by a secret hidden camera that was beaming images across the playing field to the boys' school! Dozens of worried parents had been phoning, something had to be done and it hadn't taken long to work out the likely culprit. After all, only one boy out of two thousand in the school had recently constructed a television camera...with a transmitter.

'I would remind you', said Miss Bolton, 'that we have already spoken with your accomplice in this matter, Des Green, who is currently confined to St Christopher's.'

'You don't deny that you planned to install this camera in the girls changing room?' asked the headmaster.

That was a difficult one, I'd thought. It had been Des's idea to break in, so I hadn't actually planned anything, but I had willingly gone along with the idea and certainly didn't intend grassing Des up. However, if I'd admitted to planning it, I would most likely have been expelled. But then, maybe that wouldn't have been so bad. On the other hand I might have to submit to being caned by Jenkins. If anyone in this room was a pervert, I thought, it was Jenkins. My backside had provided him with more hours of entertainment that could possibly be healthy for any grown man. There was no way I was going to allow that to happen.

My parents had until now, remained quiet throughout my grilling, but somehow, sensing my predicament, my father suddenly asked, 'Headmaster, do you in fact have any evidence that my son ever entered the girls' school?'

'Well, no *evidence*, not as such.'

'Well... do you seriously believe these lads could have not only gained access to the girls' shower room but also by some miracle concealed this device? It's the size of a small suitcase!'

Miss Bolton addressed my father with a scowl of disapproval, 'These are very serious accusations, Mr Middleton. We have a duty to take such matters seriously and fully investigate...'

'I appreciate that you have a duty to look into any accusation,' my father agreed, 'but have you actually considered that the thing requires plugging into a power socket! Do you not consider this was just a bit of a fantasy, and a case of boys being boys? I think this is all going a little too far. It seems to me to be based on little more than a lot of gossip and hearsay.'

At that point I was asked to leave the study and wait outside. I got up, head still bowed, and left. Waiting in the hallway outside I could occasionally make out the sound of my father's voice raised in my defence. Ten minutes elapsed before the door finally opened and my parents emerged, my father carrying the camera under his arm. He said, 'It's all okay now son but I must say you do have a tendency to tread where angels fear.'

My mother ruffled my hair, 'Don't worry, Will. Nothing else is going to happen,' she said gently. 'It's all been dealt with, but we do need to have a little chat when you get home tonight.'

11

"I was one of the 'puzzle children' myself – a dyslexic.... And I still have a hard time reading today. Accept the fact that you have a problem. Refuse to feel sorry for yourself. You have a challenge; never quit!"

Nelson Rockefeller

BEING DYSLEXIC in the educational system of the sixties was difficult. The problem was, I didn't know I was dyslexic... neither did my teachers; to them I was just plain thick. There were no text books on dyslexia to guide them and no helpful advice from experts. My parents did their best to help with private tuition, but to me it was all boring and totally unintelligible. I even struggled to comprehend basic maths, which in 1967 considered "base 12" to be a great idea for humans.

'Why do we have a system based on twelve, sir, when we only have ten fingers?' I asked my harassed maths teacher, as he attempted to address the class of over thirty on the subject of percentages and the British pound. 'I think, if it was based on ten, it might make more sense, sir,' I said.

'Middleton, our system is based on Anglo-Saxon,' replied my teacher with irritation. 'It was introduced by Charlemagne to the Frankish Empire,' he scrawled the words on the blackboard in white chalk, '.... and is perfectly straight forward. *Four* farthings equal one penny, three pennies equals' one threepenny bit, which is twenty five percent of one shilling and that is five percent of one pound. *Twelve* pennies equal one shilling, *twenty* shillings equal one pound and one pound and a shilling equal one guinea.'

Turning to the rest of the class, he asked, 'So what is fifty percent of one pound?'

Most of the class responded in unison, 'Ten shillings, sir!'

'Maybe if I had twelve fingers it would make more sense,' I muttered with frustration.

I had been trapped in a learning time warp for over five years, where the only thing clear was the certainty that to achieve anything in life, I'd have to trust my own impulses and rely on my own wits.

My school had a strategy for most things that involved teenage boys' impulses, whether or not compounded by dyslexia. The tactic was simple. Occupy enquiring minds and deflect impulsive behaviour with structured activities such as field sports, cross country running, canoeing or for the very adventurous, a spot of rock climbing. This approach enabled boys to gain their adrenalin rush in a safe controlled environment. Of course, every child is different – I chose an alternative path. At the age of thirteen I discovered the importance of "supply and demand" by establishing my next business – the manufacture and supply of explosives.

Misspelt circulars, typed on my dad's Smith-Corona, boomed in bold letters: *Gunpowder: two shillings per oz – Dynamite two and sixpence per oz – Gelignite five shillings per block.* Sales literature circulated the school in a whirl and as orders stacked up, my bedroom took on the appearance of a laboratory with raw materials piled high on the Dexion racking that once held the stocks of chewing gum cards. Quickly I recruited Des and a new mate, Tom Wilmot, to help with production. Even with staff costs, profits far exceeded the meagre outgoings on the raw ingredients: saltpetre, charcoal, sulphur, sodium chlorate and magnesium flash powder, all obtained from willing local pharmacists, an ironmonger and a photography store. Of course what I was producing wasn't exactly gunpowder and certainly bore no relationship whatsoever to dynamite or gelignite... it was however *very* popular with teenage boys, all obsessed with anything that went bang!

Twelve individually wrapped ounces was my minimum quantity order. Priced at just one pound, the small outlay produced twelve sizable explosions. With each sale I secured another satisfied customer who'd return typically a dozen or more times before becoming bored. Twelve sales produced twelve pounds from each boy... For the first time, maths tables registered visually in my brain. With a catchment of over two thousand punters, I quickly worked out there was a potential turnover of more than twenty-four thousand pounds. I set a conservative target of securing sales of around fifteen percent of the market which amounted to well over three grand. All of a sudden, percentages made wonderful sense!

Over the weeks, pungent mushroom clouds of sulphurous blue flames rose unexpectedly from around the school, much to the alarm of the increasingly perturbed teaching community and with production in full swing, it was only a matter of time before something went seriously wrong.

In just three weeks of trading, I'd purchased a second-hand speed boat and when we weren't fulfilling orders, spent most weekends happily on the Solent with Des, just occasionally ignoring the 5 miles per hour speed limit. With money to burn, I'd also purchased my own Bell and Howell 8mm camera and plunged into the movie business.

The tiny boat swayed, its engine racing, the hull crashing back down into the clear waters of the Solent, sending an exhilarating cascade of spray into our faces. Des swept his soaked blond hair from his sunburnt face. 'Faster, Will, faster!' he yelled.

Pushing my Polaroid glasses firmly back onto the bridge of my freckled nose, I pulled back fully on the throttle lever, the bows lifting clear of the water as the Evinrude outboard revved higher. We swept through a bend, zapping past speed limit signs, riding high and fast over the river. Des whooped with delight. Between us sat Tom, our new recruit. He was just eleven years of age, painfully thin and freckled. Aside from assisting in the explosives 'factory', Tom was also starring in our new 8mm horror epic, *Teenage Zombie*. He clung to his seat in sheer terror, his mind preoccupied not with his script, but with the thought of imminent death by drowning.

A mile up river I eased back on the throttle and steered for the isolated mud bank. Des leapt out holding an anchor line and scampered onto dry land, his long skinny legs protruding from faded cut off jeans, coated in thick river mud. 'Yuk! This stuff stinks!'

'Stop complaining,' I said, carefully handing over my shiny new camera and tripod. 'Set it up over there by the edge,' I said, pointing.

Today we were filming one of the last scenes; the zombie's final demise. Tom was already in his costume of ripped jeans and a shredded t-shirt coated with fake blood. His face was still green from seasickness and the panic of what was to come but Des added a liberal coating of slimy river mud and ketchup to complete the effect. 'Okay, Tom,' I said, discreetly scanning about for any unwelcome adults, 'all you have to do is a long, sluggish Frankenstein type walk, with your arms out stretched, slowly down the bank and into the river, then disappear under the surface.'

'If you could give us a few bubbles as you go down that would be great!' shouted Des, directing from behind the camera.

Tom glanced down at the icy waters, his bottom lip beginning to quiver, 'But my mum said I wasn't to get messy again!'

'She'll never know,' retorted Des, 'you've got fresh clothes.'

'She always knows... everything!'

'How can she?'

'But it looks yucky and it's freezing!' pleaded Tom.

'It'll be fine, Tom,' I said, encouragingly, attempting to assuage my feelings of guilt. 'It's summer, the water's warm.'

Tom adopted the practiced pose of the past few days, stomping Frankenstein-like down into the murky waters. Without pausing, he continued as the water rose up to waist level. He turned momentarily in my direction, sad eyes pleading, hang dog expression on his face. Silently, I motioned him on. Suddenly he lost his footing, tumbling headlong under the icy water, disappearing completely from view. 'Cut!' I yelled.

'Brilliant! said Des, as Tom resurfaced moments later, spluttering, several yards out from the bank.

'Help' he yelled, struggling to stay afloat. 'I'm out of my depth! I can't swim!'

'Shit!' I exclaimed, leaping into the boat and releasing the line as Des watched, grinning from the bank. I reached out, grabbing Toms outstretched hand, dragging his scrawny, sodden body into the boat.

With hindsight, Tom's fear was probably understandable and his mother's unease undoubtedly justified. Tom had only just recovered from filming the opening scenes where the zombie had emerged from its grave – the school cricket pitch. Filming had taken place late after school at dusk, an ideal time we'd thought for a zombie to crawl from its grave.

We'd borrowed a couple of shovels from Tom's garden shed and dug a hole deep down until the ground became hard and the colour changed to a light clay. Peering down into the freshly dug pit, Tom was unnerved, but Des was confident. Whipping out a crumpled drinking straw he explained, 'Just stick this in yer gob, and breathe through it like a snorkel – you'll be fine!'

With the camera running, and its speed set to maximum for a slow motion effect, the last clods of soil were shovelled over Tom's freckled face. The effect was as dramatic as his acting was dynamic; he leaped screaming from the grave, the Bell & Howell capturing every last frame in striking slow motion. Everyone was impressed, except for Tom's mother, who had to deal with two weeks of nightmares and a nasty recurrence of bed wetting! It had taken until now to lift the curfew and allow him back on set to film the final scene.

12

*"It's all common sense, but unfortunately common
sense isn't all that common."*

A fire marshal, on the safe use of fireworks

T HE DROWSY SILENCE of the early evening was broken only by the occasional squeak of a bedspring and the flick of a page as Tom, sprawled on my bunk, scrutinised my latest issue of *Parade*. Under the bed, happily munching on a crunchy sock was Sukie, my chocolate brown poodle.

A heavy vapour of petroleum and sulphurous chemicals lingered in the warm summer air. Des was sitting behind me at a small table, carefully filling one ounce packs of powder whilst I busied myself at the main work bench with the production of a large 'dynamite' order. The ingredients were simple... take our standard mix, add a little petrol from my parents' lawn mower to dampen the powder and some setting agent, then compress into moulds and leave to dry. When dry, wrap in red art paper, printed "Dynamite!" Twenty sticks were already drying on the window sill when Des got up, stretched and wandered over.

As I turned, the blast of expanding gas enveloped us like a muffled thunderclap. There was a searing flash of yellow-white flame – whummmp! Des was thrown from his feet by the force of the blast, the gold tip of an unlit *Sobranie Black Russian* protruding from his stunned face, his Ronson comet cigarette lighter clutched in his outstretched hand! The impact of the blast had thrown me to the floor knocking the wind from my lungs. I couldn't hear anything except for ringing. I stared up in disbelief through the cavity that was once my window as pages of burning naked girls whirled into neighbouring gardens like confetti. Orange flames licked the exposed ceiling joists, and through the absent plasterboard ceiling I could see missing roof tiles and wisps of cloud in an otherwise blue sky.

There was a moment's shocked hesitation as the room filled with blue sulphurous smoke. The three of us scrambled to our feet and ran for the hallway, dodging burning embers, slamming the door firmly behind. I looked into Tom's shocked and blackened face, my ears still ringing from the blast, 'Do you think my parents heard?' I asked. He didn't answer, or had I simply gone deaf from the blast?

My sister was the first to appear, dashing from her bedroom with a: *"I'm SO going to tell on you"* look pinned to her face. Behind us, detonations, fizzes and crackles continued to rattle my door and in the distance rose the shrill sound of fire sirens. I was suddenly aware of a desperate whimpering and scrappling from behind the door – I hadn't gone deaf. I gingerly cracked it open – my bed was on fire, a single remaining curtain burning and smouldering wreckage everywhere. It was as though a bomb had literally exploded. Sukie bolted through the tiny gap, eyes wide, proud pom-pom tail drooping, her coat of tight chocolate brown curls an ashen grey. Shaking, she leapt into my sister's arms as the acrid smoke began wafting into the hallway, making it difficult to breath. I slammed the door shut again.

My ears were still ringing; everything happening in slow motion... the next sound was the crash of the back door flying open and the thud of urgent footsteps, followed by my parents' shocked faces. 'Oh, shit...' said Des, his voice sounding distant, the Black Russian finally dropping from his lip. 'You've done it this time, mate,' he said, 'they were in the shitting garden!'

I could see that my mother was distraught and I'd never seen my dad looking quite so shaken, but seeing the three of us standing there in one piece with Jane and Sukie, all clearly in shock, their relief was instantaneous and palpable. The sound of the fire engines got louder, then cut off completely as they pulled up outside. For a moment there was near silence, apart from a last few fizzes from behind my door.

I stood, head down, my left ear still ringing, miserably waiting for the deserved confrontation and whatever punishment was to come, but it didn't happen, it was simply too big an event for a normal chastisement. Instead my mother wrapped me in her arms and gave me an enormous silent hug of relief – there would be words, but that would all come later. At that moment, there was just relief. Suddenly firemen charged through the house, trailing hoses behind them. My parents led us to the safety of the garden. I'd got away with something that I shouldn't have… sadly my little business venture had lasted less than a month before coming to the most dramatic and abrupt end.

It was weeks later, almost 3.30 in the afternoon and Tom and I were moping about my redecorated bedroom awaiting Des's arrival. After the explosive end to my second business, and the flop of *Teenage Zombie,* money was tight. At twelve years of age, I'd fallen into the classic trap of living up to my means. Unfortunately those means had ended suddenly, but my expenses hadn't. The mooring fees for the speedboat had to be paid and were overdue. There was also an outstanding bill for an engine service. And there were more than a dozen kids at school with prepaid dynamite orders, all expecting refunds. If I couldn't come up with a plan and quickly, things could become messy.

They say that as one door closes another opens, but for the moment I couldn't see it. *There has to be a way out of this, I know there is,* I told myself. I needed to focus on the *whole* picture, not just the immediate problem.

The three of us had been fed up for weeks but, according to Tom, Des had apparently come up with a solution to our problems. Suddenly a secret series of taps resounded from my window and Des climbed in. 'Nice new frames,' he joked. He had a rucksack on his back and a silly grin on his face. 'Wait till you guys sees what I've got,' he announced, pulling the bag from his shoulder and retrieving a reel of 8mm film.

'Is that your idea?' I asked glumly.

'Just get the projector out, mate; you're gonna love this.'

I loaded the reel and switched on the projector. Des' black and white movie flickered silently against the freshly painted wall. The acting was dire but the content mesmerising. We all stared as a pretty girl strolled nonchalantly through the woods, stopping at a secluded spot. She spent a few moments provocatively pouting and examining her fingernails, then looked about fleetingly before stripping off for no logical reason. Now completely naked, she lay down in the long grass which unfortunately covered just about everything we wanted to see.

The film lasted less than three minutes. 'All very entertaining,' I began as Tom got up to flick on the light, 'but as always, you can't see the good stuff and I don't see how it resolves the cash... shit, Des!' I stopped mid sentence. 'Whoa! Steady on ...what are you doing?' Des was standing before us, trousers down, dangly bits tucked away neatly between his legs!

'What do you reckon?' he asked, matter-of-factly, striking a pose.

Tom rolled his eyes in my direction. 'I think you need to pull your trousers back up Des.' I replied uneasily as I averted my eyes.

'It's what they look like!'

'It's disgusting,' said Tom.

'Looks a bit like Kirk Douglas's stubbly chin!' I added.

'Better get used to it mate, it's what they look like,' replied Des wryly, as he pulled his trousers back up. 'Look, I can get these films from the *Exchange and Mart* for less than a pound a reel...' he went on, '...and we can charge at least that *per person* at the school movie club to watch them.'

'Nobody's going to pay a pound if you can't see any of the interesting bits!' said Tom derisively.

'My point precisely,' said Des, gesturing pointedly at his trouser area. 'We edit them... we add just a few very well chosen, tasty frames!'

'You mean we film your...' my words trailed away as the genius of his idea sunk in.

'We'll make a killing,' I murmured.

'As long as they don't find out,' Tom said. 'If they do, it'll be like the camera thing all over again and we'll be the ones getting killed!'

Once we'd got over Des dropping his trousers, we quickly got down to the detailed planning. 'Here,' I said, holding the film up to the light. 'This is the scene where she lies down naked. We could easily add a few extra frames there. We could film it down at the local woods.'

'What are we waiting for?' said Des.

'I think we should watch the movie again first,' said Tom.

Later that afternoon, with the sun fading fast, we set up in a secluded spot deep in the local woods. The area looked very similar to the scene in the movie with the naked girl. It all felt a bit pervy as Des quickly stripped off and lay down in the undergrowth, attempting to adopt a similar provocative pose to the girl in the film. The camera was set to go. 'Okay Des,' I said furtively glancing round, 'can you get rid of your... you know what?'

Quickly he folded the protruding proboscis out of sight. I peered through the viewfinder, zoomed in and squeezed the trigger. All we needed were a few teasing, tantalizing frames!

For over a week, earnest speculation mounted through the school grapevine – this time our film club production was a professionally produced movie from a very dubious Soho source. Demand was massive. On the night of the showing more than forty boys packed expectantly into the sixth form common room for the three minute show. Another fifteen argued outside that they should be allowed in, despite not having the required entry fee. A blur of excited chatter filled the stuffy room. Des dimmed the lights and I flicked on the projector. Each boy had happily paid the one pound admission fee. Silence engulfed the room, the only sound the clatter of the 8mm projector. Everyone was mesmerised, engrossed, as the girl wandered nonchalantly through the undergrowth before discarding her clothing. The camera panned over her naked body, suddenly there was Des's mock beaver! A collective gasp of excitement left everyone's lips, followed by a riotous cheer, then gasps of shocked admiration and murmurs of sheer delight at what they'd viewed. I could barely contain my laughter; fortunately any escaping sniggers were lost in the overall roars of excitement. The final frames flickered as the film ended.

'That went down well,' I whispered to a grinning Des.

Almost immediately chants of 'Encore, encore,' broke out around the room, accompanied by over eighty stamping feet, rattling the prefabricated timber building. A quick whip-round produced another sixteen pounds for a second showing. 'What the hell, can't do any harm,' I whispered to Tom. 'And it'll more than cover the production costs,' I continued as he rewound the celluloid epic and rethreaded the projector.

For a second time the girl began discarding her clothing and the camera lingered momentarily over her body, the frames jumping slightly as Des's missing manhood provided another collective gasp of appreciation. Suddenly the lights flashed on! I turned to see a stunned Mr Jenkins standing in the doorway, his eyes locked onto the still dimly flickering images, hand frozen on the light switch. A blast of icy cold air filled the room from the open door. 'Oh no,' squeaked Tom, 'this is so embarrassing ... my mum'll kill me!'

Instinctively I stepped back from the projector, as though it were infected. 'Middleton, Green, Willmot!' he barked, 'Headmaster's study tomorrow morning at 9.30. And turn off that filthy film immediately and hand the reel to me!' Jenkins eyes narrowed as he scanned the room, 'I want the names of every single boy here.'

13

"What does not destroy me, makes me stronger."

Friedrich Nietzsche (1844-1900)
German philosopher

NOW, MORE THAN two years later, I was fifteen years old and today was my last school day – my very last, and I couldn't wait for the final bell and official release that would set me free into the big wide world. That would happen later this afternoon when the headmaster would address the term's leavers at a special assembly. After that, I could wave goodbye to the stuffy classrooms and meaningless lessons forever.

Over the past week there had been little if any work to do other than handing back books and clearing my desk. I'd had various meetings, most of which related to how to sign on for work at the local unemployment office and there had already been two meetings with Mr Cheavers the careers master. However, for some reason I'd just been called back for another; this time my housemaster, Mr Jenkins would also be present.

I made my way down the hallway and knocked on the door. 'Enter!' I levered down the aluminium handle and stepped inside. 'Ah, William Middleton, come in and take a seat.' I made my way across the familiar woodblock flooring and sat as instructed in front of the polished desk. *What was all this about* I thought *and why was Jenkins here?* None of the other boys had been interviewed by the careers master for a third time. I wasn't at all sure what was going on. *Could they be trying to stop me from leaving,* I thought. *Or was I in some other sort of trouble again?*

'I'd like to come straight to the point, William,' announced Mr Cheavers. 'You're leaving school today with no academic qualifications and as far as I'm aware, you currently have no immediate job prospects. Is that correct?'

'Yes,' I replied.

His head shook with disapproval. 'So what exactly are your plans, William?'

'I want to be a racing driver or stuntman,' I replied.

'Don't be stupid, boy,' clicked Mr Jenkins. He flicked open a file and handed it to his colleague.

I said nothing. Mr Cheavers took a few moments to study the contents, 'I see you didn't even sit your eleven plus, William,' he asked sternly. 'Is that right?'

'Yes, sir,' I answered, still uncertain where this was all leading.

He turned a few pages before reading Mr Jenkins summary out loud. 'Unpredictable, preoccupied and doesn't mix well with the other boys,' he concluded. He closed the file and handed it back to my housemaster. 'The only teacher you appear to have impressed, William, is Mr Ascot, your science master, and much of what he says relates to your construction of that television camera!' Again, I didn't answer.

'There was also the unfortunate *corruption* of my film club,' added Mr Jenkins. 'An entire roomful of boys got themselves thoroughly over excited, and I had to deal with the irate phone calls from their mothers.'

Knowing how he despised me I couldn't help adding, 'Oh yes, I'd forgotten about that... I think you still have my reel of film, Mr Jenkins.'

'That was destroyed!' he retorted, slightly too quickly.

I locked eyes with him, 'Oh, I see,' I replied – clearly challenging his authority. I hated Jenkins and thought him creepy. He'd made my life at school a living hell, just like Mr Wickham. Jenkins seemed to consider everything I did as rebellion. If I *had* rebelled, it was purely coincidental, a result of frustration.

Mr Cheavers appeared to smile. 'I don't know that we've ever had quite such a resourceful young man at this school before. It's a real shame your creative endeavours aren't reflected in your school work. Now William, you need to understand that you can't simply set your sights on becoming a racing driver or such. It simply doesn't work like that.'

'Why?' I asked. 'How does it work?'

This seemed to stump him momentarily. 'Well... it just doesn't, and anyway, you'd need a great deal of money to start racing for example. You need to set your sights on something far more achievable. Perhaps a job on the building site labouring? Or at the nurseries – there are many of those locally, or one of the factories? There are numerous openings at the local exchange.'

At that moment the door swung open and the headmaster entered. 'Sorry to interrupt gentlemen,' he said. 'I just need to collect the files.'

'We were just trying to get through to young Middleton here, headmaster,' said Mr Jenkins. 'He's leaving us today and seems to think he's going to become a *racing driver!*' he lingered mockingly on his last words.

The Headmaster turned to me, spitting the words, 'You have been a problem from day one, with no good reason, Middleton. I don't see why it should change on your final day. Listen to me! Unless you sort yourself out, you will never amount to anything – is that clear?' He collected the files, turned and left the room without saying another word. There was a slight pause. Everyone was taken aback by what seemed to be a direct attack.

I sat there, feeling broken. My face must have registered a slight flicker of shock, because Mr Cheavers quickly added, 'Well, William... you're a very resourceful young man so I'm sure you'll find something out there. Who knows, maybe you'll surprise us all.'

Two hours later we filed into the assembly hall for the last time to hear a series of specially scripted speeches prepared in our honour by the various teachers. At the end of the leaving ceremony, a few dozen boys made their way up the steps and onto the stage to be presented with special awards – books, plaques or trophies. The headmaster shook each by the hand and posed momentarily as proud parents snapped photos. I had tried hard at school, but none of my achievements were considered worthy. In fact, nobody from the lower sets received anything.

A little later, I made my way out of the school gates for the final time with the headmaster's last words to me still ringing in my brain – *You'll never amount to anything, Middleton.* Burning anger coursed through me, causing the muscles in my shoulders to tense up. I could feel the twitch of a pulse flickering at my temple. I turned to Des, spitting the words, 'that's *their* assessment ... I know what I want to do and what I'll be, and it's not going to be labouring on a building site!' My voice had dropped an octave. Something inside me knew these past years were all wrong. I hadn't missed a day's school in over seven years. I had always tried my best, never been late, and always completed my homework, although I'd forgotten to bring it in on time occasionally. Even through my father's illness, my mother always ensured I was smartly turned out each morning in my school uniform. And even when terrified, and after running away from my Draconian boarding school that first night, I was back the next morning and although still scared, stuck it out. I'd been beaten black and blue for most of those seven years, occasionally lashed publicly with a leather strap and forced to fight for the gratification of teachers in a boxing ring. Regularly I'd been hit around the head by a teacher-propelled black board rubber and every day ridiculed – all by the very guardians expected to provide my education and nurturing. And I wasn't an isolated case; I'd seen others that had shared my fate.

It was all so wrong, the cruelty and injustice; the huge classes, the general disinterest and abandonment of the teachers, the lack of care. It was all completely beyond justification – I had so wanted to learn. I couldn't help being dyslexic! Whatever became of my future, however I evolved, the outcome would greatly be based on these foundations of waste and resentment.

'It's not their job to tell us we're just fodder, Des!'

'Okay, steady on mate...' he replied. '...was that all they said?'

'Oh, no! There was a lot more. Apparently I'm unpredictable, preoccupied and don't mix well with others. The only thing Cheavers said that made any sense at all was that I'd need to find a lot of money to get started. Of course there were no suggestions on how to get it. I think they were preparing me to *"embrace the likelihood of my impending failure!"'*

'You've always been pretty good with those big words, mate... and finding the dosh. I'd have just told them to get stuffed! Anyway, I'm going to train as a sparks.'

'A what?'

'A sparky... an electrician, mate. It's damned good money on the building sites once you're qualified.'

'I didn't mean to sound like...'

'I know you didn't, mate,' he said, punching my shoulder.

'I don't expect you to understand, Des. It's different for you...' I regretted my words the moment they left my lips. His life *had* been so very different from mine. Whereas I'd been surrounded with love, he'd spent most of his life in children's homes with no understanding of affection and only the vaguest memories of his family. As a result, he'd rebelled against the school, the system, the world, everything. I suppose that's what drew us together.

Two kids with totally different backgrounds, united in one area – us versus the system! All I knew, was I wanted to do something, something to prove the educational system was wrong. I wanted to shame them, not just for me but for all the kids that had wanted to learn and get ahead but had struggled and been abandoned.

'It's just been such a waste of all these years!' I said grimly.

'Ranting against the school is pointless, mate. Anyway, we had a few laughs and played a few games didn't we?' he said with a wink.

'Yes, we did,' I replied, 'and there's a whole world full of games out there Des... let's go play!

For years we'd been inseparable, but now a new world of work was leading us down different paths. Two weeks later Des moved from Southampton into a temporary home set up by the local council for older teenagers in Sussex, where he began his apprenticeship as an electrician. Around the same time I started work as a trainee test engineer at a local electronics factory. We parted as good friends and swore we'd stay in contact but it didn't happen. It would be almost three years before an extraordinary opportunity would reunite our friendship.

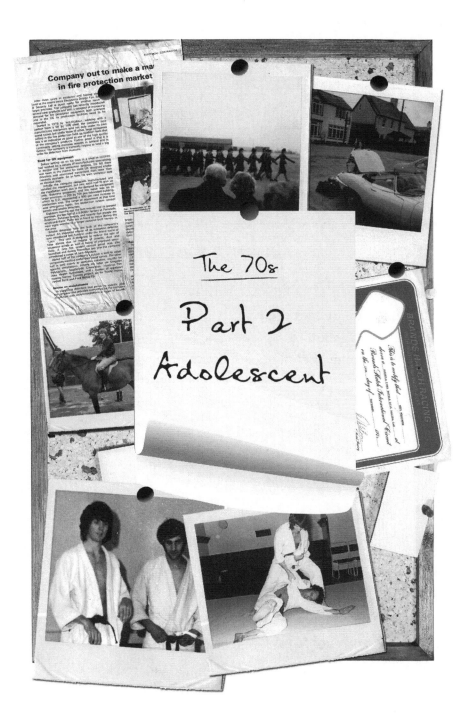

The 70s

Part 2

Adolescent

14

Approximately 3 Years Later

I S THAT WILL?' a familiar but slightly deeper voice asked.

It was almost midnight and I was standing in the hallway of my parents' bungalow, concerned that the ringing phone had woken them. Cradling the handset to my head, trailing the long lead behind, I stepped into the lounge, closing the door quietly behind. 'Yes.' I replied slightly irritated, 'Who's this?'

'It's Des, Des Green!'

'Des?'

'*Des!,*' the voice repeated. 'Your old mate from school, Des! How many Des's do you know? Don't tell me I never made no impression on you, mate.'

'Shit, man!' I exclaimed, 'it's been years. How the hell are you?'

'I'm doing well, mate. How are things with you?'

'Okay. I'm still working in electronics. I haven't quite made my fortune yet, but I'm working on it.'

'Ah, I was hoping you might say that. I just might have a little bit of business to put your way, if you're interested.'

'Always interested in making a few bob, if that's what you're saying?'

'I'm talking a few hundred quid, maybe several, if you're interested.'

'Definitely... what is it?'

'It's to do with some alarm systems over here in Worthing.'

Knowing Des's background I was immediately a little uncertain. 'What do you mean...' I hesitated, '...*alarm systems?*'

'Fire alarms mate. Electronics stuff. We'll need to get together for a chat if you're interested. I'll get my boss to send you some technical crap to look over,' he said. 'Can you drive?' he added.

'Yes.'

'Got a car?'

I hesitated... 'Err, yes I suppose I have.'

'Great... If you're free next Friday, you could scoot over here for a pint and a Chinese in sunny Worthing. I've got a little flat on Tarring Road, and there's a few spare blankets. You can kip on the floor overnight – we'll see my boss on Saturday.'

The following Friday I jumped into my beloved E-type roadster, dropped the hood and inserted *Pink Floyd* into the eight track player. I pressed the starter and the Jaguar engine burbled into life. The E-type was my first proper sports car, a 1961 flat floor model with a 3.8 litre engine with triple SU carburettors, described by Enzo Ferrari on its launch as: *"The most beautiful car ever made"*. Fifteen years on, and despite having several previous owners, it was rapidly becoming a classic, yet I'd paid just eight hundred pounds for it as a rusting hulk at the local car auction. It had taken the bulk of my spare time and most of my wages but the end result had been worth it. I'd spent most of the last eight months lovingly restoring it and had already been offered three times what it cost.

It was winter and the chill wind buffeted my hair as I cruised the motorway and down along the coastal road in the direction of Worthing.

'Shit man...' Des sighed, as I pulled up outside his flat and ratcheted up the handbrake'... what a babe magnet!' he cooed. It was mid October, yet despite the cold he wore a thin black T-shirt. A cobra tattoo snaked its way up one arm and his chin was adorned with a week's stubble. Although taller, he'd become skinnier with sharp cheekbones, his grubby drainpipe jeans serving only to exaggerate his gangly look. For just a fleeting moment though, I could see the old glint of excitement in his eyes, like when we were kids. A half-smile played on his mouth, but it was brief. There was a tired sadness in his pale young face. He shook his head, 'How the fuck did you get one of these at your age, man? It's just so unfair.'

I gave a noncommittal shrug.

'You're seventeen, man,' he went on. 'The insurance alone must cost a fortune!'

'Three hundred quid to be precise,' I said. 'And that's third party only. It's some company I've never heard of. Doubt they'd ever pay out if I stuffed it.'

We made our way into Des's flat and slumped into a pair of grubby armchairs facing an ancient television. Beside it sat a video recorder with a stack of lurid, pornographic VHS video tapes. Des sprawled back, his leg over the arm, foot swinging. Looking around the apartment, I could see walls had been demolished, forming one large living area, one wall covered with new pine wood-panelling. But wherever you looked, the work was unfinished; debris lay everywhere.

For the next hour we sat and reminisced. In so many ways we were complete opposites but by our second beer, it was as if we'd never been separated. Des expanded on everything his boss had sent the previous week in the post. 'It's not a bad job,' he went on. 'Pays reasonably well but hours are pissing long. They're just a small family firm,' he added. 'They've got this deal to fit alarms in these old codgers' homes. Trouble is, the boss's son priced it up wrong and the equipment cost is three times what he'd allowed for.' Des had told his boss he knew a whizz electronics guru, who could custom design and build everything at a fraction of the price – and that was where I'd come in, prompting the near midnight phone call.

By our fifth beer, we were stumbling our way through unfamiliar streets to his local Chinese. The restaurant was situated in Steyne Gardens, slightly east of the main town, about a mile-long walk from his flat. A police car shot by with its siren wailing, iridescent blue lights flickering about the busy streets, adding an air of drama and menace to the frigid Friday night.

Half an hour later we made our way up the steps and into the Jade Garden. The walls were painted a garish pink-blue and along them snaked carved golden dragons. It was past ten and the place was full to bursting, vibrant with people eating, drinking and smoking. Everywhere the buzz of busy chatter, the voices melding into a single drone; more than twenty tables, all protected with plastic covers, each with a bright artificial flower in the centre and all but one table laden with delicacies. Crossing quickly, we wound our way across the restaurant, through the overpowering haze of cigarette smoke mingling with aromatic oriental flavours that permeated the air, and sat down.

Overhead, more golden dragons writhed, coiling through elaborate blue-red lanterns from which maroon silken tassels hung forlornly, yellowing bulbs struggling to illuminate the garish interior. Opposite our table a large tank of bobble-eyed goldfish surveyed the evening's visitors curiously through their grimy green glass. I'd only visited a Chinese restaurant a couple of times before, and that had been a far more restrained, dignified dinner with my parents. I studied the sticky menu consisting of dozens and dozens of pictures, each dish a brightly coloured temptation. Eventually, Des beckoned to a young oriental looking waitress and ordered for the two of us. She disappeared, returning moments later with two pints of icy beer. 'By the way, this is Will, 'he said, introducing me, 'William Middleton. We're old mates, we go back a long way. Used go to school together when I was living over in Southampton.'

'What you do, Will?' she asked with a big smile.

'I haven't quite worked that one out yet,' I replied uncertainly. She turned and made her way back through the crowded tables to the kitchen.

'So, you certain you can build this stuff?' Des asked, watching the waitress disappear.

I took a sip of beer, 'It's simple stuff,' I replied, pulling out a pen and flattening out a thin paper napkin. Des watched as I began sketching out electronic circuitry. 'The control unit is little more than a battery charger, charging a back up battery and powering the smoke detectors around the building,' I explained. 'The only complicated part is that it has to monitor the wiring in case of faults and activate the alarm bells if any detectors trigger.'

'Doesn't it have to be approved or nuffing?'

'No, not even the big companies like Chubb have approved systems yet ... they just say they're built to the British standard.' I reached into my inside pocket and pulled out the slim booklet his boss had sent me. 'Here,' I said. 'British standard BS3116, it's the latest spec for automatic fire alarm systems. Your boss also sent me some marketing stuff from Chubb. I've already gone through it, there's nothing to it. I could make something almost identical.'

He cocked his head, 'But how do you detect smoke?'

'That's a bit more difficult,' I agreed, 'but I'm working on it.' There was a small seed of uncertainty in my voice. 'With luck I'll work it out in a week.'

'And without luck?' he asked.

'I'll sort it, don't worry. Compared with building a TV camera it'll be a piece of cake.' I said with a smile.

He shrugged slightly, as though recalling our childhood days, 'If you can make this stuff there'll be good money in it. All the old codgers' homes in town are being forced to install the stuff and at the moment only big specialised companies are doing it and charging fortunes!'

'I'm thinking bigger... what about the whole country?' I said. 'If they have to install these systems in Worthing, they'll be doing the same in nursing homes everywhere. This could be big, very big!'

The waitress returned and began covering the table with delicacies: sweet and sour pork, rice noodles, chicken curry, pancake rolls, roast duck in some kind of sticky sauce and a platter of mixed fried rice. 'There's enough here for ten, Des,' I exclaimed as I battled with my first pair of chopsticks.

'Who knows, maybe we'll get lucky,' he replied, admiring the waitress's trim rear as she scurried off.

'Do you know her?' I asked, in between mouthfuls of sticky pork.

'Sort of,' he replied. 'Her name's Ching Lan. Her father's the cook and her mother's French, or Belgian or something, I think.' He downed the last of his beer in one swallow before adding, 'She goes to the local college and works here most Fridays. Also goes to my judo club on Thursday nights. She's a yellow belt. I've been going for over two years, since I arrived down here. Just picked up my first Dan, black belt. You should come down and give it a try; it's great for picking up the birds.'

As Des talked, I got stuck into the other dishes. I wanted to try everything, but in no time I was filling up. 'I'm stuffed and I've only tried a few dishes,' I said.

Ignoring me and gesturing at the returning waitress with his chopsticks, he said, 'Her name's supposed to mean something about a bountiful orchard or something...' he shrugged. '...I don't know, maybe it's not bountiful, but I think it's beautiful though,' he slurred, as she came over and removed a couple of empty platters from our table. 'Two more pints, darling,' he requested with a lopsided grin.

'You drunk again, Des,' she said reproachfully, gathering up our empty glasses.

Ignoring the chastisement, he looked directly into her face, 'That's it, it means beautiful, beautiful orchard, doesn't it darling. Wouldn't mind ploughing that little orchard of yours one day... or is it a garden?' He let out a loud belch which seemed to rebound around the restaurant forever, causing diners to turn in our direction.

'In your dream, Desmond,' she replied scornfully. She gave me a smile and for some stupid reason I began blushing. She grinned again, turned and returned to the safety of her father's kitchen.

'What d'you reckon, mate?' Des slurred.

'She's cute,' I said.

'Yeah!' he replied lustfully. 'She says she's twenty, but I say she's younger, what d' you reckon?'

I shrugged.

'Bet you've had one or two in that Jag of yours, mate.'

'Not really,' I replied evasively.

'Not really?' he gave me a sideways look. 'You're not hanging onto it for the right girl are you, mate?' he replied mockingly.

'No! Definitely not... any girl would do,' I said looking longingly at Ching Lan, who was now bent over a nearby table clearing more dishes.

'Tell you what, mate. Come back next weekend and we'll nip over to Brighton to the Queen Ann,' he said. 'It's a stonking place... I guarantee you'll get laid.'

15

THE BASEMENT BAR of the Queen Ann had now been our customary Friday night starting point for more than a year, the aim always the same – chat up some girls for that promised night of wild sex. For more than a year, it had always ended the same pitiful way, with the two of us slumped together, barely coherent, reciting *Monty Python* sketches. Peering up at the open treads of the stairwell, we lived in hope of a quick flash of scanty knickers as girls tottered their way cautiously down the torturous open spiral stairway in short skirts and high heels. 'Do you reckon we're becoming perverts?' I slurred, in between John Cleese style chants of *'Albatross! Get your Albatross here!'*

Des slumped back in his seat, giving my question the serious thought it deserved. Finally he replied with his usual lopsided grin, 'No mate, we've been perverted for years!'

Over the past year, the fire alarm business had been developing well. The first three systems had long since been designed, built and delivered and we'd now begun installing our own jobs throughout Sussex. I'd rented a small unit, little more than a shed on an industrial estate, to build and store the equipment. Des had given up his old job and now worked for me full time installing the systems I designed.

It was yet another Friday and the air was, as always, thick with smoke as we made our way deep into the gloomy cellar bar and slouched into our usual seats at the bottom of the spiral staircase. 'We've got to fix all these false alarm problems, Will,' Des yelled. 'The last job in Chapel Road went off twice last night!'

I nodded in agreement. I had to admit, it was slightly perplexing. Everything worked fine when we tested it but then, for some unaccountable reason, we'd get a flurry of false alarms, usually around eight each morning, and then at random times throughout the day. Abba's *Dancing Queen* was rebounding off the confined walls, the melodious beat blocking any possibility of serious talk, so I left Des and pushed my way through the four deep crowd that permanently occupied the bar. A blue neon sign flickered its usual welcome as I shouted my order, attempting to compete against hundreds of watts of sound pulsating throughout the building. 'Two scotches with a dash of Coke in each,' I yelled. I hated scotch, but over the past year it had become another tradition, the intention being to get plastered as quickly as possible. The first round was always a single, the second a double, the third a quadruple. After that we'd become creative – an ambiosonic was eight scotches, a hexagantica sixteen. We'd never needed to get past that point.

Returning with two tumblers of potent liquor, I was surprised to see Des, deep in conversation with Ching Lan and a plump, buck tooth girl in white spandex whom I'd never met before. 'It's true,' the toothy girl was insisting, 'people have disappeared from up there.'

I slumped back down into my seat and handed Des his drink, 'Hi Ching Lan,' I said, 'what's up?'

'We just go dancing at Kingwest disco,' she said, 'drink here first. This my friend, Clare,' she gestured towards her mate of about twenty with lank mouse-coloured hair. I caught Des's *don't fancy yours*, expression. In contrast, Ching Lan looked stunning in a white t-shirt, short suede boots and skin tight blue hot pants that revealed every crease and curve of her taut little body. She smiled at me, and said, 'Not seen you for while, William. You no love me anymore? I thought you loved me?' she sighed teasingly.

Taken aback, I spluttered, 'Ermm...I've been busy with business problems. We keep getting false alarms. I've got to drive all the way down to Torquay next week to fix a job.'

'Oh, Torquay! My uncle, he live Torquay. Maybe you give me lift down when you go?'

'Absolutely...' I stammered, 'Ermm... just let me know and I'll pick you up,' I said, barely able to grasp that the moment I'd dreamt of, was materialising before my eyes. 'So... what's all this about the woods?' I added, trying to act nonchalant.

'UFO's,' said Des with a disinterested shrug, 'strange lights in the sky, people being abducted, aliens and generally creepy stuff!' a half-smile smirked across his face.

'It's true!' insisted Clare. 'It's in the local papers.'

I shook my head. 'What, people being abducted?' I asked in disbelief.

Her eyes transferred to me. 'Not sure if it's people or their dogs,' she admitted, 'but it says they disappear from Chanctonbury Ring, then return days later! It's really, really spooky.'

I laughed. 'Sounds to me as though the dogs just got lost,' I replied mockingly.

.My comment clearly hit a nerve. She gave Ching Lan a nudge, as though it was time to leave. Ching Lan looked about furtively, before passing Des a small wrap of something which he pocketed without a word. He gave me a look, a look that said *don't ask, mate... not now.* I ignored it anyway; I knew he'd been smoking some very weird stuff for months.

'You stay at Des's house tonight?' Ching Lan asked as she turned to leave.

'Yes.'

'Maybe I call you tomorrow,' she said tantalisingly. She smiled, then turned and disappeared off to the nearby disco, leaving us to more drunken debate on knickers, aliens and the prospects of my trip to Torquay with Ching Lan. Sometime during the night, as the scotch tally rose and adolescent banter on aliens probing poodles progressed, a brilliant idea evolved... A little prank destined to hit the headlines under the name of *The Mystery Whistler!*

Whenever we weren't at the hut working, Des and I would tour the various Judo clubs along the south coast. Since being introduced to the sport by Des almost a year ago, I'd trained around four nights a week, every week. My skills had become instinctively sharp, and although I was tired from the unrelenting workload, I was fit.

Sensei Joe Robinson stood 6ft 2ins tall with a large muscular physique. He was in his mid-forties and had his sandy coloured hair, cut with a boyish fringe. He was a 8th Dan judo world champion and also held a 5th Dan black belt in Wado-Ryu karate. As a well known stunt man and actor, he'd appeared in dozens of films. When he wasn't on a film set, he ran the only full time karate and judo dojo on the south coast, situated on the first floor of a damp and slightly rundown building in Vine Street, at the back of Brighton. It was he who'd awarded me my judo blue belt and orange belt in karate.

He considered himself to be my Sensei or teacher and was clearly unimpressed seeing me back in his dojo after a two months absence, proudly wearing my newly awarded brown judo belt.

'When did you get that?' he asked gruffly.

'Last week.'

'Who awarded it?'

'Des,' I replied.

'Let's see if you deserve it!' was his only reply. He clapped his hands loudly and the practice session that was going on stopped instantly, everyone returning to the edge of the mat, kneeling obediently in an orderly line of seniority.

Sensei Robinson called out for my first opponent and a tall broad shouldered chap, around the same age as me, wearing a brown belt, stepped forward smiling. I watched as he swiped aside a fringe of hair from his eyes. He checked, and then rechecked the knot on his belt – *perhaps a sign of nerves*, I thought.

Sensei Robinson beckoned us forward and I took a couple of steps onto the mat and bowed, my eyes never moving from my opponent. 'Hajime!' Sensei announced sharply, the Japanese word meaning *"begin"*; the signal to start the match.

I took a further step forward, leaned in and gripped the lapels of my opponents' gi. Immediately he attempted to block me, but failed and slipped his hand around my back. I felt his grip lock onto the back of my belt and knew instinctively he was about to try a hip throw. He began pushing and pulling, attempting to take control of the contest but his arms were rigid and I could sense each move before it began. He turned in for the throw, but I fended it off without difficulty. Using his own momentum, I eased him forward by his lapels, taking him fractionally off balance and in the same micro-second spinning in and dropping to my right knee. In that instant his body lifted, momentarily airborne, a split second later, crashing downwards. To the line of spectators it appeared he would drop on his head, but at the last moment I lifted, pulling up on his gi, sending him crashing down safely onto his back. 'Waza-aris!' yelled Sensei Robinson whilst raising his arm parallel to the mat – the second highest score achievable. Unfortunately though, I'd pulled up fractionally too sharply for an outright win and my opponent hadn't landed flat on his back. He was however clearly dazed, winded and disoriented.

Rolling first onto his stomach he brought his legs up, forming his body into a tight protective ball, inevitably leaving his back exposed. Reaching around from behind, I again grasped his lapels, levering back in a scissor action whilst wrapping my legs around his waist. I dragged him over, hauling him back with all my strength. I could feel his resistance draining, then the tap of submission. 'Waza-ari, awasete Ippon,' bellowed Sensei Robinson, holding his arm out parallel to the mat, and then raising it vertically. I'd won. I released the hold and we both stood and bowed, first to each other and then to our sensei.

I was about to return to the edge of the mat when I realized the test had only just begun.

Turning to the next in line, a yellow belted teenager, Sensei Robinson nodded and the next contestant rose, stepped forward and bowed.

As each opponent stepped forward, I allowed the lower grades a few moments dignity before consigning them to the mat or wrapping them in an arm lock or a choke. With my heart pounding, sweat saturating my gi, the line up continued; two more yellow belts, one orange belt, three blue belts and finally another brown belt. Finally Sensei Robinson nodded his approval before stepping forward smiling. He bowed and took hold of my sweat soaked gi. A few moments elapsed before I found myself flying through the air and slamming without quarter onto the mat, my right arm instantly wrapped in an excruciating lock. I tapped frantically to be released.

I rose, bowed and joined the rest of the students, pointedly taking my place at the end of the line, ahead of the other two brown belts.

Sensei made no further comment until later that evening, when to my surprise he called me over, wrapped a muscular arm around my shoulder and said, 'Not bad, Will. Not bad at all. Oh, and don't forget, before you leave tonight, I think your dues are a little outstanding.'

* * *

'Found it at the local Army Surplus store,' said Des proudly, as he unlocked the back of his Transit van and hopped inside.

I'd almost forgotten our drunken banter and gawked in sheer amazement. It was a huge hulking thing, taking up the entire back of the van. 'Shit, Des!' I exclaimed, 'What the hell is it?'

'It's supposed to have been used by the bomb squad for some sort of training exercises. It's a dummy 500lb bomb.' he announced, 'Cost me a fiver.'

'You sure it's a dummy?' I asked incredulously, without taking my eyes from it.

He raised an eyebrow. 'Will, mate, they don't sell *real* World War Two bombs down the high street! I reckon it'll make a brilliant alien space ship,' he said, tilting the device up by a tail fin. 'It looks just like a real rocket, don't you think?'

I had to agree it did look like a small rocket, and it was only last weekend that we'd been talking about pulling off the alien hoax. 'I suppose we could give it a bit of a paint job,' I said, 'and add some 'alienish' looking lettering down the sides. That might help.'

'I think it needs something a bit special,' said Des, 'something to cause a stir.'

'What... something more than tripping over a 500lb bomb?' I replied sarcastically.

'*Alien spacecraft!*' corrected Des.

'Okay, a 500lb spacecraft,' I agreed.

He picked up a powerful work torch, flicked it on and held the lamp against the glass fibre casing. 'Look, if you fitted some sort of lamp inside, the whole thing'd glow and light up all the strands in the casing. Looks a bit science 'fictiony' don't you think? Couldn't you put a lamp inside and make it pulse, like a heartbeat or something and give off some sort of futuristic sound?'

The idea was intriguing, 'Yes,' I said, now running with it, 'and if we planted it up at the copse at night, we could make it so it only triggers if someone shines a torch at it!'

Over the next week, I tinkered away on the electronics whilst Des worked at his flat on the spacecraft's appearance. The glass fibre casing had now been sprayed grey with unintelligible Cyrillic style lettering down the sides. He'd also scorched it with a blowtorch, to give it a look of having entered the Earth's atmosphere. 'Don't you think the lettering looks a bit Russian?' I asked.

'Naah, nothing like it,' Des replied.

We'd carefully cut out a panel to install the electronic circuit board, battery and a large base loudspeaker. And there were a series of light sensitive photocells attached to the control board through the casing. Des dimmed the lights and I switched the device on. In the dark it was completely dormant, but as I shone my torch at it, the thing let out a hideous piercing scream. A gradually escalating throb followed, like a rising heartbeat matched by a spooky pulsing glow as if awakening some demonic internal intelligence. There was simply no doubt, this thing was now very, very spooky and that was in Des's lounge. If you were to trip over it in the middle of the night up at Chanctonbury Ring...

16

"I stopped reading science fiction once I saw that the UFO was real. It became science fact that just hasn't been proven yet."

Mike Bird

FOR DECADES there'd been rumours of UFO sightings at Chanctonbury Ring. It was a desolate windswept hill top, crowned by an enormous ring of beech trees high on the Sussex Downs. The site had been well known amongst archaeologists for decades, their excavations unearthing Roman remains dating more than two thousand years. The place had not only gained a reputation for UFO's, but also for witchcraft, ghosts and all sorts of unearthly goings on. What's more, it was a favourite spot for couples in search of privacy and tonight they were our target.

Dusk was quickly fading to a shadowy darkness as we made our way along the rough gravel footpath, over a stile and up a steep rise that led towards the huge circle of trees at the top. Des was holding the front of our impressive "alien space craft", I bringing up the rear, clasping the end section by its tail fin. High up in the distance I could see an outline of the famous beech trees.

It took a good thirty minutes to reach the top. I paused for a moment, watching the dark clouds forming in the night sky. Behind us and to the south, I could see the twinkle of lights in the nearby town of Worthing.

Suddenly, just ahead, I caught an unexpected shadow of movement and then the silhouette of a couple appeared out of the darkness, a white scarf fluttering around the girl's neck. They strode quickly past us back down the hill, completely ignoring our impressive craft and disappeared into the shadows. 'You reckon people see a lot of alien space ships around here?' I asked Des.

'If you believe what the papers say, all sorts of strange shit happens here. Apparently, if you run around the trees seven times, Beelzebub appears and gives you a free bowl of soup. You do have to give him your soul in return. And you have to do it at midnight and anticlockwise or no damn soup.'

I instinctively flashed a look at my watch, it was just past 8.30. I hesitated, glancing back down the hill, then looked back at Des through the darkness, 'Are you sure this is the place to be doing this, Des?'

'We couldn't find a better spot,' he insisted, 'people are convinced aliens land here. A couple of years back, a group of nutters spent a whole night up here, scaring the shit out of each other and making recordings and stuff. They're supposed to have lost the use of their arms and legs, seemed to last about five minutes. I reckon they were just pissed or smoking some strange shit.'

Clutching Des's cumbersome UFO tightly, we continued stumbling further up the hill towards the trees.

Suddenly, just ahead, I heard a voice and the sound of suppressed giggles coming from behind a large tree. Des nodded in the direction of a clump of nearby bushes and we crouched down, fumbling along as silently as we could. Carefully positioning the alien craft, Des switched it on and we retreated back into a dip surrounded by undergrowth. For what seemed like hours we lay there in silence, only occasionally hearing a muffled voice or giggle in the distance. Finally I got up and checked my watch. 'This is pointless,' I whispered. 'It's gone 9.30 and nobody's taking any notice. Maybe we should find somewhere else, somewhere with more life.'

We got up, gazing around through the mist which had started to descend. A cold wind was now sweeping up the hill. The place was deserted. 'Perhaps we should try down town, or maybe further along at Arundel?' Des agreed with frustration.

Dejected, we gathered up our elaborate craft, turned and made our way back down the hill.

A little later we arrived in Arundel and made our way down Mill Road to the local Black Rabbit pub. The place was situated on a bend of the River Arun, with an extensive floodlit terrace and superb views of the local castle and river. It was a popular spot with locals and was buzzing when we arrived. Des parked his van at the top of the slope that ran down to the pub. He carefully unpacked the UFO, switched on its electronics, positioned it at the top of the incline and gave it a gentle shove.

For a moment, nobody moved as the device rolled to the bottom, resting by a startled Golden Retriever. Suddenly the UFO's photocell picked up the surrounding floodlights and it began its spooky, rhythmic pulsing light show. The dog's owner jumped up, staring in alarm. He took a few steps cautiously towards it and squatted down. Straightening back up, laughing, he turned to his expectant friends who were also now on their feet, announcing in the style of Inspector Clouseau, 'It's a *bomb*, but *not* of the exploding kind!'

'Oh shit,' I exclaimed, striding down the slope. 'I give up, doesn't anybody get it? It's supposed to be a damn UFO!' Pushing my way through the small crowd that was gathering around the device, I made my way to the bar. 'I'll get us a couple of pints before they close,' I called back to Des, who with the help of some revellers was repositioning the device on a picnic table, like an elaborate centrepiece.

On my return, I collapsed into a seat and taking a swig of cold beer asked, 'So, what do we do now with it?'

Des raised his pint in my direction and shrugged, but his reply amounted to just that.

I hesitated for a moment, then as nonchalantly as I could manage, I said, 'Changing the subject completely...' I paused, 'I have a question to ask you.' I took another sip of beer, wondering how to phrase my question. 'Is there anything going on between you and Ching Lan,' I finally asked.

My question hung for a moment before he answered. 'Going on?' he cocked his head, peering around our bizarre table centrepiece. 'What do you mean, going on?'

I shifted uncomfortably. 'You know what I mean, Des... *going on!*'

'Oh, you mean... like that? Oh, shit no,' he sighed. 'We're just mates. I know her uncle, he supplies me with some shit ... why?'

I shrugged casually, as if brushing off the thoughts that had occupied my head for over a week. 'I'm giving her a lift down to Torquay tomorrow night, dropping her off to her uncle's place in the morning before I try to sort out that fire alarm problem.'

'You jammy little sod...' a mischievous grin curled the corners of his mouth. 'When you get back, I want to know everything that's happened, mate... every gruesome little detail. Okay?'

'Yeah, I don't think so...' I hesitated, as a couple wandered past, admiring our table display. 'One question, Des,' I asked hesitantly after the couple had passed.

'What's that?'

'How the hell do I stop it going off the second she touches it?' I asked quietly.

'What do you mean, mate?' he asked, grinning.

'Come on, Des, you know exactly what I'm talking about... I almost shot my bolt last week when she turned up in those skin tight hot pants... I've been waiting for this for years! If she goes anywhere near it, it'll go off like...' I glanced at our device, '... like a bloody five hundred pound bomb!'

He gave me a wry smile. 'You just need to relax mate.... get a few drinks down you. Stop getting so worked up. Take a small bottle of scotch with you and if you stop to get something to eat, have a few beers. When you get to the hotel and she disappears to the loo, get the scotch down you, like at the Queen Ann. It'll chill you out.'

'You reckon?' I questioned uncertainly, a small seed of doubt sprouting in my mind.

'So, what are you going to do with the UFO?' I asked, draining the last of my beer.

'Well, I don't want the thing back at my flat and unless you want it, I reckon I'll dump the thing,' he took a sip of beer. 'There was a car park just down the road, near the castle. I'll leave it there.'

* * *

The room began spinning the moment I left the bathroom. Fighting hard to stay on my feet, I zigzagged in the general direction of the double bed where Ching Lan had already draped herself expectantly, a sheer white sheet pulled up to her shoulders, the fabric undulating above the sensuous curves of her body. Reaching the bed, I tugged back the sheet, staring down at her. My eyes swept up and down her curves, stopping abruptly at her tiny feet encased in a pair of short white ankle socks! *Why on earth has she kept those on?* Shaking my head, I glanced back at her toned body, her small breasts and jet black hair, tied back in a single glistening braid, coiling sinuously on the white pillow.

All of a sudden it hit me, a stirring that was quite the opposite of what I wanted and I silently cursed Des and his advice. Feeling increasingly queasy and still fighting the revolving room, I dropped the towel from my waist, letting it fall to the floor and slid in alongside her. Immediately she rolled over, straddling me with her slim, powerful thighs. Leaning forward, she traced the outline of my jaw and grinned mischievously. 'You love me, Will Middleton?' she purred, leaning further in and nibbling my ear. She whispered, 'Tell me how much you love me, say in my language,' she breathed softly, her warm breath caressing the side of my face, 'Tell me, Will. You say, *wu – ai – lin.*' I tried to repeat the words she wanted to hear but my mind was somewhere else – my stomach, where the chicken vindaloo was now having a very serious disagreement with the quart of whisky I'd swallowed in the bathroom.

I tried to do what I thought I was supposed to do, clumsily touching parts I had never touched before, but whatever I did clearly wasn't having the right effect. She pulled herself up, her face flushed, flicking wayward strands of black hair from her face. Her eyes flashed with frustration as she sat back, 'What wrong, Will? Me ready *now,*' she said, staring down defiantly. 'Why *you* no ready?' She shrugged accusingly. 'I no turn you on?' It must have been at that moment, that the vindaloo finally erupted...

It was almost mid day when I woke face down, naked and alone, with my head pounding. I stared at my wristwatch in disbelief as the telling red digital display faded into oblivion. For a few moments the fog in my brain obscured my senses, then it all came crashing back and I shuddered at the memory... *Never again* I told myself, I don't even like scotch...

You'd have thought by the age of eighteen I'd have known all there was to know about the female form, but no amount of distance learning could have equipped me for last night. I was totally unprepared, despite the years of fraught research. I could never have imagined just how smooth and warm that curvaceous body would be – well, I'd imagined it for months, but the reality was so different. I suppose that after all the years of waiting, the image was still a shock and the hastily gulped scotch on top of the curry we'd eaten en route, hadn't helped. Through the fog invading my brain, I could vaguely remember her cute little backside and the final defiant swing of her plait as she'd stomped off the bed. I must have blacked out seconds later.

The hotel room stunk like a brewery and for the first time I noticed a horribly large stain running down the bed to a pile of vomit on the floor. *That's going to be tough to explain away,* I thought. Turning onto my back, carefully avoiding the stain, I stared up at the ceiling as flies buzzed around me. The room was sweltering in the summer heat. I closed my eyes, trying to refocus my brain but when I reopened them, the room was spinning again, in odd circles. I eased myself up, clutching the wardrobe for support and then veered cautiously across the room, heading for the shower. As I stood beneath gushing warm water, my head slowly began to clear and I soothingly massaged shiny pink hotel shampoo into my scalp and temples. I groaned with disbelief as last night's fiasco replayed over and over in my mind, cringing at my own stupidity. Why the hell had I listened to Des? I hated scotch anyway... I only drank it to drown out inhibitions. That's it; never again I told myself.

I returned to the bedroom feeling a little better but still unable to get the image of last night out of my head, and downed a bottle of complementary water, gulping it in one go. As I searched for my clothes, the reality finally dawned that Ching Lan had gone – for good.

Once dressed, I opened the windows and did my best to clean up. As I left, feeling very embarrassed about the state of the room, I handed over a ten pound tip to a confused chambermaid waiting in the hallway. 'I'm really sorry,' I said sheepishly, 'the room's in a bit of a state.'

A week had passed since the failed UFO prank and I was eating breakfast at my parent's bungalow. My father was engrossed in the local paper. Suddenly his expression changed and he adjusted his glasses. In his sternest tone of voice he exclaimed, 'William! Tell me son, this isn't you and that friend of yours, Des Green!' He held out the paper, pointing at the headline: *"Arundel evacuated – Mystery Whistler Attacks!"*

Even though I was eighteen, I knew I was in for it whenever my father used my full name. I took the paper and quickly scanned the short article in gaping disbelief.

"A hoax 500lb bomb resulted in the town of Arundel being cordoned off on Friday night by the Army Bomb Squad. Arundel castle itself was evacuated after caravan park attendant, Tom Baker discovered the sophisticated device in a waste area. 'I was just completing my rounds' explained Mr Baker, 'when I found the device which had been carefully concealed amongst the rubbish. When I bent down and shone my torch at the device it let out a terrifying whistling sound!' The device was subsequently taken away for forensic examination..."

Shifting uncomfortably in my seat, stunned by what I'd read, I stuttered, 'But...but, it wasn't me,' I insisted. 'It was all Des's idea! It was just supposed to be a practical joke... a fake UFO!'

My father sunk down in his chair with a groan, 'Oh, William! What are we going to do with you?'

17

"Screw it, let's do it!"

Richard Branson

B Y EARLY 1975 my alarm systems were being installed into nursing homes all along the South Coast, and as word spread, demand continued to rise. With help from my father, I'd already moved the business from my bedroom into a small shed on an industrial estate in Sussex, employing Des as my installation engineer and first full time member of staff.

In the same year, the *Wall Street Journal* published an article headed *'Goodbye, Great Britain'* – the article was stark and to the point, telling anyone that would listen to get out of any sterling investments. The UK economy was on the verge of a total meltdown. Despite the general gloom and despair, my niche business continued to thrive and in 1976 I took on a second member of staff, Mrs Kemp; a very efficient lady in her mid fifties with steel-grey hair and sensible brogues. Immediately she set about organizing the office with proper books and records.

By March of that year, Harold Wilson had resigned as Prime Minister, James Callaghan had been elected and the value of the pound was plummeting like an out of control elevator, setting off major economic shockwaves. Industrial disputes were breaking out daily and strikes becoming widespread, yet still, against this backdrop, guided by instinct rather than knowledge, my fledgling business continued growing. The trouble wasn't getting orders, it was getting paid. Usually, despite Mrs Kemp's efficient chasing, it took around two months from completion of an installation before receiving the payment. Enquiries came in most days and fresh orders were piling up. My problem was cash flow, I urgently needed money for parts to fulfill new orders and pay wages. But in the economic climate, banks were refusing to lend money, especially to a twenty-one year old with no experience or qualifications. In all the uncertainty, the one thing I knew was that my survival would be precarious without proper financial support. I needed to find a backer almost as urgently as I needed to resolve the false alarm problems which were giving both of us more and more sleepless nights.

For over a week I'd been urgently working on a new smoke detector design. The previous week, by sheer chance, we'd finally discovered the baffling explanation for the constant false triggering. Although the problem occasionally occurred in the hotel jobs, the majority of nursing home installations regularly false alarmed. Even more baffling, there was a peculiar pattern. It usually started around the same time each morning and one room in the Torquay installation appeared particularly prone to the mysterious problem. I hadn't seen Ching Lan since our abortive night, so Des accompanied me on this latest trip. He'd somehow discovered the details of that fiasco, and mercilessly ribbed me about it throughout the entire journey.

As the detector was said to regularly false alarm at around 8.30 each morning, we'd set off early and by eight had arrived, and I was up a ladder in Major Drummond's room. I'd encountered the retired officer on each of my previous visits. Like most of the occupants, he was in his late eighties but unlike the others, he was quite a character, having served in both world wars with a commission in India, in the colonial service.

He was still tucked up in bed, suspiciously scrutinizing us through squinting eyes, his sprouting facial hair giving him the appearance of an enraged sea mammal. Climbing back down the ladder, I reported to Des, 'It appears to be working perfectly; I honestly can't see anything wrong with the thing.'

'Damn newfangled machine!' yelled the Major, his jowls now quivering indignantly. 'Goes off like clockwork every damn morning without exception *and* last thing at night. I could set my watch by the blighter!'

'I don't doubt you, Major,' I replied politely. 'It's just that it seems to be working okay now.'

'Blithering thing,' continued the Major ignoring me. 'Darned thing! Damn little red light blinks at me all night long!'

'Yes, Major…' I replied with restraint. 'I'm sorry about the L.E.D. but it's just to show it's working okay.'

'*Doesn't* work! That's the blessed point young man!' thundered the Major. 'Doesn't work, blasted thing… should be removed!'

At that moment two nurses arrived, wheeling in a commode. One, the younger of the two, had a newspaper tucked under her arm. 'Good morning, Major,' announced the older nurse cheerily. 'Sorry we're a little late for your ablutions this morning. Paperboy arrived late.'

'Don't know the meaning of the word punctuality nowadays. Little buggers should be strung up! That'd sort them out!'

'Quite, Major, but they'd be dead then, wouldn't they?' replied the older nurse matter-of-factly.

'Wouldn't do it again though, would they, little buggers…how we did it in India you know. Need discipline… spot of national service, that'd sort them out!' he added, flinging aside the bed clothes to reveal a pair of blue withered testicles and a shrunken penis, nestling in a bed of grey pubes.

'Now, Major,' said the older nurse sternly, bending down to retrieve his discarded Windsor-blue, striped flannelette pyjamas, 'we've spoken about you sleeping in the noddy before, haven't we? It's not fair on the junior staff, and you need your pyjamas to keep warm.'

'Poppycock woman! Simply can't abide the itchy things. Not good for one you know... need air to circulate!'

The younger nurse, trying hard to suppress a snigger, positioned the commode by the Major's bed side, and then turning to us with a big grin on her face, gestured that it was time to leave.

Still aghast at what we'd just seen, we rapidly left for the sanctuary of the hallway. We stood in silence with our backs to the door as a grumble of wind rose from the other side.

'That wasn't very pleasant!' I whispered, as a volley of farts rang out from behind us. Running a hand through my hair, I added, 'Anyway, it's really weird how the detector seems to be working fine.' Suddenly a nose wrinkling stench began seeping from beneath the Major's door. An instant later, alarm bell's rattled into life around the building and a few yards away, in the nurses' office, a repeater light flashed its urgent warning.

'Damn and blast the blistering thing!' bawled the Major from the other side as a further long-drawn-out squeal of escaping gas emanated, rapidly crescendoing into a series of irregular machine-gun bursts.

'Shit...' I said slowly, '...what the hell's happening?' Then suddenly reality hit me.

'Precisely,' replied Des with a nose wrinkling grin. '*Shit!*' Raising a hand to stifle a laugh, he added, 'You've invented the world's first fart detector, Einstein!'

In truth it wasn't funny – I had not only invented the world's first 'fart' detector, but I'd also installed around two hundred of them in dozens of old people's homes up and down the south coast – every single one would have to be changed! The original detectors turned out to be sensitive to practically every gas imaginable – the volatile Major, our key in finding the fault, just happened to be exceptionally gassy.

My mistake when dreaming up the original design had been to use a silicon chip commonly utilized in the bilge of ships, to detect the buildup of dangerous gases and prevent explosions. This chip was intended to detect *any* carbon based gas, and it had worked brilliantly when I'd tested it with smoke. I'd never imagined how the detectors would be affected in a confined nursing home environment by countless sulphurous whiffs – a vile pot-pourri of methane, hydrogen and dimethyl sulfide, all merging with propellants from competing industrial-strength air fresheners, the combined compounds drifting hauntingly throughout the buildings, targeting chips at random.

'How does it work?' Des asked, peering over my shoulder at my new design as I soldered a field-effect transistor into a bird's nest of components.

'It's a small americium ionization chamber,' I explained, 'and I'm passing a minute current through the air that's being ionized by the americium.'

'What's americium?' he asked.

'It's radioactive material, a minute piece of nuclear waste,' I explained.

Des stepped back in alarm, 'Where the fuck did you get hold of shitting nuclear waste, man?'

'It's nothing to worry about, it's a minute amount, less than you'd find in a luminous wrist watch. What should happen, is the transistor will sense the change in current flow, as smoke enters the ionization chamber and triggers the alarm.' I attached a test meter to the output of the device. 'There, try blowing some smoke at it.'

'How do you know all this stuff?' he asked, whilst removing a cigarette from its pack.

'Simple. I just look at what the other big boys are doing, and then do it better.'

'But it is safe?' Des asked, still uncertain.

'Absolutely,' I replied. 'The americium ionizes the air, allowing you to pass a current through it, and the carbon in the smoke disrupts the current flow. This is going to be the real money maker,' I said. 'The big companies are charging a fortune for these. I reckon we can make them for a couple of pounds each. Forget running around the country installing alarm systems. We need to be concentrating on manufacturing... churning these things out in thousands.'

Des lit his cigarette, exhaling a small cloud in the direction of the sensor. Immediately the meter registered, the needle climbing to a set point and a moment later, a bleeper began sounding.

18

"Love is the flower you've got to let grow."

John Lennon

WHENEVER WE WEREN'T working or involved in adolescent pranks or behavior, we'd scout the south coast judo clubs in what was usually an abortive search for girls. It had been that way for more than three years and I was now twenty-one.

It was mid August 1976 when we stopped off again at the Wick Judo club near Littlehampton. There was always plenty of fresh talent at the club, mostly in their mid to late teens, generally dispatched there by parents to learn the art of self defence. We welcomed them, like wolves inspecting a new born lamb straying into their lair.

We'd just set the mat out when the latest lamb wandered uncertainly through the door. Her younger sister, Barbara, had been a regular for almost a year, but this new girl was distinctly different. She was around five foot two and slim with dark brown hair held back in a pony tail. I strolled over as nonchalantly as I could manage. 'I'm Will,' I said. 'Will Middleton.'

'I'm Beth,' she replied, smiling shyly. 'Beth Turner.' She had sparkly brown eyes and, as I later discovered, was nineteen years old. 'Like the place?' she asked.

I shrugged, *'The place?'*

'In America?' she said. 'Middleton House or is it Middleton Park – it's in South Carolina, I think.'

'Oh, yes! We're somehow connected with it, but I've never been there. It goes way back to my great, great grandfather, Henry Middleton. How do you know about Middleton Park?'

'I'm Anglo-American. I was born over there, although I grew up in England. Does that mean you're very rich?' she asked jokingly.

'That'd be nice,' I said, 'but unfortunately no, I'm very poor. I do have plans to change that situation though.' I smiled but was suddenly struck dumb and couldn't think of anything else to say. Des had bet me a fiver that I couldn't get past the first five minutes, and as usual he was about to be proven right. Standing there feeling rather awkward, with him watching on the sidelines, I felt myself blush. At that moment if I could have, I would have fled, changing my entire life's path but I held my ground, finally managing to add in a strangulated voice, 'As this is your first night, I could teach you break falls if you'd like?' She nodded yes.

Later that evening my success continued when Beth and her sister agreed to join Des and me for dinner at the local Chinese. It was 10 pm by the time we arrived and the Hong Kong Garden was packed, with a John Lennon track playing in the background. We were shown to an empty table. 'Beers all round?' Des asked.

'Just water for me, please,' Beth replied softly. 'And a coke for you Barb?' she said, turning to her sister.

'So, what do you do for work,' I asked, attempting to start some sort of conversation.

'I'm still at college, studying music, but I'm working part time at a local nursing home, mostly dealing with false teeth and bottoms!' she added giggling. 'At least it keeps me in pocket money. What do you do?'

'I've got a business making fire and security systems.'

Des was still studying the menu but having already downed his first pint, he chose that moment to peer over the top and administer a loud belch, adding, 'He's also planning to be a famous racing driver.'

I grinned sheepishly at Beth, 'That was some time ago, when I was a kid.'

'So, do you race?'

'No, it was just a childish dream.'

'You should always follow your dreams. If that's what you want to do, you should go for it. I'm planning to join the army.'

'The army!' I replied, 'Why the army?'

'I love music,' she replied. 'I'd like to play professionally, so I'm thinking of joining the Women's Royal Army Corps Staff Band. As I say, you should follow your dreams. If you want to race you should go for it.'

'He's too busy building his electronics empire,' said Des with disinterest as the waitress arrived to take our order. 'A chicken curry and house fried rice,' he said.

'I'll have the same,' I added, 'but with a couple of pancake rolls.' I turned to Beth, who was studying the single card with her sister. 'What are you having?'

'We're not very hungry,' she said. 'We'll just share an egg foo-yung please, but no mushrooms.'

'I'll have to remember all this for our next date,' I said, smiling, 'You're Anglo-American, dislike mushrooms and only drink water!'

She cast a look at her sister but said nothing. I gave Des a look that said *I've just got myself a date* – but he was distracted, admiring the young Chinese waitress.

A few uneasy moments passed before Beth broke the silence, 'Did you see the horrible crash on the news last week?'

'The Niki Lauda accident?'

She shrugged. 'I don't know who it was but it looked terrible. I think it was somewhere in Germany?'

'It was Germany, at the Nürburgring,' I agreed. 'Up in the Eifel Mountains. James Hunt and Lauda were on the front row,' I said. 'Hunt was on pole.'

'What's pole?' Beth asked.

'It means he was fastest in qualifying, so he had the best starting position on the front of the grid,' Des chipped in, momentarily tearing his eyes away from the waitress' shapely rear.

To the millions watching on television or lining the track, it had appeared Lauda was already dead. All around the world, people had watched in horror as flames enveloped the scarlet Ferrari. In the centre of the soaring blaze, Lauda could clearly be seen, still strapped into his cockpit, slumped to one side – a white-flamed funeral pyre, the Ferrari a crumpled mass of twisted high-tech aluminium and magnesium.

The race had begun with the track still damp, the thirteen miles of twisting tarmac quickly drying. That's when it happened. On only the second lap, Lauda lost control at over 160 miles per hour, slamming into the barriers, then bouncing back across the track, disgorging fuel and bursting into a fireball. His Ferrari was then dramatically hit by two more cars, Harald Ertl's Hesketh and Brett Lunger's Surtees. Surely no one could survive the inferno that ensued. Yet amazingly, despite life threatening injuries, Lauda returned, swathed in bandages, just thirty-nine days later. Only one point was to separate Hunt and Lauda by the time the season's finale took place beneath snow capped Mount Fuji.

Formula One had had been growing significantly over the past years and each race was now watched by around 30 million viewers all over the world. The final round at Mount Fuji was to be a cliff-hanger, and then, adding to the drama, it rained heavily. Many drivers protested saying it was too dangerous to race. By the end of the second lap, Lauda pitted and withdrew, saying that the conditions *were* too dangerous. James Hunt ultimately finished third, becoming World Champion and at once a mega star, appearing in chat shows and television commercials and even alongside comedians, Morecambe and Wise.

Stories of Hunt's off track exploits also filled the newspapers. On the night prior to the Mount Fuji final, rumours abounded that he and Barry Sheene, the motorcycle world champion, had been ensconced in an all night orgy with around thirty British Airways stewardesses in Hunt's luxury suite at the Tokyo Hilton.

Watching the on-track swashbuckling between the calm, clinical Lauda and the hot headed, unpredictable Hunt, had rekindled my childhood aspiration to race and if further motivation had been needed, Hunt's alleged sexual exploits had provided all the incentive necessary to a naïve, hot blooded twenty year old – if that's what racing drivers got as part of the package, I'd wanted in on the deal. But with no family involvement in racing and no karting background other than a few years messing around in the school playground, I had no idea how to begin. I was also very aware that my clock was ticking; at my age most drivers were already well established – I was yet to find a way in.

For the last fifteen minutes Des had been pestering the young Chinese waitress. 'I think I'm in love,' he said, admiring her narrow waist and slim legs. 'How is it you say "I love you" in Chinese?'

'Wu ai lin,' I replied, without thinking.

'Can you speak Chinese?' Beth asked, clearly impressed.

Des cast me a knowing grin. 'He *used* to have a Chinese girlfriend,' he answered helpfully. She tried to get him to say it during moments of . . .'

'We broke up a long time ago!' I added quickly.

'Seemed like it was only the other week to me,' added Des sarcastically. 'Shit man, that hurt!' he exclaimed as my sneaker collided hard with his shin. 'What the hell was that for?'

Beth flushed slightly as the answer to her question became clear.

From that night on, we met whenever work or chores didn't get in our way. For me each date was the same, like the fizz or sparkle of champagne, but Beth was less sure. She came from a large family, both brothers and one sister having already left home. The remaining elder sister was clearly unhappy with my arrival and her disabled mother very unsure of my intentions – as a result I felt awkward when visiting the house.

As a family they were close and had always done everything together. My arrival threatened to change what had, until then, been a well ordered life of schooling and college, the girls dealing with the cleaning, polishing and other chores. My life had been very different, having been brought up by various nannies; living in a hotel, privately educated and now running my own business, I was slightly more experienced and independent. I was also two years older than Beth but despite her reservations, over the weeks that followed, we went everywhere as one; cinemas, restaurants, and ultimately for long passionate weekends in the New Forest, where I introduced her to my love of horses. In no time we'd become inseparable and within a couple of months, were engaged.

Over the next two years we spent all our free time in each other's company, took our holidays together and went horse riding; me cantering ahead over the moors, Beth trailing way behind, a worried look on her face. Less assured, she found both ends of the animal equally unpredictable, convinced the creature's only interest in life was to throw her to the ground or stamp on her size 4 feet. I however, lived for the freedom those weekends provided;

the heady combination of skin tight jodhpurs, friction, horse sweat and hormones were intoxicating, but then business would predictably get in the way and an exhibition, big order or trip, would sweep me off and split us apart for days or even weeks.

Over the past two years my firm's alarm business had grown exponentially and the new smoke detector was a major success. Propelled by legislation, we were now manufacturing them in their thousands, primarily branded for several of the UK's foremost providers.

My new business plan of principally manufacturing, rather than building *and* installing worked well, but Des hated it. He despised being restricted to the shed, often working sixty hour shifts, soldering components to circuit boards or packing products, ready to dispatch. For months he'd started arriving late, sometimes not at all, occasionally disappearing for days, even weeks at a time, generally becoming increasingly unreliable.

19

Just try me once and I might let you go, but try me twice, and I'll own your
soul... If you try me be warned this is no game. If given the chance, I'll
drive you insane. I'll ravish your body; I'll control your mind. I'll own you
completely; your soul will be mine. The nightmares I'll give you while lying
in bed, the voices you'll hear from inside your head, the sweats, the shakes,
the visions you'll see; I want you to know, these are all gifts from me....
...then it's too late, and you'll know in your heart, that you are mine, and
we shall not part.... Come take my hand, let me lead you to hell...

Unknown author

DESPITE ALL THE positive achievements, the success
brought with it ever increasing cash flow problems. I
desperately needed more finance and I also urgently had
to find larger premises.

My accountants provided the solution: George and Herbert
Deakin, two brothers looking to find a venture to capitalize. Both
were in their sixties, both experienced in manufacturing. They
owned several factories in Brighton and Lancing, mass producing
ovens for the catering industry.

Gerald Palmer was the senior partner of accountants Palmer,
Johnson and Brindthorpe. Mr Palmer was in his late fifties,
dressed in a dark pinstriped suit, overweight and heavily jowled
with an impressive mane of unruly silver hair and a trim goatee.
He was sitting behind his desk, intense blue eyes focused on the
file of papers he was holding. Behind him, practically all the wall
space was adorned with books or certificates. Palmer's tired face

broke into a broad smile. 'This is, in my opinion, an extremely good offer, Will,' he said, caressing his greying goatee thoughtfully. 'It will take away all the uncertainty and provide you with the premises you need, plus the finance to grow.' He got up from his chair and made his way over to a coffee machine and poured two cups. 'Black or white?' he asked.

'Black please,' I said, 'and no sugar.' I took the proffered cup and looked out of the window, deep in thought. 'But I'll lose control,' I said, turning back to him.

He shifted in his seat. 'You would retain forty eight percent of the company; they would hold twenty six percent each, so you remain the largest shareholder.'

'But I lose control,' I repeated emphatically. 'There are two of them and they'll always vote together, so I'll always be out voted.'

He shrugged, then smiled. 'Maybe,' he conceded. 'But it's a decision only you can take.'

'I don't think it's right; I don't think they understand the business. They're in their sixties, I'm twenty one. I've built the business from nothing. I know I've flown by the seat of my pants, but I've got it right more often than not. If these guys take control, I think we'll end up disagreeing, and then they'll simply out vote me!'

A slight frown creased Palmer's forehead, 'Will, at twenty two, you'd own forty eight percent of a company, with a four thousand square foot factory on a prime industrial estate, with a *proper* workforce. The existing overdraft will be underwritten and you'll have a company car, guaranteed financing, a good salary and dividends each year on your shares.'

'Dividends are set by the directors,' I said. 'If they don't want to grant a dividend, they'll have the power to withhold it.'

'They'll want to keep you happy, Will. You're the one that understands the technical side. That's your ace. Take this step and the company could be worth millions in a few years. There aren't many twenty two year olds that could achieve that.' He gave me a wry smile, adding, 'I have a boy your age. He considers it an accomplishment to get out of bed by mid-day. You should be proud of what you've achieved, Will. Take my word for it; this is an opportunity to move into the big time.'

In my mind's eye, I could see the big factory, the work force and the sparkly new company car. The negotiations had already taken several weeks and I'd also spent days talking it through with my parents. Gerald Palmer was awaiting my final decision. In the silence of the room I could hear Mr Palmer's laboured breathing. A few seconds passed before I looked up and smiled faintly. 'Okay,' I said slowly, 'I'll go with it.'

The legal theatrics lasted for weeks, with various documents being produced for signatures by both sides. I was divested of my controlling interest, the shareholding rearranged as Mr Palmer had advised. My role changed from Managing Director to Technical Director. Gerald Palmer and my parents felt it was all a wonderful opportunity...I wasn't fully convinced.

Work began a few weeks later on remodeling one of the brothers' many factories, a nineteen-fifties brick built, two storey building in Portslade, East Sussex. Existing grimy cream internal partitions were demolished and the surrounding walls painted a surgical white. A large open-plan production area was formed, with two long lines of assembly benches and a separate test and packing area established at the far end. The floor was re-tiled and an overhead line of fluorescents installed, to brightly illuminate the entire working area. A large storage section was fenced off securely at the start of the production line, the overall effect being to force a methodical progression from the arrival of component parts along the assembly line, to the test area and finally, to dispatch.

At the entrance, three comfortable sections were partitioned off in glass, one for me, one for Mrs. Kemp my indispensable secretary and a third as a sales department and showroom.

By the end of the first month we were employing four girls on the production line, plus a test engineer and, alternating between the store and the packing area, Des, supervising production.

By the end of the third month, I'd designed a swish line of emergency lighting and secured orders from major distributors for more than two thousand units per month. The production line was buzzing, and now boasted twelve girls, two test engineers and an apprentice, with Des now officially employed, in his new position, as factory foreman. The following month, we took on a full time sales manager, having sweet-talked him away from Chubb on a salary of twenty five thousand a year plus a company car, on the understanding that he brought with him double his salary in new business.

By the sixth month, Des had resigned, finding the discipline and daily demands of the increasing work force too much, despite the obvious rewards. His previous unreliability had worsened, starting in the first few weeks, arriving late, then days of unexplained sickness. But there was something else, something in his eyes, a deep sadness I couldn't comprehend. Our paths in life had been so very different and yet we'd always bonded. It was as though he didn't have the will or the energy to keep up.

For weeks I'd phone, but he'd never return my calls. Then one evening after work, I arrived unexpectedly at his flat in Worthing. I was surprised to see Ching Lan open the door. She let me in. The place was in semi darkness, Des hunched in one corner of the lounge, leaning against the unfinished pine panelling. He was unshaven, gaunt, his skin bleached white, body emaciated, and dark blue shadows had formed beneath his eyes.

'What's up, Des?' I asked, concerned. His eyes flickered momentarily, but he barely acknowledged me, remaining slumped on the floor between the piles of dirty cushions. In his lips he held a sort of hollow pipe or straw and in one hand a slither of shiny foil. Beneath it he clasped his old comet lighter, a jet of flame glimmering in the gloom.

I watched, perplexed, almost hypnotised in the near darkness, as the orange-blue flame flickered gently beneath the foil, sending shadows of light across the darkened room. Wisps of vapour rose out of the black tarlike granules crumbled on the foil, writhing up like uncoiling serpents. As each vapour swirled up out of the mist like a dragon's tail, Des followed it across the foil with the pipe, breathing in the mesmerizing haze. The effect was almost instantaneous. His eyes snapped fully open. 'Holy shit, that's good fucking stuff!' he said, then instantly his body relaxed as though warmth had enveloped him, his breathing becoming shallow.

Turning to Ching Lan, I whispered, 'What's he doing?'

'Des chasing dragon,' she breathed almost reverently, her eyes reflecting the enticing glow. 'You want try?' she added eagerly.

In that moment, I instinctively knew that Des's attempts to escape from the pitiless world that had deserted him, had opened an irreversible chasm between us. I'd lost my best friend and what I was watching was just too overwhelming, 'No... no way!' I replied without hesitation.

I got up and bolted for the front door.

As the first year in the new factory drew to an end, I was employing around thirty people, most of them on the production line, and all at least ten years older than me. My parents were elated. I was now twenty two years old – *at last,* they thought *, he's grown up!*

Production was at full capacity, orders piling in every week. Each morning I'd arrive at 7.30 in my latest 'investment', a 1967 metallic silver Aston Martin DB6. I'd found the car on yet another trip to the local auction and spent all my spare cash painstakingly restoring it. The DB6 gave me the impetus to carry on, as each night I collapsed into bed around midnight, totally exhausted.

When I wasn't designing a new product, securing another contract or manning an exhibition stand at Olympia, I'd be training or interviewing a new staff member. But since Des had departed, all the pranks had stopped, there was simply no fun. After he left, only very occasionally was there time to meet up for a chat or a beer with Beth and me at the Queen Ann. When we did meet, he appeared distracted, disinterested and agitated. All attempts on my part to discuss his habit and the negative influence of Ching Lan were met with an almost feral rage. Drugs took away his pain and his growing, insatiable hunger for the packages provided by her, dominated his life more and more as it rapidly spiralled out of control.

By the age of twenty three, I too was totally exhausted, but in my case from over work. I was becoming increasingly disillusioned and on the verge of my first burnout.

On reflection, the deal was doomed to fail. The brothers had no understanding of electronics, or the need for ongoing development. In the late seventies, the first microprocessors had been developed and I could immediately see that a revolution was just around the corner. But age brings with it experience, and at that time, I had the drive and vigour that foresees the future and impetuously runs with it. What I didn't see or comprehend, was the deepening recession and need for security.

George Deakin was of average build, and stood five foot eight with greying hair; he now scrutinised all financial matters. His brother Herbert was two years his junior, a little shorter and somewhat overweight. He had little to do with the day to day running of the business and spoke far less often, but when he did, he spoke with a breathless wheeze.

'We need to completely redesign our systems using microprocessor technology,' I said. 'These new chips are going to revolutionise the industry, dramatically simplifying installations and could virtually eliminate false alarms.'

George Deakin poured his second cup of black coffee and sat back, thoughtfully stirring in several spoonfuls of sugar. The fraught meeting had already lasted an hour and neither of the brothers was impressed with the thought of further investment.

George gave a weary sigh. 'Will, how can a little chip possibly do any of that?' he asked somewhat patronisingly.

'The chip's effectively a computer,' I explained enthusiastically. 'We'll programme them to interrogate our new second-generation detectors, for a series of preset criteria, before allowing them to trigger. Each detector could be coded and so individually identified by our control systems. These systems and the detectors will in future be able to "talk to each other",' I said excitedly, 'identifying that a *real* fire exists and showing precisely where it starts in the building. The control system's contain a constantly evolving database for each location, always learning, building up a virtual footprint of each detector's environment, so they wouldn't false alarm with the first whiff of smoke...'

'Hmmm... I'm sure', 'interjected the younger brother, a bored expression etched into his face. He leaned back in his black leather chair. 'Sounds like sheer lunacy to me, flights of fancy,' he went on, head shaking. For the last half hour he'd been sitting, arms rigidly folded across his chest, eyebrows knotted into a deepening frown. 'You need to focus on the *real* world, Will,' he wheezed, 'not some fiction, where you imagine inanimate objects talking to each other.'

George Deakin wearily rubbed his temples. 'I have to say, Will, we're a little disappointed. We've already invested in the original designs and neither of us have the slightest confidence that chips or "microprocessors" will be anything more than a fad.'

'But we could be world leaders,' I pleaded. 'We're small, so we can move fast... I could develop the systems within weeks, a few months at the most. The big companies would take *years* to catch up.'

From that point there were ongoing disagreements, as the two brothers instigated a new system of rigid control. My opinions were considered rash and ill conceived. The new inflexible measures threatened to derail any further development, interfering with my creativity as a designer. I became increasingly bored with merely overseeing the ongoing mass production as little more than a factory foreman. I began to dread each new day but out of all the friction, I gained a fresh and surprising insight... this was absolutely *not* what I wanted to be doing.

Although Beth and I had been engaged for over two years, no date had been set or even discussed. We weren't in any hurry, and both knew our careers were drawing us down separate paths for the time being; my only question was how long I'd continue working with "the brothers". Whilst my future was clouded by uncertainty, Beth's was not. A week earlier, she'd broken the news I'd been dreading – she'd finally signed up to join the Army, as a percussionist in the Women's Royal Army Corps Staff Band. 'It's just for three years,' she said softly. 'Remember, Will, this is *my* dream. I've always wanted to work as a professional musician. It's important that we follow our dreams.'

'But won't you be gone for months at a time?'

'No, I'll be based at Guildford, and once I've completed my six weeks basic training, we'll be able to see each other most weekends.' It was then that she handed me an unexpected gift, a present that would ultimately change both our lives forever; a large manila envelope on which she'd inscribed a heart and the simple words "Follow your dream!"

I flicked it open, pulling out a brochure from the famous Brands Hatch Racing School, along with a voucher for a try out day at the track.

24th November 1979

Les Ager was a slightly rotund, fifty-eight year old instructor with silver grey hair, and when not strapped into a race-prepared Talbot Sunbeam, he stood five foot four inches in his blue lace up race boots. '*Lovely. Lovely* boy,' he cooed, as I hurtled the Sunbeam into Paddock Hill bend for my penultimate lap. 'Now... much later turn-in for Druids, Will, and remember, clip the apex late!' he yelled with unabated enthusiasm. 'That's it, you've got it, boy!' he bellowed with excitement as I exited the hairpin, clipping the curbing with the right front wheel. '*Lovely! Lovely* boy, now up a gear and take bottom bend flat out this time, no need to lift!'

At last it was beginning to flow and I was having more fun than I'd had in years. I was going faster and faster, with Les shouting encouragement all the time, 'Oh, you *lovely* boy!'

Earlier that morning

Beth had accompanied me to the track the day before and we'd stayed overnight at a small B&B nearby, arriving at the circuit early Saturday morning. Seeing the track for real had been electrifying; my whole body tingling with excitement like the feeling of Christmases long since passed. The weather was bright and sunny as we made our way up into a grandstand and watched the cars circling the ribbon of tarmac that snaked its way before us.

Later, we walked through the tunnel, under the circuit to an office, and signed in. The trial started with a briefing in a small room with large windows overlooking the track. Then I was fitted out with a set of red fireproof overalls plus a safety helmet and introduced to Les and the car I was to drive.

The interior of the Sunbeam was no more than a shell, all comfort removed, only functionality important. In place of its original upholstery was a pair of light weight, ridged bucket race seats, each fitted with a six point race harness.

I pulled the safety helmet over my ears and attached the strap under my chin, the sounds of the track instantly muffling. Easing myself into the driving seat of the austere interior, Les leaned across from the passenger side, to help me fasten the Willans harness. I turned on the ignition and pressed the start button. The engine throbbed into life as a mechanic slammed shut the door. I stretched out my arms and gripped the wheel, pausing for just a moment. Then, selecting first gear, I released the clutch and exited the pit lane.

After several laps of getting it wrong, trying to go too fast too soon and generally over-driving the car, I pitted, and Les took over.

Now, effortlessly careering through corners, smoke bellowing from the tyres, he pitched the car one way first and then the other. I sat, rigidly clinging to my seat, feet firmly braced against the bulkhead, wide eyes fixed directly ahead through the windscreen, my heart pounding as we hurtled down straights and through bends. It all seemed terrifyingly fast, but totally in control, as he happily chatted whilst sliding sideways at 90 miles per hour into a corner. I couldn't help but compare him with my beloved Dad, who, at the same age had never exceeded a sedate 70 miles per hour in his life! The whole excitement exuded by this grey haired instructor as he showed me the correct lines, turn in and braking points was incredibly infectious.

Les pitted the car and we swapped seats, but this time as I drove, attempting to emulate my grey haired instructor, I heard his dulcet tones cooing encouragingly '*Lovely! Lovely* boy!'

During the lunch break Beth and I studied the list of my driving faults that Les had completed on an analysis sheet. Beth read it out to me as I hungrily devoured a large cheese and ham baguette.

'Well darling, he's given you eighty-one percent, so it can't have gone too badly...'

'It was fantastic.' I grinned. 'Even better than sex.' I looked up at her, 'Well... almost as good!'

Beth ignored me as usual and continued reading my first decent school report.

'It says you need to brake before changing gear but shouldn't touch the brakes as you go through the bends. And you're turning in too early on some corners but too late on others.'

I looked up as I finished my baguette and nodded in acknowledgement before turning my attention back to a pack of cheese and onion crisps, which as always, I struggled to open.

'Shall I go on?' Beth asked.

I nodded again and she continued, 'It says you're approaching the corners on too tight a line, and sometimes miss the clipping point. And then it says you're not heel and toeing.' She looked up at me with a grin on her face, 'Sounds like someone's finally got you dancing, darling! What's that mean?'

I shrugged, 'I haven't the foggiest idea,' I replied. 'Let's go find out.' I tipped my head back, pouring the last remnants of crisps into my open mouth. 'Oh... did you want some?' I asked, somewhat crestfallen.

'No darling!' Beth replied laughing, 'You were obviously very hungry!'

One hour and another briefing later, I lowered myself carefully into the moulded seat of my first Formula Ford single-seater. I pulled the helmet over my head and the hubbub of the track disappeared. A mechanic leaned in, helping to strap me in.

'Right! Just five laps... okay?' I nodded in reply. He went on, 'You're going to find this very different to the Sunbeam, so take it easy to start with.'

I grinned back through the slit in my visor. I loved everything about this thing; the smell, the excitement, the anticipation. It was like being strapped into the cockpit of your own fighter aircraft, sent out to do battle on the track. I looked down at the simple dashboard just comprising a few switches; a rev counter, and a water temperature and oil pressure gauge. The mechanic leaned back in, switching on the ignition and pressing the starter button. The harsh engine note vibrated through the chassis as the gauges rose, the rev counter flicking in time with the engine. Stepping to one side, he indicated I was clear to go. I selected first gear, raised the revs to just over 2000 as instructed, and exited the pit lane, leaving my first tramlines of rubber bubbling on the pit lane.

Over the next two months, I attended the school each weekend, each session being more fun than the last. I entered their winter series of races in the school's Sunbeams, always finishing in the top third, but never managing an outright win.

I'd become totally hooked. I'd always known what I'd wanted to do; I just hadn't known how to start. It was as if somebody had turned on a light, illuminating the path ahead. Now I knew precisely where my future lay, and plans rapidly took root and began growing. But to follow my childhood dream, would, to my parents, appear irrational and foolish. Still buzzing from my last school race, I chatted with Beth on the phone. 'My parents are going to kill me,' I said.

There was a slight hesitation before she answered, 'Why Will? What have you done?'

'Well, I haven't *yet*'...I paused for just a moment. 'But I'm about to.'

'What is it?' she sounded a little anxious.

'I'm going to resign.' I finally said. 'I want to drive full time as a professional driver. You know that's what I've always wanted!'

'Yes. But what about all the hard work you've put into your business? Are you sure it's the right thing? Is it what you really want? Are you *sure*?' Beth asked, picking up on my hesitation.

'More or less...' I replied, clearly still uncertain.

'Which one is it, Will, – more... or less?'

'More,' I said, a mischievous grin entering my voice, 'Definitely *more*!'

'Then *go* for it darling!'

And so I finally turned my back on the security of the electronics business and walked away from the four thousand square foot factory and my handsome salary. Selling my beloved Aston Martin for three times what I paid, I bought a hopelessly outdated Lotus Formula Ford with the proceeds and, to keep up appearances, another rusting restoration project; my first Italian supercar – a metallic silver De Tomaso Pantera.

For the next twelve months, I proceeded to crash into every Armco barrier and piece of catch fencing I found. When I didn't crash the Lotus, it broke down in protest, probably in fear of being propelled towards yet another barrier or hapless competitor.

20

"The day which we fear as our last is but the birthday of eternity."

Lucius Annaeus Seneca

BETH HAD BEEN in the Army for over a year when I got the phone call.

'It Ching Lan,' the voice said almost inaudibly.

'Hi, Ching Lan,' I replied, 'long time, how are you?' I said, surprised to be getting a call after all this time. The phone went silent. 'Ching Lan, are you there?' I asked.

'Yes,' she said hesitantly.

'What is it, what's up?'

'It Des...he gone.'

'Gone?' I echoed lamely.

'Gone...he dead!'

My parents had for some reason, always disapproved of my friendship with Des, even attempting to have us split up when we were in the same class at school, but they too were shocked by his sudden death. I'd never been to a funeral before, and Beth was unable to come, being committed to her service in the Army, so my mother accompanied me on a cold wet afternoon to the Worthing cemetery to celebrate Des's short life, and mark his passing.

A priest began saying some words. Furtively wiping tears from my eyes, I watched as the polished wooden box containing my friend's body was lowered slowly into the ground, the last rays of light glinting off the brass plaque on the casket lid.

I felt guilty... could I have done more, could I have stopped him? My thoughts revived memories. In my head I could still hear his playful voice; joking, scheming, encouraging me to come up with some brilliant new master plan. Casting my mind back, I thought of our nights out at the Queen Ann and the drunken sniggers as we attempted, and always failed, to pick up girls. I remembered our pranks like the "mystery whistler", and our years touring the local judo clubs when he'd been so fit and strong.

They'd found him slumped in his van, a syringe still imbedded in his arm – *death by misadventure* had been the official verdict.

I looked around, there were very few mourners. But all stood still and silent, some crying. A few threw clods of earth into the grave.

Ching Lan had wisely stayed away – I would never see or speak to her again – but years later I'd hear of her death, also by a heroin overdose.

My mother drove us home. I sat, still partially in shock, numb, mutely thinking of our early days at school with the film club, the TV camera episode and the explosives business, all the stuff we'd got up to when he was strong and outspoken, when we were both naïve. How could he now be dead?

I remembered it was he who'd started me off in business – the first systems going off all hours of the day and night with the early "fart detectors". If it hadn't been for him I thought, I'd never have met Beth! A last emaciated image of Des drifted into view; bone thin, a defeated look on his gaunt, lost, yellowing face. We'd been the same age but from such different backgrounds, yet drawn to each other from the first day we'd met. Back then I'd never imagined he'd end up turning to drugs as a means of escape.

The 80s

Part 3
Races and
Legal
Wrangles

21

"I want to be up front racing."

Dale Earnhardt

I WAS CURRENTLY TWENTIETH in the championship, which meant I had absolutely no chance of achieving anything more than a healthy overdraft, any reserves of cash long since gone. The previous week, I'd traded in my ten year old Lotus Formula Ford for a slightly more up to date Royale, so I now had a racing car that was only five years out of date, but naïvely, I still attempted to take on teams with brand new cars, fresh engines and tyres plus a small army of mechanics. I only had Ian, who, with no formal training, did his best to run my "team".

Ian had just turned eighteen and was tall and skinny with short cropped brown hair and a spotty complexion. He'd left school a year earlier, with a host of 'O' levels, unlike me. However, whilst I knew where I was going, he had no idea whatsoever and had happily tagged along for the ride ever since. He was loyal and willing to take on whatever jobs were necessary, so long as I managed to fill his constantly empty stomach.

Some weeks earlier, endeavouring to fulfil that commitment, I had secured a lucrative deal with a catering company at Gatwick, who produced pre-packaged airline meals in foil containers. In return for a tiny sticker on the race car, we had taken delivery of more than fifty cartons of precooked chicken supreme, all neatly packaged up, storing the perishable produce alongside our cans of diesel, petrol and oil in the boot of the car. This was Ian's first race since suffering three days of projectile vomiting and diarrhoea which had followed a weekend's gourmet feast from which I'd seemed strangely immune.

We arrived at Brands Hatch, via the rear paddock entrance at just after 7.30am. Having put in for a weekend's leave, Beth had joined us and was fast asleep on the back seat. Ben the security guard emerged from his wooden hut and offered a cheery smile, handing over an envelope filled with passes. 'How'd you manage it, Will?' he asked. 'No one else gets extra passes.'

I took the envelope and peered inside. 'Woohoo... looks like I hit gold this time... fifteen... no, twenty!' The previous week I had phoned the race organizer, John Nichol; a great guy that was always willing to help, and begged him for the extra passes for the sponsors attending the race. In truth, the only sponsors I had were merely providing me with printed team T-shirts that I could sell for a few pounds but it all helped.

'There's a caravan show in the lower paddock,' said Ben, 'you'll have to set up in the top half.' He strolled over to the wire gate and pulling it back, beckoning us through.

'I'm famished,' said Ian as we made our way into the upper paddock. 'I could do with some breakfast if the clubhouse's open.' He looked hopefully in my direction for agreement.

'Ditto,' I acquiesced.

In the paddock we quickly selected a perfect spot close to the signing on office and scrutineering bay. Beth woke up and the three of us carefully wheeled the Royale, with its "Sussex T-Shirts" logos, backwards off the trailer and covered it with a tarpaulin, taking care to secure it down with some rocks and bricks, and then made our way over to the Kentagon for breakfast.

Inside, the place was packed. As we sat munching away at eggs, sausages, bacon and toast, Ian pointed to a man sitting at the bar drinking coffee. 'Do you recognise that chap?' he said, pointing with a ketchup covered knife.

'Shit!' I exclaimed, 'it's the guy from TV, the actor chap, what's his name...'

'Gareth Hunt,' said Beth, 'from *The Avengers*. He's quite dishy!' she added, suppressing a grin. 'What do you think he's doing here?'

I was already on my feet, heading in his direction, intent on finding out. As always, I had no idea what I was going to say but this was an opportunity not to be missed.

'Hi,' I said, lamely, offering a slightly greasy hand. 'I'm Will, Will Middleton.'

'Hello, Will,' he replied in a deep, rich familiar voice I'd heard so often on television. 'How are you, and what can I do for you this fine morning?'

I grinned sheepishly, 'Well... quite a lot I expect, if you don't mind?'

It turned out that he was at the circuit taking part in a celebrity race, driving one of the race school's Talbot Sunbeams. 'Buggered if I can get the hang of that first corner,' he said, 'Paddock Hill bend? I've been practicing half the week. Still get it wrong.'

Ironically on television he was playing the part of a character called "Gambit" who was supposed to be a suave, sophisticated ex racing driver turned crime fighter, so he was expected to put up a good show, not trail behind at the back of the pack.

'I'll be going out to qualify in about an hour,' I said, confidently. 'I can talk you through it if you like and you could watch my lines from the Paddock Hill Grandstand.'

A little later, my new best friend, Gareth, having already posed for photos by my race car and now bemusedly decked out in our sponsor's T-shirt, made his way to the grandstand to watch me qualify my very second-hand Royale, with its worn out engine and old tyres.

Making my way up the slight incline and out onto the track, I weaved the Royale back and forth, attempting to heat the three year old Dunlops supplied with the car – *"They'll be fine..."*, the guy had assured me as I'd peeled off the last of fifteen hundred pounds – *"Still shit loads of tread left..."* he'd said, tapping the fossilised rubber with a sturdy Doc Martin.

Down Cooper Straight I sped, knowing the famous actor was watching, scrutinizing my every move for tips. I turned into Clearways with the Royale sliding wildly – *whoa, that was a bit weird,* I thought. *Never mind, Gareth is watching!* I floored the throttle, flat out in top gear down the pit straight. Ahead, Ian was holding out a blank pit board indicating his place along the pit wall. I shot past and up the incline underneath the starting gantry, then over the brow, 90 miles per hour, 6000 revs registering on the counter as the 100-metre board flashed past. As taught by Les, I aimed directly at the marshal's post, then punched the brake, noticing as the front wheels locked in clouds of smoke, that Gareth was standing alongside the marshals directly behind the barrier, doubtless an honoured guest. With smoke still billowing from the locked wheels, I fought for control as Gareth's perplexed expression switched to one of alarm, his piercing blue eyes widening beneath his mop of thick curly hair.

At the last moment Les Ager's relaxed tones rang out in my head – *off the brake, lovely boy! That's it! Oh, lovely, lovely!*

As I lifted, the Royale veered sharply right, slamming sideways into the steel barriers, its fibreglass bodywork shattering into shards, everything now happening in slow motion. The front left wheel detached completely and looped its way majestically downhill in a series of arcs as the marshals began waving yellow warning flags. Still gripping the wheel, I tilted my head and through the slit of my visor stared directly into Gareth's shocked eyes.

Slowly I released the six point harness, and amidst clouds of escaping steam, stepped calmly from the mangled wreck. Gareth, now relying on many years of acting, was endeavouring to hold himself together, 'Are you okay, Will?' he asked seriously, trying hard to suppress a mischievous grin that was creeping across his face.

'I'm fine,' I said with a weary sigh. 'Pride's a little dented,' I added, now grinning beneath my helmet, 'but not quite as badly as that thing!' I gestured at the wreck being manhandled off the track by the marshals.

'Well, if there's anything I can do to help...'

'Thanks,' I said, returning a flicker of a smile as I removed my helmet. 'I may well take you up on that!'

Later the same day – Brands Hatch

A mobile crane lowered the Royale sadly onto the trailer and Ian set about removing any bits that were likely to drop off on the journey home.

With the car wrecked and with Gareth's home phone number tucked safely in my pocket, Beth and I set off for a look around the caravan exhibition in the bottom paddock. *It was always possible I might find a sponsor*, I thought.

Some time later, I stood with Beth, listening intently as a short man in a flashy race suit chattered away to a potential backer, 'Ermm... I'm looking for around a grand,' he said. 'Um... that would be for the whole car though,' he added hesitantly. 'Ermm, ermm, it *could* be repainted in your company's colours... if you wanted?' he said, beseechingly handing over a dog-eared paper. The man scanned it briefly but seemed unimpressed. He smiled politely and began moving away. 'You could always consider part sponsorship...' the short man's pleading voice tailed off as his eyes then focused on me. I wandered over to the display car and bent down, unclipping one of the typed flyers held in place by a bulldog clip.

The old Crossley Formula Ford was finished in black, with Douglas Print signwritten down the sides. 'Are you interested in racing?' his voice enquired eagerly from behind.

Straightening up I heard myself reply, 'Well, possibly....'

'If you're interested, I'm looking for sponsors,' the little man said smiling eagerly. *Aren't we all?* I thought.

He was of similar age to me but stood only five foot two, with a thick mop of brownish hair that was already beginning to recede at the temples and bore more than a passing resemblance to the singer, Phil Collins.

'I see...' I said, trying to sound like a potential backer. 'What are you looking for?'

'Well, ermm... I'm looking for a couple of thousand pounds,' he replied hesitantly, then quickly added, 'but, um... for that you could have most of the car and it could be painted in your company colours, if you liked. What do you do?'

'Oh, the black would do quite nicely – we're a family business of undertakers,' I replied gravely.

'Oh, ermm... an undertaker?' I could hear the alarm in his voice.

'Yes. I recently inherited the business,' I continued. 'We're trying to find ways of giving the profession a more up to date look. I was actually thinking of advertising somewhere on the track,' I said. 'Which bends have most crashes?'

'Um...' his mouth opened and closed a few times giving him the look of a stunned goldfish, no words emerging.

'Of course, they don't have to be fatal,' I added quickly. 'That wouldn't be very tasteful. We'd just like to let people know we're around... you know, if needed.'

'Oh, er, I see...' I could see the uncertainty in his eyes. He dropped his cigarette and stubbed it out with his raceboot.

'Do *you* crash often?' I asked, noticing for the first time the name badge on his race suit. 'Robert Allan, is it?'

'Yes, Rob Allan...' he said, offering me his hand. '...and well, ermm, there are quite a few crashes in this formula, but I try to win.'

Frowning, I gave him a weary sigh, 'Pity,' I said. 'Not as spectacular as going up in flames. That would be far more in keeping with our line!' I replied as dryly as I could manage. I could see Beth's face was on the verge of cracking up so quickly stepped over to examine the displayed car. 'Have you considered offering advertising space on its underside?'

'The underside?' he repeated, clearly now unsure if it was a wind up or a genuinely eccentric potential backer. 'Well, you can have the underside for free if you take the rest of the car,' he said, giving me the briefest flicker of a smile.

'Do you think you could give the bodywork some sort of flame effect?' I enquired.

'I'm a graphic artist, so I'm sure I could come up with something you'd like.'

'Well, I'll give it some thought,' I said. 'Okay if I take one of your information sheets?'

'Yes, that's fine,' he said, sounding a little disheartened, 'my phone numbers on the bottom if you're interested in discussing anything further.'

I began to move away with Beth, 'It's quite scary how you manage to come out with such twaddle, and make it sound convincing,' she said sotto voce.

I shrugged, still scanning the flyer. 'You know this stuff he's written isn't at all bad,' I said. 'It's just the way he's presenting it, and he's certainly no salesman. You'd think if he's a graphic designer and has a printer for a sponsor, he'd get a professionally produced brochure for a start, not this scrappy piece of paper...' I paused for a moment, thinking back to my bartering days at school, the seed of an idea forming. 'Now...there's an idea,' I breathed.

To progress through the formulae, I needed to find a sponsor, and finding a sponsor ranked somewhere close to finding intelligent life in Westminster – next to impossible.

How could I sell the idea? I thought. *Why would anyone want to sponsor me?* *Well, I've Gareth Hunt for a start,* I thought, *and he's prepared to help!* Thinking back to the wheeling and dealing of my school days, I'd always had difficulties with *written* words, but rarely when it came to presenting something face to face – selling an idea. But I didn't exactly have the most up to date race car to "sell" or a top team to catapult me to the front of the grid. And without proper backing, I wasn't able to test, so my only opportunity to learn on track or practice against more experienced drivers was during an actual race. I also had no idea about mechanical setup, how to make the all important tweaks to make the car go faster. I needed to break through all these barriers and I needed to do it quickly. The key to everything, I concluded, was presentation!

Armed with the promised support of Gareth Hunt and having studied Rob Allan's scrappy handout, I began to formulate a plan. Over the next few days I reshaped his flyer, picking out key points and highlighting the objectives of sponsorship. I also persuaded Gerald Palmer, my accountant, to write a short section of text outlining the tax benefits of corporate sponsorship and the payback in terms of corporate hospitality.

Three weeks later, following meetings with two local companies, a paper supplier and a printer, I was holding the proof of my own glossy ten page full colour sponsorship brochure, produced for free, in return for their names on the race car. The next step was getting the race car – a new one.

I decided I'd had enough of crashing out in Formula Ford 1600s, and I wasn't getting any younger, I needed to get a move on. *Why couldn't I jump to the next formula,* I thought, *Formula Ford 2000?*

"RJ Hair" wasn't on the whole the sexiest sponsor to have on the side of a race car but if they'd provide the necessary funds, that was all that mattered. They were a large fashionable chain of hair salons planning to expand, opening their latest outlet in Brighton's trendy Churchill Square. John, the senior partner, stared back at me, his eyebrows now knotting into a deep frown. He was in his late thirties, used to the far less stimulating chatter of ladies having purple perms or artfully disguising the shiny patches of his male clientele. For the last half hour he'd listened intently to my sales pitch as I'd enthusiastically outlined my exciting proposition.

'So, we'd have your guaranteed assurance, that if we purchase this Delta race car for you Will, Gareth Hunt will open our new Churchill Square salon?'

'That's correct,' I said. 'And of course you'll have the Delta itself on show for the actual opening, prepared in your corporate colour scheme with RJ graphics at no extra cost.' I handed over a copy of my smart new brochure, which appeared to endorse a well funded and highly professional team.

For a few moments he studied the glossy pages, eyes narrowing. He looked up. 'And we could keep the graphics on the car for the first race?' he asked.

Got it! I thought... 'Yes, that would be no problem at all,' I replied, trying hard to suppress my excitement.

A slight grin spread across his face and he offered me his hand. 'Okay, Will. We have a deal. Who do I make the cheque out to?'

With a new car, a gleaming new (1950s) transporter/ mobile home and the stickers of more than a dozen sponsors, it looked like I'd arrived and was suddenly a major player. The reality was very different; I had just about enough cash to pay the race entry, race fuel and the diesel to get us to the track.

22

"Dream as if you'll live forever, live as if you'll die today."

James Dean

Brands Hatch – 2nd August 1981

I WATCHED IN DREAD, knowing there was absolutely nothing I could do. A six point harness clamped me rigidly in place; captive. Gripping the wheel of my stricken Delta, I braced myself for collision, as the midfielder accelerated directly at me; this time it was really going to hurt! Agh! Then nothing...

The shock of the impact echoed in my unconscious mind, waking me momentarily and I attempted to sit up, but the pain was unbearable, disorienting, a blazing white brightness burning in my skull. Something or someone was trying to hold me down. Suddenly the light changed to iridescent flashes of blue accompanied by the wail of a siren. A face came blearily into focus. 'Don't move son, you're going to be fine,' a man whispered calmly. 'We're just cutting you out of your suit ... okay?' Cautiously I dropped my head back onto the stretcher – *not the new suit, don't cut the suit,* I thought. Then darkness...

A nurse's voice, 'Hi Will, how you are feeling?'

'I hurt ... everywhere!' I replied.

'You're doing just fine. We're keeping an eye on you overnight,' she said, pouring water into a glass and feeding me painkillers. 'Beth, your fiancée, has been on the phone, asking about you.'

'Is she coming?' I asked.

'I think there's some problem getting leave. She's in the Army isn't she?'

I nodded painfully. 'Yes, she's in the Women's band, in Guildford.'

'Well, I think she's actually in Canada... some kind of military tattoo? Her boss isn't being too sympathetic about allowing Beth back. She sends her love and she's going to phone you in the morning.' The nurse slipped a tape measure around my waist and made a note on my chart.

'What are you doing?' I asked. No answer, just darkness...

Daylight. A group of four doctors in white coats, stethoscopes draped around their necks entered the ward, accompanied by a female nurse. She pulled the curtain around my bed, isolating us from the rest of the patients. A doctor began an examination, whilst chatting to his colleagues. 'One of two drivers admitted, following accidents at Brands Hatch yesterday,' he began, directing his briefing at his colleagues. He studied my chart. 'Mr William Middleton. Arrived 3pm yesterday by ambulance, with concussion; ribs eight and nine broken right side, third degree burns to both legs and puncture wound to left shin.' He paused for a moment holding an x-ray up to the light. 'Looks like there's a cracked vertebra as well,' he added.

'Doesn't sound too good when you put it all that way,' I chipped in.

The doctor's mouth reflected a wry smile. He turned to me, pale blue eyes encircled by wire frames. 'They do say – *"What doesn't kill you makes you stronger,"* Mr Middleton, however in your case I'd have to say you're pushing the boundaries somewhat.

Perhaps you should consider something a little safer in future? Bull running maybe? '

'We learn from our mistakes,' I conceded.

'Well, after this last weekend, you must be quite knowledgeable!' he replied with a grin. He held up another x-ray image, and turning back to his colleagues, added. 'Puncture wound may have been caused by the steering column shearing off in the crash. Nice clean injury, no debris according to the pictures.' He lifted the bed sheet examining my legs first, and then leaning over me, he began probing my side. I gasped in pain. 'Possible damage to the right kidney,' he went on. 'Some signs of internal bleeding last night.' He replaced the sheet, studying me momentarily. 'Know your limits Mr Middleton or you'll run out of luck.'

'I wasn't anywhere near my limit... in fact, I wasn't even moving,' I added ironically, 'a guy just crashed into me. Anyway, we make our own luck.'

He shook his head, his reply amounting to just that. 'Well, how are you feeling?' he asked.

I shrugged 'Fine, I think, except for my head and side. They hurt like crazy. Any idea when I can go home?'

'We'll be making a decision on that over the next few days,' he replied with a slight wave of dismissal, eyes switching back and forth between me and the chart. 'Do you remember what happened?' he asked.

'Yes, as I said, I was T-boned by another driver.'

The doctor removed a torch from his breast pocket and leaning back over me shone it into each eye in turn. 'Any problems with your vision?' he asked.

'Only when someone shines a light in my face,' I replied drily.

'Quite!' The torch clicked off. 'What about dizziness?' he added.

'No, nothing like that, just pain in my side and head.'

'Good, very good, at least the old grey matter's still okay. Can't say the same for your helmet, I'm afraid. Smashed to bits apparently! Anyway, I'll pop by tomorrow to see how you're doing.' They all turned and moved on to the next bed.

Another nurse came over.

'Damn, that helmet was three hundred quid's worth.' I said. 'And that prodding really hurt!'

She smiled as she plumped up my pillows, 'Best three hundred pounds you could have spent.'

I pushed myself up painfully into a sitting position. 'And the suit, that was another three hundred!' I replied dejectedly. 'I remember now, they cut me out of it.'

She fed me some more pills. 'The tablets will help with the pain' she said, 'but I'm afraid I'll be disturbing you every few hours for more measurements. They're a little concerned about the internal bleeding.'

'Okay.' I replied gloomily.

'Cheer up! At least you're in one piece,' she said, pulling back the curtains, 'and there's certainly nothing wrong with your memory... that's very good.'

I woke to the sound of wheels squeaking on hard tiled flooring, accompanied by a slight whirring noise. I'd been dozing... I looked up. He was strapped into a black motorised chair covered with racing stickers, his legs and spine paralysed, his motionless head supported by padded restraints.

'Hi Will,' he said, 'I'm Paul.' His chair moved towards me in a series of small jerks, its motor controlled by a permanently clenched right hand. Clipped to one side, a clear plastic bag hung, partially filled with urine, its tube snaking up his immobile leg. No older than twenty, a mass of crooked muscles and twisted nerves, his gaunt face was lined with pain. Yet, imprisoned in his cruel world, he was smiling at me.

A nurse had asked if it was okay for him to visit me. 'He lives in our high dependency unit,' she explained, 'he's been there ever since the accident. He always likes to visit other drivers when we get them.'

'What happened to him?' I asked.

'He was brought in from the track around two years ago... competing in a race and went off backwards into the barriers, breaking his neck.'

I cringed at the thought of it – a moment's mistake only, but in that moment everything had changed forever; life in a wheelchair, being dressed, fed, cleaned, undressed, put into bed.

Becoming seriously injured, particularly the thought of being paralysed or losing my legs, had always been a secret fear, but it was just that... a *secret* fear. We know the dangers; we know it could happen ... we just put the thought to the back of our minds. But I had talked to Beth, and even given her the private phone number for a well known surgeon – a precaution, just in case it was ever needed.

Paul and I sat quietly for a few moments before he asked, 'So, what happened?'

'I was going to ask you the same thing,' I said, 'but wasn't sure if I should.'

'It's not a problem; at least it's not anymore,' he replied evenly.

A nurse brought some tea. Paul sucked his through a long stripy straw as we sat talking. 'I was in a Formula Ford race at Brands,' he went on, 'a few years back. Crashed on the second lap,' He thought for a moment before adding, 'A group of us broke away from the main pack. I was challenging for second place, trying to outbreak a guy into Paddock bend. I got hit from behind. Everything happened so quickly; I spun a hundred and eighty degrees, ended up backwards in the barriers at Paddock bend. My head restraint snapped with the impact and my helmet went back through the roll cage,' he paused, the next words were spoken in a murmur. 'The worst bit's waking up every day.'

The expression left my lips without thought. 'Shit!' I said.

'You could say that,' he sort of shrugged, the only way he could, more of a facial gesture.

'I'm sorry...' I said, 'really sorry.' Listening to him with my few injuries made me feel like a fraud.

'It's okay. As I said, it's not a problem...I now live here in their Elmstead Unit. Anyway... what happened to you?'

I watched Paul sucking up the remains of cold tea through his swirly straw as my thoughts turned to last weekend. 'It was the challenge race for the *Pace Petroleum 2000 event*,' I explained, 'My first race in a Delta and I'd qualified fifth. In fact it was my first ever race in a formula 2000 car. I'd just got a new sponsor, a big chain of hair salons, and they'd paid for the car. I'd also managed to get a personal backer, Gareth Hunt, and he'd been helping with promotions.'

'The actor chap?' asked Paul, taken aback.

'Yeah, he's playing a character called Gambit in *The New Avengers*. He's supposed to be a suave ex racing driver turned spy. He's a really nice chap. It's thanks to his backing I got the deal just two weeks before the race.' I gave a weary sigh. 'Then it all went wrong...'

23

> *"I think we all wish we could erase some dark times in our lives.*
> *But all of life's experiences, bad and good, make you who you are.*
> *Erasing any of life's experiences would be a great mistake."*

Luis Miguel

THE DELTA FELT good and positive, the Dunlop slicks giving much more grip than my old Formula Ford 1600. By the third lap a group of us had separated off and I'd moved into fourth, challenging Nigel Corry for third. I drifted out of Graham Hill Bend, along the short back straight, inching closer all the time to Nigel's Royale. As we entered Clearways I eased up the inside but he cut me off.

Nipping back under his rear wing to reduce drag, we drifted out of the sweeping right hander, into fourth gear, slipstreaming down Cooper straight, flat out in top gear. My pit crew held out a board, "P4", "48.9", "7 laps to go". We blasted past, beneath the starting gantry, up over the brow, over 100 miles per hour, 6600 revs registering on the counter. The 200-metre board flashed past and I shot out of the slipstream, punching the brake but Nigel moved across and our wheels interlocked momentarily. With sweat running down my face, stinging my eyes, I flicked the Delta at the apex and floored the throttle; 6900 revs as the car bottomed in a cascade of embers. Side by side up the hill, 98 miles per hour as we approached Druids. Now I was level alongside but my entry was far too tight. I hit the brake and flicked into second gear, 50 miles per hour as I turned in, my front inside wheel almost touching the red and white kerbing, the back of the Delta already breaking away as I fought for control. Nigel braked deep into the bend, taking the classic line and late apex as I spun out of the hairpin in a cloud of acrid smoke. The engine died, my stationary car straddling the exit.

Marshals raced to raise yellow warning flags as I twisted my head in the direction of the looming pack now exiting Druids. Russell Spence swerved his Royale, dramatically missing me by millimetres, David Mercer and Charlie Kirby took to the grass on either side of the track. I watched in dread, the six point harness clamping me rigidly in place ... captive. Gripping the wheel of my stricken new Delta, I braced myself as Richard Martin accelerated directly at me....

Disturbing dreams began to invade my mind as I slept – Paul's pale face appearing before me; his emaciated body, and the squeak of the wheelchair, the sounds of his laboured breathing. His words possessed me, gripping me like a vice... Then, intertwined with Paul's words, the doctors voice: *concussion! ... ribs broken!... burns to legs!... puncture wound to shin!... cracked vertebra!* The powerful thoughts and tangled images, something between memory and fear, became a virus, invading the pathways of my mind, the seed taking root in my sleep the night following my meeting with Paul. Negative, disorienting dark thoughts endangering my hopes, dreams and ambitions... What if the unthinkable *should* happen? All racing drivers know it could happen, but we never quite believe that it will... not to ourselves... what if it had happened or did in the future... what would happen to Beth? We'd planned to marry as soon as she finished her service in the Army. What if we'd got kids?

The watch alarm bleeped on the bedside cabinet, waking me from the nightmare. Carefully I pushed myself up against my pillows and looked about the hospital ward. Other patients were still sleeping, the room cloaked in shadows, but a light was glowing dimly in the nurse's room just outside the ward. I glanced at my watch, exactly six o'clock, the alarm set from two days earlier. My head still ached and my tongue felt like cotton wool. I took a drink from the tumbler on the bedside, and cautiously eased myself out and onto the tiled floor. I desperately needed a cup of tea. Unsteadily I made my way towards the nurse's office and tapped softly on the door. There was no response, so I knocked a little harder until a female voice responded.

The night duty nurse was in her mid twenties with almond-shaped eyes and tanned skin, her dark hair piled up beneath her white nurse's cap. She looked tired. 'Hello Will,' she said raising a hand to stifle a yawn. 'How are you feeling this morning?' She put down her pen and stretched.

'A lot better thanks,' I replied. 'Don't suppose there's any chance of a cup of tea?' I asked pleadingly.

'Sure, come in and pull the door to. We don't want to wake the other patients.' She got up and flicked the kettle switch. 'We get a few in from Brands Hatch most weekends,' she said.

'I know. I met one of them yesterday!' I said.

'When did you start racing?'

'Couple of years ago, although I did play around with go-karts for a time when I was a kid, but nothing serious.'

'Were you always into sport?' she asked.

'I do a bit of horse riding now and then... I suppose that's a sport?' I shrugged, 'I was into Judo once but that was a few years back. It was a good way of getting rid of aggression when I was angry with the world. Trouble was I was always getting hurt, but other than that, not really.' I said. 'I've never been into team sports anyway.'

'That's a bit unusual, isn't it?'

I nodded. 'I was at private school and it was very sporty. I hated it. Playing sports was a sort of badge of honour; trouble was I didn't feel any loyalty to my school, so wherever possible I avoided it. Not a lot of point in trying to win for a regime you dislike.' I said thoughtfully, watching her pour the boiling water. 'I suppose it is a bit strange thinking about it... I'm probably the only one from any of my schools that went into professional sport.'

'Milk and sugar?' she queried.

'Just milk please,' I replied, still thinking.

She handed me a steaming mug of tea. 'What does your fiancée think of you racing... doesn't she worry?'

The virus was instantly back in my brain like a knife wound. I shrugged. 'Possibly,' I said evasively 'but if she does, she hasn't said anything. She has a strong faith,' I added. 'She believes there's a higher power watching over us.'

'What about you, do you have the same belief?'

I paused, sipping my tea. I wanted to believe, I told myself, and I did believe. But deep down inside there was uncertainty, a dissenting voice that wanted answers to all the questions where Beth simply relied on faith... But then there was another more patient voice, counselling me, asking me to keep seeking. 'Yeah,' I finally managed, 'I suppose I do.'

I looked around the ward at the grey faces peeking out from beneath their white hospital sheets. I'd been in St Marys four days now and time was passing slowly. I was getting increasingly restless.

A volunteer arrived, pushing some kind of trolley with a phone. She plugged a lead into the wall behind my bed and passed me the handset. 'It's your fiancée, phoning from Canada,' she said.

'Hi Will, are you okay?' an anxious voice asked.

'Yes, I'm fine, Beth, just a bit stiff. How's Canada going?'

'It's okay. Lots of different bands from all around the world... What have you done? Is anything broken? They wouldn't tell me much.'

'I've broken a couple of ribs and got a few burns on my legs.'

'Burns!' she repeated in alarm. 'Did it catch fire?'

'No! Just the damn fire extinguisher! It went off automatically in the crash and caused freezer burns on my legs.'

'What about the internal bleeding? The nurse said you were being monitored overnight.'

'That's all okay,' I said, 'I'm fine. I'll be out before the end of the week, honestly.'

Another volunteer appeared, pushing a trolley filled with an assortment of newspapers and magazines. I selected a copy of *AutoSport*, the bible of motorsport. Flicking through pages I found the *Pit & Paddock* section. A heading instantly leapt from the page: *Will's hairy escape! by Marcus Pye.* I scanned the article – *all publicity is good publicity*, I suppose, or so they say.

Turning to the report of the weekend's race, I pressed the call button on my bedside. A few moments later a nurse appeared. 'Hi Will, what do you need?'

'I was just wondering... do you think there's any chance of me going home today?' I asked.

'I'll ask your doctor, but I think it's unlikely. He'll be seeing you on his rounds before lunch. You can talk to him then,' she said. 'So, who won the race in the end?' she asked, motioning at my open *AutoSport*.

'Chap called Tim Davies, he's Welsh.' I said, scanning the report. 'He's very good.'

'Never heard of him.'

'You will do, he often wins.'

'You can't be doing too badly yourself if you were in third place.'

I laughed, 'I was in the challenge race when the accident happened, it's a sort of qualifying race. I don't think Tim Davies would know what a qualifying race is!'

She didn't seem convinced and left me flicking pages.

The afternoon came and with it the doctor with the pale blue eyes and wire rimmed glasses.

'You're going to be here for another week or so, I'm afraid,' he said with grim resolution.

'That's impossible...' I stuttered. 'Look, I really do appreciate everything but my next race is only two weeks away and I've got to get the car fixed!'

'I don't think you'll be fit to race for a few months, Mr Middleton, certainly not in a couple of weeks. The broken ribs may be painful but given time they'll heal. The burns on your legs however could easily become infected and we're not sure yet about the damage to your kidney.'

Later that afternoon, against all medical advice, I signed my own release papers and made my way stiffly to a waiting taxi. Opening the passenger door, I tossed a bag of *Hydrogel* dressings I'd been given for my burns onto the back seat and eased myself painfully into the front seat alongside the driver. As he set off, I flicked open the doctor's report, prepared for my GP, turning a few pages. It didn't make good reading but, thinking back, my reports never had.

24

"Mistakes are a part of being human. Appreciate your mistakes for what they are: precious life lessons that can only be learned the hard way. Unless it's a fatal mistake, which, at least, others can learn from."

Al Franken

THE TAXI WAS AN OLD Subaru Leone, its driver in his late fifties. He fired up a cigarette and cracked his window down an inch. 'Don't mind if I smoke?' I didn't answer as the smoke was already drifting, the question rhetorical. I settled back for the thirty minute drive from Sevenoaks to Brands Hatch, the scene of my recent downfall.

On arrival, I was pleased to see the Delta's transporter, an old 1950s school bus, was still parked where I had left it in the lower paddock, on the morning of the race. The old bus wasn't merely the race car's transporter; it also served as my temporary mobile home.

Less than three months ago, I'd removed all the seats, fitted a ramp and roller shutter door at the rear and had been living in the thing for the past eight weeks along with my faithful "mechanic" Ian and another friend who'd recently joined us, John. The idea was that before next season, we'd convert the front into proper living accommodation, but for now our lodgings amounted to just one large open workshop with three makeshift beds. Also sharing the restricted lodgings was 'Deadly Doris', a six inch Mexican Red Knee tarantula who, having swapped life in the scrubland of Panama, now resided happily in an aquarium beside John's mattress.

As I entered the bus, I removed my jacket, dumping it on the floor alongside a pile of filthy clothes. It was Thursday, a general test day, and the high pitched drone of racing engines circling the track reverberated in the air. I stood beneath the stark florescent lighting surveying the wreckage that was once the Delta. 'It's a total mess,' I said dejectedly to my team. The car was banana shaped, two wheels hanging from their uprights, the steering wheel buckled, the nose and green bodywork missing, destroyed by the impact. Even the seat I'd been strapped into was smashed. I rolled my shoulders, attempting to ease the tensed muscles in my back and neck. 'Is it fixable?' I asked.

'Anything's fixable,' Ian replied, 'It's just whether it's cost-effective to do it.'

'It'll cost a fortune,' I said morosely. 'It'll need a new chassis for a start. Why the hell did the guy ram me like that?'

'It might help if you stopped spinning in front of people!' Ian said mockingly.

'You were lucky to get out of that as well as you have,' John added, tapping one of the suspended wheels with a smelly trainer.

I tried to dismiss his words... I didn't need reminding of what *could* have happened; I was still reliving those possibilities. 'Maybe you should sell it for spares and move on to a different formula?' he went on. 'Perhaps it's time to get that golden tongue of yours working again and persuade some poor sponsor to hand over another nice cheque.'

'I know I made a mistake,' I said ruefully, 'I took too tight a line, but everyone else missed me. The guy hit me – actually accelerated straight into me!'

I knew the division between triumph and failure in this sport was slim and the reasons often subjective. Just qualifying at international level was an achievement, getting you close to the best of the best. Crashing out if you were pushing hard was no real disgrace, but as I was discovering, it was also painful, both physically and financially, bringing with it, potential legal ramifications.

I had just picked up two more small sponsors and was supposed to be competing at the next races but both the car and I were a wreck. Gareth had already offered to help and the sponsors were unlikely to sue given the circumstances, but they would quickly become disillusioned. They were in this for sound business reasons, after all that was the concept I'd sold them. I had to face facts; the guys at the very front were fighting a narrowly defined pathway to Formula One but the rest of the pack – many were just fighting! There for a weekend's blitzkrieg, happy to ram, force or barge a competitor off the track.

But there was something else, aside from the fact that I wasn't yet fast enough, and all the crashes. At six foot two, and weighing 168lbs, I would always be at a disadvantage in a single-seater, regardless of any latent ability. I had to face facts; I was already over the top at twenty-seven years of age. I was too old, too tall, too heavy and too late. I would never be able to take the path I dreamed of, not to Formula One. But as John suggested, there *were* other possibilities.

Overhead, fluorescents buzzed and flickered like irritating strobes. Ian brewed instant coffee, the aroma filling the bus, mingling with the everyday odour of diesel, petrol and dirty laundry. I swallowed a couple of painkillers and sat watching deadly Doris scurrying about in her little abode. 'How long do these things live?' I asked, flicking a rancid sock from my mattress.

'Females can live up to thirty years,' John said, dropping a live cricket in front of Doris, 'but males have a much shorter life span.'

'So Doris is going to be with us for another thirty years?' asked Ian nonchalantly.

John sipped a milky coffee and shrugged. 'Well, as long as *she* isn't a *he,*' he replied with a wry smile.

Doris froze at the sight of the tasty morsel before her. We all peered quizzically through the glass at the twitching red and black abdomen. 'How do you know?' I asked, 'Has it got a tiny todger?'

As though on cue, Doris reared up, revealing her under-belly, black and orange legs twitching hypnotically at her quarry. 'If it's got one, could you see it?' asked Ian.

The cricket appeared as stunned as we were intrigued. Six of Doris's forward facing eyes focused in on her prey. 'Don't be daft! You'd hardly expect it to be dragging a big pair of furry red bollocks behind it, would you?' replied John sarcastically. 'Anyway, you can tell it's a girl by the speed it whips a cricket's head off!'

As John spoke, Doris uncoiled like a spring, but incredibly, her dinner responded even quicker, leaping onto her back in an instant, locking onto her thorax with its forelegs, hitching a ride. Doris scurried about indignantly, her rear binocular vision focusing in on the galling gryllidae. 'Now that is one quick cricket!' John said, 'Perhaps we should put *him* in the Delta.'

Doris continued furiously circling her domain, every tendon, ligament and muscle straining to dislodge the beastly bug, which hung on relentlessly like a bronco rider. 'Shit!' exclaimed John. 'The bastard's attacking her!'

'How do you know it's a him?' asked Ian.

'Piss off, Ian... seriously, it's attacking her!'

Suddenly Doris stopped her frantic circling, quivered momentarily, and then lay motionless except for an occasional erratic twitch. A small pool of blue liquid oozed from her back, a moment later the roach disappearing eagerly inside the now gaping crater – Deadly Doris was dead!

Nobody spoke, except for John, who simply managed to repeat the same word, 'Shit! Shit! *Shit!*'

25

"Like success, failure is many things to many people. With Positive Mental Attitude, failure is a learning experience, a rung on the ladder, a plateau at which to get your thoughts in order and prepare to try again."

W. Clement Stone

A YEAR HAD PASSED since crashing the Delta at Brands Hatch, and since then I'd been busy promoting racing to just about anyone who'd stand still long enough to listen. Somehow it appeared to be something that I was surprisingly good at. It was like breathing, it just came naturally. If I could get in front of the right person, despite lack of preparation, I'd somehow instinctively find the words, and usually walk out of the office with a deal and very occasionally, even a cheque. Of course, at this point I wasn't finding the really big sponsors, but I was managing to pick up a host of smaller ones.

With regular sponsorship income, my team had not only rebuilt the crashed Delta, but also purchased a brand new Royale Formula Ford. Over the winter we'd also started converting the old bus into a comfortable two car transporter with separate living accommodation. Our makeshift home was now divided in two, with a cramped, though still unfinished living space at the front and an equally small workshop at the back. We'd removed the windows and panelled over the openings with aluminium, to conceal the race cars. Over the past week we'd also been adding the finishing touches to our living area: a sink, shower, kitchen, four comfy bunks, a TV and a massive water storage tank, plus heating system.

Now with two cars, my team had the facilities and assets to not only compete, but also to hire out a second car and generate urgently needed additional income. Increased cash flow meant increased track time, and my close relationship with the barriers slowly became a little less confrontational, but despite occasionally managing to stay on the black stuff long enough to finish, I was still at best, a midfield runner, a long way from winning.

It was April 1982 and we were parked outside my parents' place, working on the transporter. Outside, the sun was high in the sky, causing the temperature inside our restricted living area to climb. John had just brewed some coffee when suddenly there was a loud rap on the door. I turned from installing a new shower pump, to see a tall, lanky guy in his mid twenties.

'Hallo, my name's Dirk,' he announced, in a distinctly Belgian accent. 'You are Will Middleton?' He was neatly dressed in light blue Chinos, blue button down shirt, and was holding a copy of the local paper with an article on my last escapade. In the absence of wins, I'd always done my best to court the media's attention in the misguided belief that any coverage had to be good news for my sponsors, but I was beginning to question that logic. The trouble was, each article tended to be predictable, always following the same pattern. The week before a race, headlines would cry: *Will's Winning Chance!* And the week after: *Will's Lucky Escape!* The lanky Belgian extended his hand.

'Come in and take a seat,' I said, shaking the outstretched hand and offering a wry grin. 'I see you have a copy of my latest adventures.'

He paused, raising an immaculate eyebrow and smiled, replying, 'Well, I noticed you crash quite often!'

For the next hour or so we sat and talked. I discovered he came from Antwerp and had a background in karting, having been runner-up in both the Belgian and Benelux Championships two years back, missing each title by just a single point. He regularly visited the south of England to see family friends who lived just around the corner from my parents' home and had known of my "heroic exploits" from various reports he'd seen in the local papers. 'I want to get into single-seaters myself,' he said.

Sensing an opportunity, and with my face breaking into a grin, I asked the obvious first question, 'Do you have a budget?'

'No, unfortunately,' he replied. 'Money, that is always the problem, is it not?'

'It is,' I agreed wryly.

It was late when Dirk eventually returned to his friends but we agreed to keep in contact and in the weeks that followed, a lot happened; we finally finished our mobile home, the lanky Belgian somehow got renamed "*Space Mouse*" and I persuaded a major corporation, *British Tissues*, to sponsor the pair of us as a two car team in both the Southern and Northern Championships, as well as the odd round in the big National Championship. The only downside to all this development, was that the total amount of sponsorship was barely sufficient to run even *one* car for *half* a season in a single series.

Some weeks later found us on a wet and rainy airfield, just along the coast at Goodwood in West Sussex. The bumpy track was formed out of an old roadway which weaved its way around the perimeter. It was a difficult circuit to get right, with adverse cambered, double apex corners and an uneven, undulating surface which, as I would discover, could easily catch you out. It was here that Stirling Moss' career had ended after a massive crash in 1962 and McLaren's founder Bruce McLaren lost his life testing in 1970.

The circuit hadn't been an active race track since 1966, but it was used regularly by teams for testing prior to a race, and I'd just completed several laps, before rain stopped our fun. We were all seated in the living area of the old bus listening as Space Mouse explained, 'I think you overdrive it, Will? You need to be very much smoother, particularly in these conditions.'

I turned back from the window where I'd been distracted by the *whup-whup* of a small red helicopter landing, then lifting again, hovering and performing training circuits. Space Mouse was sitting between Ian and John, carefully sipping coffee from a plastic mug. 'It's almost dry again,' I said, looking at my wristwatch and back to Dirk. 'There's just over an hour before they close the circuit for lunch. Do you fancy taking the Delta out for a few laps? I'll watch you from the first corner; maybe pick up a few points.'

I watched from the first bend, a fast sweeping right-hander with a double apex called *Madgwick*. The car shot past, leaving a small plume of spray in its wake. Just the sight of it lapping at speed caused a tingle of excitement to run down my spine. Ian clicked the stopwatch as I watched the re-sprayed white Delta vanish into a haze of mist. Being the only car on the track with no other noise, we could clearly hear the downshifts, the crackle of the overrun and changing engine pitch as Space Mouse made his way down the straight and around the back of the circuit, through Lavant and down towards Woodcote. Again the Delta flashed passed in a blur and Ian clicked the stopwatch. 'He's almost equalled your time,' he said, 'and the track's still damp!'

Ten minutes later the car was back in the pits and it was my turn. I lowered myself into the restrictive cockpit and firmly fastened the belts. Raising my hand, I gave John an OK signal with my finger and thumb and he plugged an external battery pack into the Delta's electrical system. I pressed the starter and the rev counter flickered as the engine roared back into life.

For the first few laps I concentrated on my lines and breaking points, remembering what Dirk had said. *Don't overdrive it, keep it smooth...* but I couldn't help myself, I wanted to be quickest.

I turned late into Madgwick and aimed for the first apex, clipping the curbing with my front right wheel, the car drifting slightly on the greasy tarmac, then back, picking up the second apex.

This was my third flying lap and with the track drying fast, I floored the throttle, flat out down the straight towards Fordwater and turned in through the slight dip, the car twitching on a damp patch. Then maximum revs into the "nameless" right-hander, holding a tight line towards the inside of the track. Sharp left, 4500 revs registering on the counter, into St. Mary's, drifting smoothly out, using the entire surface, exiting on the tricky adverse camber. Approaching Lavant, 90 miles per hour, 4th gear, I positioned the Delta to clip the second apex, taking the corner in 3rd with one long smooth sweep, then back up into 4th gear. Powering down Lavant Straight, I ironed out the kink at over 100 miles per hour and down into the double apex Woodcote corner. I punched the brakes and turned late, clipping the second apex as the centrifugal force tried to drag me from the circuit, then hard back onto the throttle before pounding the brake, flicking into 2nd for the chicane. Ahead Ian was holding out a pit board with "1.19.8". *Not bad,* I thought. That's almost a second faster than Dirk, but the track was almost dry.

With excitement surging through me, I scorched the pit straight, 6000 revs, 110 miles per hour. *This was going to be the quickie!*

In the last microsecond before Madgwick, I punched the brakes, flicking the nose at the first apex, turning in deeper and later than before, but suddenly the car felt nervous, the nose turning in but the rear oversteering alarmingly. Instinctively I flicked the steering left, controlling the drift, my foot still planted hard on the throttle but with the car drifting wide, I completely missed the next apex. Suddenly, travelling at over 90 miles per hour, I hit a bump in the track, a second later wildly pirouetting out of control onto the wet grass like a Catherine wheel, discarding body sections as I spun, the slick grass actually accelerating me faster towards the banking at over 100 miles per hour. In an instant, everything was still and calm. Strapped securely in my cockpit, I somehow floated, cocooned from reality. With bemused calm I watched the late afternoon sun inverting mysteriously through my visor, framed by clear blue sky and fluffy clouds, the raw rasp of the pinto engine suddenly muted...

For a moment I was struck by the lack of sound, but a moment later, a crashing thud reverberated through my cocoon as the inverted Delta impacted with the ground, its roll cage digging into the soft soil. The momentum arrested the car, completing its gymnastic display with a slow motion side-wards flip back onto its wheels...everything suddenly and permanently still.

With the engine stalled, there was no noise other than the sound of my own breathing and the occasional *tick, tick* of the cooling exhaust. I unclipped my belts and stepped unscathed from the remarkably undamaged car and slumped down on a rear wheel. Back on the track, the circuit's red danger lights had flashed on. A few seconds passed and I heard the ambulance shoot out in search of my remains.

Looking up, the sun was still high in the sky overhead and the little red helicopter was back, *whup-whup –whup*, its shadow fluttering over me like an enormous insect – *Interesting*, I thought, my adrenalin rush slowly subsiding, the seed of another idea forming.

With the session stopped, Dirk, Ian and John were already sprinting down the track, knowing only that I'd last been seen soaring through the air, heading in a generally easterly direction towards Chichester! Suddenly I heard the sound of shuffling feet. Looking over, I saw everybody clambering over the bank. 'Will, are you okay?' somebody called.

'Yes, I'm fine,' I said. 'Bit of a bump back there in the middle of the track, isn't there!'

'Catches a lot of people out,' advised the marshal, 'but only if you go off line.'

'You don't say,' I replied dryly.

26

---

*"If the only tool you have is a hammer, you tend
to see every problem as a nail."*

Abraham Maslow

I T WAS TWO weeks later and we were again sitting in the old
bus, but this time at Cadwell Park circuit in Lincolnshire,
trying to analyse my last laps of yet another practice session. 'I
watch you on the approach to Park bend,' said Space Mouse,
taking a measured sip from his Diet Coke, 'and you still go into
the corners way too fast and get all locked up. You almost lose it,
then somehow scrabble through, but it is not *clean*, you know? And
I hear, you are on and off the throttle... you must be *smoother* and
only commit to the power one time, when you can accelerate
cleanly through the corner. Think back to basics,' he went on,
'remember friction circle theory...'

'Err... friction circle theory?' I repeated.

He gave me an uneasy frown. 'You never hear the term *friction
circle?*' Space Mouse asked in disbelief. I gave a noncommittal
shrug but said nothing.

I listened as he continued. 'It is very important in racing,' he
went on pedantically. 'Only this way can you understand the grip
boundary of your race car!' He looked over to Ian and John and
caught the blank look on their faces. 'It is also important when
setting up the car for mechanics. It tells you what must be
adjusted to get the maximum out of the chassis.' They both
looked back as though he was speaking in Flemish. 'How else do

you know why the car is losing grip, or why it is too slow?' he went on passionately. Then turning back to me he added, '...or ends up in the barriers!'

I hesitated. 'I thought that was just misjudgement. When I'd gone too fast?' I said.

'It is not that simple... If you were going *that* fast you would win races, would you not? Or be at least up front? I think your problem is you still overdrive it...' he paused as if trying to find the right words. 'Imagine you are at a track... perhaps Brands Hatch. You head flat out into Paddock Hill bend. You slam on the brakes at the very last moment, almost to the point of locking the wheels. The tyres will be at the limit of their traction – yes?'

I nodded slowly, trying to take it in, 'Yes, I suppose so,' his words reviving memories of Gareth Hunt's stunned Arctic blue eyes, as I slid headlong towards him.

There was a slight pause, then he patiently continued. 'So, if you try to turn the steering at *that* point, the car, it loses traction because there is no more lateral grip available. But, if you apply *less* brake, the braking force is no longer on the limit of the friction circle. Then the car *will* turn, because you *now* have lateral grip available, so you can accelerate *cleanly* out of the corner instead of scrabbling about and losing time. No?'

'No... I mean yes,' I replied, still unsure but not wanting to be the only one in the lesson again who didn't understand.

He cleared his throat. 'It is just simple maths, Will,' he went on laboriously, 'a simple equation. I write it down for you.' He picked up a spiral bound note pad and began writing what looked like a load of mumbo-jumbo in neat tidy script. 'Look!' he said excitedly, holding the pad out so we could all see it. '$F = L \times Cf$,' he said, sounding horribly like a Flemish version of Mr Jenkins. 'Where F is the traction force and L is the load on the tyre and Cf is the co-efficient of friction for the tyres on the track surface.'

I listened in horror as the world I'd come to love turned into a terrifying maths class. 'So you're saying there's some sort of mathematical formula for going quick?' I finally asked.

'Well, yes!' he looked at me in disbelief, 'or at least for *not* crashing. But on the track you obviously cannot actually calculate these things... but you must understand them, so you can do "the calculations" instinctively. Did you think it was just about driving around in circles and changing gears?'

I gave an evasive wave and for the next hour sat trying to absorb racing theory: friction circle theory, slip angles, traction force, contact patches and weight transfers. 'Anyway,' Space Mouse concluded, turning to Ian and John, 'Remember what I said about "slip angle". It is all to do with the tyre's contact patch in its relationship with the wheel.'

We all wisely nodded in unison, and with that our meticulous theory training came to an end.

Over the months that followed, Space Mouse and I became the best of friends but with two cars to run, and four mouths to feed, the minute budget was quickly depleted and by August, Space Mouse had returned to Belgium.

Ian and John had also become bored. The three of us had had a lot of fun and I'd learned a lot, but I now needed results, and I needed to move on, but unlike in the past, I now had some experience and a better understanding of what I was doing.

As the season drew to an end, I sold the old bus and the now restored, gleaming De Tomaso Pantera, and with the cash, ordered the latest Van Dieman Formula Ford two thousand, installed my somewhat worn engine from last year and found a professional, experienced mechanic. Over the months that followed, I secured my first lap record at Lydon, then a front row qualifying position followed by a pole position and two third places at Oulton Park. But to be taken seriously, I needed results in the big National Championship, and to get that, I needed more backing and a *top* class engine. And at that point in 1983 there was only one engine to go for, a German built Zack.

Three weeks and many phone calls later, we were back at Brands Hatch for the new season. We set off to find a good spot to set up camp and off-load the race car equipped with its brand new three thousand pound Zack engine. Driving into the paddock, I noticed several of the top teams had already arrived and was surprised to see frenzied work being carried out beneath bright arc lights, all of them busily removing engines from their race cars and installing replacements.

'Wonder what they're all up to at this hour?' I asked Derek, my new mechanic.

'Who knows,' he replied. 'I could do with some breakfast.'

With a last glance over my shoulder at all the frantic activity, we made our way to the Kentagon. Inside, despite the hour, the place was busy as usual. We pushed our way through the crowds to the counter and placed our orders.

'Heard the news?' a voice enquired from behind.

Turning, I was greeted by Simon, a mechanic I'd chatted with many times before. He was in his late forties and well respected, having worked for years with the Lotus Formula One team.

'No, what news?' I replied turning to greet him. 'And what are you doing down here... I thought you were working up at Snetterton this weekend?'

'Just got a job running a sports prototype for a driver in the national series.'

'Oh, is it any good?' I asked.

'Yes, it's a good little series. Eight races spread up and down the country and the drivers are quite competitive. You should take a look. So, have you got caught up in this engine palaver?'

At that moment my expression must have changed because Simon's smile vanished. 'Oh... you don't know?'

I swallowed nervously. 'What engine palaver?' I said, a feeling of dread already spreading through me.

'Zack engines,' he shrugged before taking a large bite of a greasy bacon sandwich. 'They've all been declared illegal. No one's allowed to run them.'

27

"A grand adventure is about to begin..."

Winnie the Pooh

HEALTH IS A GIFT we all take for granted ...until it's gone. As delicate as a spider's web, it can be snuffed out in an instant, leaving our life's dreams shattered and the toughest, dwarfed in despair – any hope of survival crushed by a devastating medical pronouncement of impending death. All these years on from his sentence, my father kept beating the odds, still very much alive. He was a fighter, refusing to give in. Love was his panacea, my parent's little bungalow oozing it from every brick and timber. I could sense it now as I turned onto the driveway, my tyres crunching against the hard gravel as the car came to a halt.

I ratcheted up the chrome hand brake, the headlights flickering in time with the idling straight-six engine. Just ahead, the bungalow was veiled in soft moonlight.

It was November and with the season over and Beth on a full week's army leave, we'd driven down to stay with my parents. For weeks Beth had been feeling unusually tired and generally rundown, and I was exhausted, so we'd welcomed the opportunity of this time together on the south coast. I eased myself out over the wide sill of my latest investment, another e-Type roadster. This one was a 1967, 4.2 litre, series 1.5 model and I'd found it around two months earlier at the local auction. It had been described as a non runner, to be sold strictly as seen and untested.

I'd successfully bid just £1200 and towed it home. Five weeks later, re-sprayed in Daytona yellow with a fresh Connelly leather interior, having replaced the blown head gasket and seized water pump, it was looking and running like new. I'd already been offered, and turned down, over £5000 for it.

Collecting our bags from the boot, Beth and I headed to the front door. My parents, having heard the car, were already standing in the opening, smiles beaming, with Ching, their Pekinese dog yapping his usual hysterical welcome. They both looked older, small and frail. 'Welcome home kids,' my mother called out excitedly as we approached. 'Now, we've saved you both some dinner. I assume you haven't eaten?'

'No, we haven't,' I replied, giving her a big hug.

'Hello stranger,' my father added in his usual dry fashion as I kissed him.

We stepped from the gloom and into the brightly lit hallway, breathing in the familiar scents of lavender and beeswax polish.

The macaroni cheese was excellent. My father pushed the remains of the dish in my direction. 'Go on son,' he urged, 'it won't do you any harm to finish it off.'

It was the first decent meal I'd had in ages. I scraped the last remnants from the bowl and continued my slightly abridged tale of the past couple of months. 'I'm getting fed up with constantly being punted off,' I said. 'And all the wasted expense on things like the Zack engine hassle.'

'I think you should give up all this silly racing lark,' my mother chided. 'It's time you two settled down and had some babies!'

Beth blushed and decided it was time to start clearing dishes. She rose self-consciously, gathered some plates and made her way quickly to the kitchen.

'Well, mum...' I replied, '...you're not getting grand-children quite yet. But I may be giving up this current formula.' I said, 'I'm planning to move up a notch or two.'

'Oh...' both parents looked at each other as an awkward silence descended.

I'd already discussed the plan with Beth and had a speech prepared for my parents but the unexpected mention of babies had erased my mind and sent my only supporter scurrying off, searching for a place of safety. There was no other way to put it, they'd know soon enough, 'I'm going to be driving a sports prototype car in endurance races in future,' I said. 'I'll be doing a few national events to start off, but then I'll be driving in the World Sports Car Championship ...races like the Le Mans twenty four hours.'

'How?' asked my father. 'I don't understand.' I could sense the frustration in his voice.

'It's actually safer,' I said – in truth it was a lie, but what was the point in burdening them with the reality? 'The cars are worth a lot more money and the drivers are a much higher standard, so you're much less likely to get punted off,' I added. 'In endurance racing, the whole mentality is to actually finish. Provided you're consistently fast and smooth, you can win.'

'But William,' interrupted my mother, who was trying but failing to keep her voice calm, 'how can you just jump into a world championship? You've only been racing for a few years!'

'I've got an international race licence, mum. That's all I need to be able to drive.' I said, desperately looking around for Beth to provide some back-up, but she was still ensconced in the kitchen, slowly washing dishes.

'But what team would employ you?' my mother persisted.

'It doesn't work like that,' I replied. 'Very few drivers are ever *employed*, most *pay* to drive. Anyway, I don't plan to join an existing team; I'm going to create my own. It'll be my own personal VIP pass into the Championship.'

'But... you haven't got a car, have you?'

'I'm looking for one,' I said. 'I know a guy that used to work with the Lotus Formula One team, he been running an endurance car in the national series. As soon as I find something suitable, he's going to help run it for me.'

My mother looked pleadingly at my father for help. I felt a sudden need to comfort them both, but what could I say? Where I saw a future of thrilling adventure, they only saw catastrophic injury or death.

'But what about the cost son?' my father finally asked. 'And if it's a world championship, doesn't that mean you'll be travelling all around the world? It'll cost a fortune.'

'That is a minor setback,' I admitted, 'but I'm working on it. Anyway, the first races will be in the national series,' I reiterated 'and I've already put together a deal with a magazine for sponsorship.'

'A magazine', repeated my father softly. 'Are they giving you the money?'

'In a roundabout way,' I replied, 'At least part of it.'

'We should never have got him that go-kart,' my mother said, turning to my father. 'That's what started all this stuff and nonsense!' My father didn't answer. My mother gave me one of her looks. Rising from her seat, she gathered the few remaining dishes from the table and left to help Beth in the kitchen. The conversation was over.

In my dream, as I descend into REM, I'm somehow outside my body, looking down on the race, witnessing everything in the third person, drifting out of a first sweeping corner and into fourth gear, flat out now in top. Flashing past the pits with rows of timekeepers and mechanics, I see the driver's head turn, stealing a glance at the pit board. In the nightmare, I know precisely what's about to happen; I've dreamt it many times since the crash, and I can't stop it. I blast beneath the starting gantry at over one hundred miles per hour and up the incline. The 200-metre board flashes past and I out-brake another car in a cascade of sparks as the Delta's skid blocks impact with the track. Suddenly I'm back in the cockpit, drenched in sweat, aiming at the apex. All around I'm pursued by other cars. I floor the throttle; 6900 revs as I bottom out in another blaze of embers; again I'm side by side with yet another driver, battling my way up the hill and into the hairpin. Suddenly I'm spinning, competitors missing me by millimetres. Strapped in the cockpit, gripping the wheel, I brace myself for the impact that always follows. In the reoccurring nightmare I'm unable to move. I see my crumpled body as the flames envelope me, a helpless witness to my own destruction. I smell my own burning flesh and taste the acrid smoke as the fire rages all around me. Suddenly the apparition appears before me as it always does. Leaning in through the curtain of flames my father releases my belts and with strong arms lifts me from the blazing inferno, whispering softly, 'Everything will be okay, son.'

I jolted awake with a gasp and sat up, sweating, my heart pounding. I'd suffered the same nightmare for months. Usually the dream was the same, but sometimes it included Paul, strapped in his motorised chair with its racing stickers, just sitting, smiling at me.

I looked over at Beth; she was curled up, still dead to the world. Settling back down, I wiped my face on the sheet and tried to get back to sleep.

The following morning I woke late and pulled on my normal weekend outfit of old faded jeans and T-shirt and walked to the bedroom window. It was going to be a bright sunny day. Beth was still curled up in bed, five foot two of brunette lusciousness. From the window I could survey the streets; red brick semi-detached houses of fifties design. The estate was still quiet; just a few neighbours out washing cars and one or two children playing, the sun beginning to peek out from behind the fluffy cumulus clouds. I wandered into the lounge where a gilt-bronze ormolu clock, a relic from our hotel, ticked tirelessly on the sideboard, next to a leather-bound picture frame. Picking it up, I gazed down at the faded black and white photo of a small group of boys, all smartly dressed in school uniform, arms crossed, eyes focused directly ahead. In the centre of the group, looking sternly forward, my old headmaster, Mr Wickham. I smiled at my own youthful image sitting there cross-legged in the front row, the only one staring defiantly in the opposite direction to my peers. Picking the photo frame up, my older image reflected back from the glass, the defiance in my eyes still there, still burning but now more controlled.

The old clock chimed, its peal breaking across my thoughts. I decided to leave Beth sleeping and walk the short distance to the local store to buy us croissants and a newspaper.

On my return, half an hour later, she greeted me in the hallway with a radiant smile and a big kiss. 'How are you feeling today,' I asked, pleased to see she was looking happier and a little less tired, though a bit unsure of something.

'I'm fine,' she said, taking my hand and pulling me towards the bedroom we shared when staying at the bungalow. 'Come with me, I have something to show you.'

Silently closing the door behind us, she went to the wardrobe and opened the door, removing what looked like a small glass tube. 'Take a look,' she said, half- smiling, still obviously unsure of my response.

Unaware of what the object was, I took it and held it up to the light. A little blue circle appeared almost to wink back at me. 'What is it?' I whispered, as if we were sharing some huge secret.

She smiled nervously, 'I think it's a George,' she said, whispering back, 'or maybe it's a Georgina... We won't know for a few months.' There was a moment's pause before she added, 'Will, I'm pregnant. You're going to be a dad!'

'*Pregnant!*' I repeated, dropping the bag of croissants in stunned amazement. 'But... but...' I shook my head slowly, trying to take it in, '...how did that happen, er, wow, shit wow...'

'I think you know *how* it happened, Will!'

'Well, yes I know *how*...' I stuttered, '...but *when* and I mean shouldn't you be sitting down or something and... I don't know... shouldn't you have your feet up or something. And shit, what about the Army and, and... wow, I mean, well ... we'll need a house and I mean ... wow!'

Later that morning, feeling a little more relaxed with the prospect of looming parenthood, we decided to let our parents in on the news. Beth wanted to tell her mother first, so we set off on the hour long drive to Littlehampton. Having never felt particularly welcome at Beth's home, I didn't relish the prospect of breaking the news that her young daughter would soon be presenting her with a new grandchild. So, taking the coward's way out, I waited in the car as Beth dropped the initial bombshell. To my surprise, ten minutes later I was invited in and amid big smiles, offered tea and celebratory biscuits. 'That appeared to go down quite well,' I said as we set off back to Southampton to break the news to my parents. 'Your mother seemed almost to have been expecting it,' I said, still in a daze.

Things didn't go quite as smoothly when we arrived back at my parent's bungalow.

'Well, my girl,' said my mother sternly, fixing Beth with an accusing glare, all memory of last night's chat forgotten, 'you'll obviously have to leave the Army and we'll need to find you a wedding dress quickly, before you begin to show.' She turned to my father, who appeared to be taking everything in his usual relaxed stride. My dad had always liked Beth and considered her a good and calming influence on his only son. And compared with my other, not too distant accomplishments, of blowing up my bedroom, the CCTV affair and having half of Arundel evacuated, an unexpected grandchild was just a walk in the park.

But my mother didn't see it that way, and continued planning. Turning to my father, she added, 'Darling, you'd better get down to your club straight away. See if we can book a date urgently for a reception.' Looking back at Beth, she said, 'We'll probably find you a second hand wedding dress in the free ads....'

Beth's growing unease mirrored my own and I interrupted. 'Mum, we're not planning to get married, at least not immediately.'

'What... but you must... what would the neighbours think?'

'It's the eighties, mum. I don't think the neighbours will be bothered,' I replied, slightly irritated.

'But, but, she can't stay in the army, William! How can she possibly stay in the army when she's pregnant?' She turned to my father for support.

Taking her hand, my father gave it a loving squeeze. 'Come on dear, let the kids sort it out for themselves. If they're grown up enough to have got this far, I think they'll be fine.'

In the months that followed, Beth and I found a small semi-detached house-wreck near Ford in West Sussex. The place was in need of a total restoration, but it was a start, and with Beth back in the army, I quickly sold the E-Type for nearly six thousand pounds. Using the cash, I made a start on the necessary work; knocking down walls, rewiring, installing new plumbing, double glazing and a gas central heating system. My parents had lovingly provided the deposit for our house, 'Consider it an early *wedding* gift...' my mother had said earnestly, with great emphasis on the "wedding" word, as my father wrote out the cheque.

With no regular income still from my racing, Beth's army salary initially paid the monthly mortgage. Meanwhile, back at the Army base, her tiny frame began expanding like a barrage balloon, her commanding office turning a blind eye as Beth's fellow band members of differing dimensions, rallied round, camouflaging the "bump" with their ever more generously proportioned uniforms. On 23rd March 1983, Beth completed her full three and a half year service, receiving an honourable discharge, amid a shower of baby gifts, her pregnancy now common knowledge throughout the camp.

St Richard's Hospital Chichester, West Sussex 13th July 1983

Beth had been in labour for more than twenty two hours when I finally slipped away to grab a coffee and a sandwich at the hospital canteen. It was past ten o'clock. Outside, all was inky black and still stiflingly hot. Today had been the hottest on record for a quarter of a century. I made my way back along the corridor towards the delivery room, pushing open the doors. Beth was being examined by a nurse. She palpated her abdomen whilst listening with a stethoscope to the foetal heartbeat. 'You're doing just fine,' the nurse said reassuringly. 'Not long now.' She plunged a needle into Beth's thigh. 'That should help you,' she said, then turning to me, 'Ah, I see the long lost father-to-be has returned. You're just in time Will.' Turning back to Beth she went on, 'Now, with the next contraction try not to push. Just concentrate on your breathing. Okay dear?'

'Is it happening now?' I asked, shocked by the sudden speed of events.

'Yes, Will, you're about to become a dad,' the nurse replied. 'Never mind the blood,' she added looking at my face. 'Just be a good boy and hold Beth's hand. Okay? I'll deal with the business end.'

I glanced anxiously at my watch. 'How long is it likely to take?' I asked.

The nurse looked up from between Beth's legs, 'You have something more pressing?' she asked dryly.

'Err no, no... It's not that,' I spluttered, 'it's just that, well, er.... it's still Wednesday,' I said, glancing at my watch anxiously. 'It's still the thirteenth!' I'd always been irrationally superstitious and had been worrying all night that the baby would be born today of all days, the thirteenth! I turned to Beth, her forehead beaded with sweat. She was groaning loudly through her gas mask, 'Beth, darling, could you hang on for just a *little* longer?' The look in her wide eyes provided the answer. Suddenly there was a massive spurt of blood. 'Oh shit no,' I said, 'that's horrible!' covering my mouth with one hand. Suddenly, feeling nauseous, the oppressively hot delivery room began spinning.

'If you're going to do what I think you're going to do, William, move to the other side of the room,' the nurse instructed firmly and without compassion. Then turning back to Beth, she added calmly, 'Good girl, its coming!'

From behind the gas mask I could hear Beth's muffled gargled grunts. A few moments later a head appeared. 'That's it! Well done!' called the midwife, 'Just one more push.'

'Oh, wow! That's incredible,' I sobbed, my eyes suddenly filling with tears, now totally in awe of what was happening. There was another spurt of blood, then moments later the shoulders slipped out and in a single sudden movement, the midwife pulled our son out and up towards Beth's stomach. At precisely one minute past eleven on Wednesday thirteenth of July, George made his entry into this world with a very healthy, loud and lusty yell.

28

---

*"The critical ingredient is getting off your butt and doing something.
It's as simple as that. A lot of people have ideas, but there are few who
decide to do something about them now. Not tomorrow. Not next week,
but today. The true entrepreneur is a doer, not a dreamer."*

Nolan Bushnell.

A RACING DRIVER lives in a world of perpetual fear – not
so much the fear of death or injury, although, as I'd
discovered since my big crash, those thoughts do exist,
hidden somewhere in the depth of the psyche. It's more the fear
of living beneath the perpetual cloud of a twelve month contract,
where each race or season could be the last. As quickly as the
previous season ends, the new one dawns and with a move to the
World Championship, the demand for a bigger budget steepened.
Towards the end of each year, backers were re-wooed and new
sponsors sought – I never knew if I'd find them, or if, having
found them, I would keep them. Hours on the phone or writing
proposals left me drained but the adrenalin drove me on. A
racing driver has no master other than his own soul, and that was
just one of the reasons I raced. I loved it.

When I was a kid, I thought racing was all about thrills and
spills. In fact motor sport is a business, *not* just a sport and if you
don't understand that, you won't last a season. I lived for the
racing but loved the business side almost as much – I found selling
the whole concept of corporate sponsorship fun. There was a part
of me that was pure, pedigree salesman, but as with everything I

did, I was unconventional. With the exception of a few set rules, I rarely had any idea in my mind what I was going to say until it came out of my mouth. To me, there was something instinctive about the type of company, product and service that would identify with the high octane world of the race track, and the financial world was one such industry.

I inserted the key, turning it, and my latest acquisition, an old Triumph TR7 convertible, burbled into life. Giving a final wave to Beth as she stood in the doorway, cradling George, I headed north in the direction of Huntingdon.

Three hours later I arrived at Lola cars and was introduced to Mike Blanchet. He was a short slim man in his early forties, with an impressive race pedigree. Rows of spotless cars perched on trestles in the surgically clean bays, as we entered the immaculate factory unit. It looked more like an operating theatre than a race workshop. We made our way to a bay where a sleek outline rested beneath a yellow dust sheet. Mike flicked back the cover and removed papers from a blue file adorned with a yellow and black logo. He paused, studying the papers momentarily. Stepping over to the yellow Lola Group C racer, he hinged open the door and added. 'It's the second of just two T610s we've built. This one is the former Ralph Cook car.' He handed over a neatly typed specification sheet and a list of spares. 'This is a list of parts that *could* be available,' the emphasis on the verb clearly indicating his preferred area of negotiation.

'What are you looking for?' I asked.

'Forty grand as a rolling chassis,' Mike replied without hesitating.

'Are you open to offers?' I said.

'Who isn't?' he replied, 'as long as it's sensible. Are you interested in it with or without the engine?'

'I assume it's fitted with the 3.9 DFL?' I enquired.

'Yes, it's a Nicolson McLaren, but it blew at Le Mans last year. No real idea what went wrong, there are no holes in the block. I know it was having the usual vibration issues, but I think it then overheated. If you're lucky, it may not be too devastating, but it's the buyer's risk.'

'I'm also thinking of running it at Le Mans this year,' I said, 'but Balestre, the FIA President, is making lots of fuss about reducing the fuel allowance, and I doubt we'd get the efficiency from the 3.9 engine. Anyway, we'll probably modify it later to run in C2 category, so we'll need a smaller 3.3 engine.' I paused. 'I'll give you twenty grand, less the engine but with all the spares.'

Back in the TR7, I started the engine and set off in the direction of Nottingham for the next and most important stage in my plan, the all important finance. On top of a one thousand eight hundred overdraft, the residue of last season's running, I now needed an extra twenty five thousand for the Lola and I needed it fast!

The next day

The maître d welcomed us like royalty. A pair of waiters appeared from nowhere, whisking us to a large secluded table. Seats were drawn back and heavy linen napkins carefully unfurled and spread over our laps. Paul Cartel was the owner of Aztec Finance and his company now spent more than three million pounds a year on national advertising campaigns alone. He'd also sponsored my Formula Ford last year, to the tune of eight thousand pounds.

'We have some wonderful veal I'd strongly recommend,' the head waiter urged with a practiced smile. Paul, my potential source of funding for the Lola, nodded back. 'And perhaps the gratin of lobster tail to start?' continued the maître'd.

The sommelier arrived and handed Paul an impressive leather bound folder. 'How nice to see you again Mr Cartel,' he gushed, 'I trust business is well in the current climate?'

'Can't complain, Albert,' Paul replied with a wink. 'With the opposition now split, it looks as though Thatcher will be back in, come June,' he said. 'I suspect the Labour vote will be down three million or more on the day.' The sommelier bowed slightly in accord but made no direct retort about the forthcoming general election. The economy had been in recession for almost two years and Thatcher's first term as prime minister had been a difficult time for any on modest incomes, but then, no such client frequented *this* establishment.

During Thatcher's first three years, unemployment had rocketed to over three million, the highest since before the Second World War. Inflation, ravaging since the seventies, still held the country in a vice like grip. An earlier miners' dispute was still rumbling on, threatening to escalate into an all out strike. Yet strangely, whilst the iron lady was unpopular in this part of the country, the successful outcome of the Falklands war had generally bolstered her popularity throughout much of the rest of the nation. It was an odd time, a time of dispute and rebellion and yet much of the nation was starting to feeling a surge of optimism as house values began what was becoming an unstoppable climb into the stratosphere. Britain was becoming a country of winners and losers, and to be on the winning side all that was needed, or so it seemed, was to own your own home. Our own tiny semi-detached had already jumped almost ten thousand in value. The fight to enter the burgeoning housing market only inflated prices further. Any home owners felt cocooned with an impression of wealth, but the only thing that gave that feeling, was their home. With the warm glow of prosperity, came a national desire to indulge. New cars were ordered, holidays booked, lofts converted, conservatories added, double glazing fitted and new kitchens and bathrooms installed. Yet for most, there was no real cash to pay for the

excesses. Finance began to reign, and Paul was the king of loans –
it's what he did.

As the nation's debt ballooned, the City rushed in, greedy to
package up and sell this mushrooming 'asset' with spiralling
interest, the investment, pension and insurance industries
gobbling up their share of the bounty. Government ministers
watched all this with glee as new business emerged phoenix-like
from the years of recession. City demands for more 'investment',
led to long ministerial lunches where regulation and restrictions
were removed. Thatcher's economy was beginning to take off.

'I'll have a glass of champagne to start,' Paul said, his head
inclining in my direction.

'That would be great!' I said.

'Could I suggest a bottle of the Chateau Cos Labory, St Estephe
Grand Cru, to follow?' the sommelier enquired. 'We have just one
bottle of the 1952 remaining. It really is a quite *outstanding* red;
silky with a highly perfumed bouquet. Quite fruity,' he went on,
'hints of cedar, plums, vanillin spice and sweet oak.'

Paul nodded his agreement to the one hundred and forty
pound bottle, handing back the unread wine list.

'So,' he said, glancing at me, as the sommelier departed,
'you've sold your Formula Ford and already have a major backer
for this Lola?' He turned his attention momentarily to a beautifully
sculpted bread roll, breaking off a small piece and slipping it into
his mouth.

'We do,' I lied. 'We'll be competing in some national races and
the Le Mans 24 hours and at least two more world championship
events in Italy and Australia.' My technique tended to follow at
least a few set rules. I never said we *"hoped to..."* or *"we needed
backing for..."*, it was always *"we'd like to represent you and are doing
this race or that race.."* and I'd *never* say we hadn't got *any* backing. I
was always just looking for a *small* co-sponsor, to top up the
existing budget and by chance, we just happened to be in a unique

position to offer quite a lot of endorsement space! 'We're simply looking for a co sponsor to help with the team travel expenses, nothing more than that,' I slipped over a colour picture of the Lola, 'and we could offer up to two thirds of the car's body work for endorsement space.' As long as I managed to get a face to face meeting with a potential sponsor, it seemed to work most times.

The waiters reappeared, placing a pair of cloche covered platters before us. At a signal from the maître d, the covers were lifted simultaneously with a flourish. 'Your gratin of lobster tail,' he announced with a small bow.

Over the next half hour, Paul listened intently as I outlined my proposition. 'So, for thirty thousand pounds we'd have space on the sides and rear wing of the Lola and twenty full colour pages in this rather dodgy magazine. Is that right?'

'That's correct and we'd produce all the graphics for the Lola as well as all the artwork for your magazine advertisements.'

'Does anyone ever look at the ads in these things?' he flicked a few pages of naked flesh derisively. 'I thought they just bought them for the pictures!' At that moment the maître d reappeared. 'Here, Albert, take a gander at these,' said Paul, flashing a page of pert breasts in his direction. 'Would *you* look at something like this?'

Without missing a beat the maître d drily replied, 'I'd have to say it's not my usual literary intake, sir.'

'Hmm, well I have to say it's a novel idea, Will,' concluded Paul as he collected his thoughts and closed the magazine.

'The price on the rate card would normally cost you fifteen hundred pounds per page,' I added. 'So in effect, you'd be getting a full year's exposure on the race car for free.'

'That's if we were going to *spend* thirty thousand pounds in this magazine,' replied Paul with a grin. 'It's not the type of publication I'd normally consider but *if* I was to, I'd never pay standard rate card. Still, it's an interesting proposition.' He sipped thoughtfully from his cup, pausing for a few moments. Finally he raised his coffee cup again, this time in a 'cheers' gesture. 'Yes, quite interesting,' his voice suddenly serious. 'Okay! I'll go with it but I'll need it invoiced this tax year.'

'That's not a problem,' I replied happily.

Paul smiled, 'I take it you'd like the cheque today?'

29

"Courage is resistance to fear, mastery of fear – not absence of fear."

Mark Twain quotes

Four weeks later

JACKIE STEWART called it "the green hell" but from where I sat, the extraordinary scenery looked stunning. More than one hundred square kilometres of woodland, with fairytale castles rising out of vibrant green meadows and dotted amongst them, Mosel vineyards. Startlingly blue lakes glinted as if dusted with diamonds, their edges fringed by dark forests of pine, spruce and beech... Of course, he'd been talking about the Nürburgring itself, a thirteen mile ribbon of tarmac rimmed with steel, not its stunning location, the place through which I was driving – the rolling Eifel Mountains.

Ian, John and I had crossed the Belgian border into Germany at 8am that morning, they having been enticed back from their brief 'retirement' by the prospect of international travel and a world championship. It was now 9.15 as we turned into the temporary entrance for the northern loop of the Nürburgring. Three weeks ago I'd taken delivery of the Lola T610 and since then, Simon, the ex-Lotus team mechanic, had been working on the car day and night. Today we'd unleash it, fitted with its new 3.3DFL Cosworth engine, prior to its entry into the 1984 World Championship event – the Le Mans 24 Hours. Although today was a test, I'd also planned to secure an all important co-driver deal, without which Le Mans was unlikely to happen. That meeting was really the primary motive for driving to the Nürburgring, but the track itself was a major draw... one of the few circuits with a straight as fast as Le Mans' Mulsanne, long enough to hit over 200 miles per hour.

I parked opposite the Amous Renn Hotel and made my way up the road leading to the improvised paddock.

François Migault had already arrived and was examining the Lola when I reached the pits. He was a slim man of about forty years, with dark receding hair and an intense gaze. A former Formula One driver, he had driven for the ill fated *Connew* team and later, for *BRM, Hill* and *Williams* back in the seventies. He smiled confidently and offered his hand, '*Bonjour mon ami,*' he said in a deep French accent, '*ça va?*'

'Hello François,' I replied, smiling, 'I'm very well, thank you.'

'I chat with Simon here. Ze car, *elle semble bien,* but you change *la spécification, oui?*' he asked with a shrug.

'Yes, we're going to run it with a slightly smaller engine at Le Mans to get the fuel economy and then we intend modifying it later to run in the junior C2 category for the rest of the races,' I replied, 'there's no way we could compete with the big budget Porsche teams, but as a C2... '

He nodded, 'Oui. And the car, it's ex Ralph Cook?' he asked.

'Yes, there were just two T610s built, this and the Guy Edwards one.'

'*Mon bon ami,* he drove this one in last year's Le Mans, François Servanin. It went well, but then it overheats,' he shrugged again, in a French way. '*Joint de culasse* … You know François?' he asked.

'No I don't,' I said. 'But it shouldn't suffer from overheating anymore, not with the smaller engine.'

'Non?' he replied thoughtfully, eyes smiling.   Having considered my reply, he nodded positively, adding, 'Ah, bon!' We stepped around to the engine bay, the Frenchman's head continuing to nod approvingly. 'You drive at the ring before, my friend?' he added.

I smiled, 'No, never... so any tips would be greatly appreciated.'

He raised his eyebrows, 'You know Nürburgring is probably most challenging race track in all the world.   Not best place to learn in a Group C car for ze first time!'

'I always like a challenge.' I replied with a grin.

'Be careful, Will...' he paused, '...ze's corners have claimed egos of some of the biggest names in racing! Come,' he gestured at a large map of the track, **'I talk you through it. It's fast, *très rapide!* About a hundred corners, many blind, many surface change... And ze jumps... watch ze jumps! Zey can somersault you off the track!'

An hour later, feeling slightly unnerved, I changed into my fireproof overalls and laced up my nomex race boots. Back in the pits, François held open the Lola's door and I inched myself into the restrictive cockpit.   He leaned in, helping to fasten the six point Willans harness. 'Ze trick with high speed corners is to turn ze steering as little as possible. Ze less steering load, ze more ze car will be in balance and less speed you scrub off with ze tyres.'

The sounds of the track muffled as I pulled on my new Arai helmet and secured the strap beneath my chin. Simon was leant over the engine behind me, a boom microphone protruding from his headset, his now familiar voice crackling in my head, 'Just take it easy, Will... remember there's a lot to learn out there... We're *not* looking for any sort of time yet. Just scrub the tyres and learn the lines, okay?'

'Don't forget what I said about ze surface,' François added, 'watch out for blind corners... don't get caught at Bergwerk! With ze overhanging trees it will be very slippery this day.'

Simon's voice crackled in my helmet again, 'Switch on the low pressure pumps...'

I breathed in deeply and glanced at the instruments through my smoked visor. Reaching out I flicked a switch. Behind me, four Facet pumps clattered into life, lifting high octane fuel from the rubber safety cell into the Lola's collector tank. Simon continued, '...don't touch the throttle, Will. I'll be operating the sliders from back here.' As he spoke, I felt the throttle move beneath my right foot. 'Switch on the high pressure pumps!' he yelled into the mike.

I flicked another switch on the dash – 90 lb registered on the pressure gauge. Back in the engine bay, Simon pumped a volatile mix into the eight Cosworth intake trumpets. I reached out and gripped the Lola's black suede steering wheel. Ian stood directly in front of me, his face fixated, concentrating, both hands held out, his palms facing me, like a policeman. I could feel the grate of the heavy starter mechanism inserting into the rear of the gearbox. Suddenly, the rev counter flickered and with a deafening roar, 450 horse power of Cosworth burst into life behind me, the engine pulsating through the chassis like a malevolent life force. Taking control of the throttle, I held the revs steady at 2000, feeling the bump of the rear body section as Simon and John lowered it back into position, securing the fastenings.

The water temperature registered 62 degrees, oil pressure 75 lb, oil temperature 70 degrees, fuel pressure now showing 120 lb. I closed my eyes and relaxed, a feeling of calm flooding through me. Simon leaned into the cockpit checking my safety harness, – the usual last words, 'You're fuelled for eight laps...' he said, '...that's almost a full tank, so it'll be heavy. Don't take it above 9400 rpm... watch yourself.' He closed the door and secured the latch. Ian stepped aside, making a sweeping motion with his right hand – *clear to go*. I selected 1st gear, lifted the revs to 4000 and gently released the triple plate clutch.

To learn a thirteen mile track with over a hundred corners, bumps, bends and surface changes is a challenge to most drivers. Throw in the financial restriction of limited track time, and then add the need to impress a former Formula One driver who, at that very moment, was observing my every move via his stop watch and the pressure becomes immense. But for me, there was my additional unique challenge – *dyslexia*. Unknown by many, dyslexia doesn't simply affect one's academic abilities. Dyslexia seriously affects short term memory ... it's the *goldfish effect*. In the time it takes a gold fish to lap its bowl, it's completely forgotten the previous lap – so it begins all over again. To the fish each lap is an entirely new experience, a never ending journey of non discovery – it has *no* short term memory!

My dyslexia was a closely guarded secret, a fact nobody in the racing or business world knew. Only Beth, my parents and my closest friend, Des, had ever known just how badly affected I was.

Fighting to concentrate, the signals constantly hitting my brain – *damn*, turned in too soon ... s*hit*, braked too late ... *bugger*, turned in too late... s*hit*, wrong gear ... s*hit*, missed the apex... Still not enough grip – tyres not hot enough, brakes not up to working temperature... I needed to go faster to find more grip, to get more down force, to get more heat into the brakes but I can't think fast enough to remember what corner is coming next!

But slowly, *so* painfully slowly, the signals hitting my brain begin to merge together as a single sensation – *a feeling of fluid movement*. I no longer have to think, the feeling has somehow bypassed my dyslexic brain – instinct is gradually taking over. Braking and gear changes become cleaner and precise, my lines increasingly accurate – the circuit etching into my psyche. Psyche, not *memory* – if you try to *think* what's coming at 180 miles per hour, you're already in the barriers!

Selecting 2nd gear I turn into the slow left hander, for my eighth and final lap, the Lola now much lighter on its reduced fuel load. Exiting the downhill kink, I line up for the fast right-hander, down into the dip, the car still feeling skittish. Four seconds later I hit the brake, into the double right hander, Hatzenbach, the undulating surface causing the Lola to dance violently about the track. A quick stab explodes the pads onto the discs part way, balancing the throttle, with another quick punch before the last right-left combination.

Accelerating up a gear, along the short straight, I'm back onto the brakes, into 3rd for Hocheichen, a right-left combination. The exit camber pins me to the track as I move back up the gears, the track narrowing. Into 5th, 180 miles per hour as I crest the bridge, the car light, the track bumpy. 170 miles per hour, 9000 revs on the counter as I hit the hump, the Lola becoming momentarily airborne. I pound the brake and turn into the double right hander, drifting out of Quidelbacher Hohe, back into 5th gear, 9400 revs, over the brow, down the dip, 190 miles per hour. Another jab on the brakes, I turn into the now thrilling left hander, Schwedenkreuz and down the short hill, the rear of the Lola briefly light.

Again I hit the brake, the four pot hydraulic A. P. calipers clamping the pads like giant vices against the spinning ventilated discs. Flicking down two gears, I'm into the 180° long downhill Aremberg corner, now carrying as much speed as I can into the Fox Hole.

Scorching the steep downhill section and over the crests, back uphill, into the blind lefthander towards the chicane. Into the dip, 160 miles per hour, the suspension fully compressed, I lift momentarily, a curbstone on the left indicating my turn in. Over the brow, I blaze past a car somersaulting into the Armco.

Ignoring it, I continue, hitting the brake, flicking down three gears for the chicane and floor the throttle.

Back up the gears for the half mile run into Metzgesfeld, I punch the brake and through the medium fast lefthander. I take a late entry through the tightening Kallenhard. The track turns, twists, as I balance the throttle, the Lola dropping into the cambered left segment of the downhill esses. The massive Dunlop slicks search for grip as we drift to the left of the track, lining up for the long downhill right hander, Wehrseifen.

Again onto the brake, I aim the nose at the second inside curbstone, back up to 120 miles per hour, 8100 revs. Hard onto the now fading brakes, the slicks peel back tarmac as the track turns right, down three gears into the left hand Wehrseifen Brücke, the slowest corner of the track. Exiting flat out through the right hand kink, ahead the Adenau Bridge and the track becomes even bumpier. I move to the inside, lining up for the steep uphill Ex-Mühle corner, the down force pinning the lightened Lola onto its titanium skid blocks in a cascade of fiery embers. Over the brow in a power slide, I snatch 3rd, 4th then 5th gear, now flat out through the blind left hand kink, ahead Bergwerk, the car drifts wide – François' words flash through my mind – *It'll be damp! – very slippery! – trees over hanging!*

Exiting on the inside, the track surface now undulating, I brake hard and late, attempting to transfer heat into the understeering front tyres. Now adopting a curved line with a late entry, I turn into the tight 3rd gear Bergwerk right hander, the corner tightening as I exit. Back up through the gears, 4th, 5th, over the brow, flat out now through the bumpy left hand kink, 150 miles per hour, uphill, 170 miles per hour, through the fast sweeps, the car now in full compression, sparks showering from the skid blocks. 175 miles per hour, I line the nose up to the fast left hand Courage corner. Pounding the brakes into submission, I flick into 4th gear. Exiting, I gently move to the left side, lining up straight for the blind right Klostertal, over the rise, the car going light as we crest the hump, a microsecond later crashing back into full compression, embers blazing from the underside, for the first time I'm flat in 4th through the right kink.

I pump 180lbs into the dying brakes, flick down two gears, turning into the 180° right hander Steilstrecke, back early onto the power, gently unwinding the steering. Uphill, then back down two gears, the banked track and uneven surface unsettling the Lola's savage five thousand pound springs, just 52 miles per hour through the 190° Karussel.

Up through the gearbox, ascending the hill, now entering the left kink over-fast and relying on down force to pin me to the track, I dab the brakes for Hohe Acht, the Lola going light as I drift out in 3rd gear, power sliding out of the corner on the polished tarmac.

I flash through the next right, powering towards the Wippermann esses, sweat now stinging my eyes. My front right wheel hits the curb stone on the exit, the rear momentarily breaking away. Turning into the blind right hander, Eschbach, the rear of the Lola again steps out as I apply power.

Through the double apex lefthander, a quick dab on the brakes for Brünnchen, accelerating along the short straight – for the first time I see a group of waving spectators to my left – the distraction costing me milliseconds from my lap time. I turn into the second right hander, back up hill, a late entry into Eiskurve. Winding back downhill through the fast zigzag of ever changing tarmac, I cut as close to the high curbing as I dare, squeezing the maximum out of the car.

I punch the brakes for Pflanzgarten as the track suddenly drops away, the Lola briefly airborne. Instantly I lift to prevent wheel lock, the car landing in a shower of titanium sparks as I stab the brakes hard again and flick down two gears into the double apex right hander. Up into 4th, all I can see is sky and trees as I approach the jump. I steer first left, a curb stone orientating me.

Momentarily we're airborne, then landing, the Lola's dampers stabilize the unsettled chassis.

140 miles per hour, operating now by pure instinct I exit the zigzag, avoiding elevated curb stones by millimetres, the chassis rebelling at the diverse camber changes. Travelling at over 160 miles per hour I can see the Schwalbenschwanz combination blurring ahead. Braking on the outside, I hit a bump, turning in. Exiting right, aligning in a micro-second for the left hander, then the second banked left, I hold a tight line, the suspension fighting the uneven track.

Accelerating up through the gears into the Galgenkopf combination, I turn in, setting the radius into the first section. In an instant, I straighten the wheel then turn into the second right hander. Flat out, 9400 revs in top gear, the Nürburg castle flashes past on my right at 200 miles per hour.

Under the bridge at Antonius Buche, flat out through the left hander, downhill into the dip, back up the hill, onto the fading brakes through the next curves, the chassis fighting the changing camber.

Lining up for the Hohenrain chicane I pump the dying brakes, into 4th gear, brake again, into 3rd gear, a final stab and into 2nd gear, 60 miles per hour, through the chicane and the next right-hander. Ahead, Simon holds out the black pit board with "IN" in large yellow letters.

François opened the door smiling, '*C'est comme ça... we* just scrub ze tyres? *C'était un bon temps: 6.49!*'

The lap time made me grin, but the "we" word said it all. This may have only been a test but he was hooked... we'd got our third Le Mans driver. *And* a pile of French francs!

30

Snetterton Circuit, Norwich, Norfolk
One week before the 1984 Le Mans 24 hours

W ITH THE SMELL of burning oil filling the cockpit and catching in my throat, I killed the engine, coasted through Coram Curve and into the pit lane. In my mirrors I could see a thin trail of blue smoke. Simon hinged open the door, grimacing. 'What the hell happened?'

'It was going fine,' I said, 'but then on the last lap it suddenly misfired and felt down on power on the straight,' I peeled off my gloves and unclipping my belts, stepped from the car. 'I'd just turned into the Bomb Hole and hit the throttle,' I said, 'then *bang*, something went.' I looked behind, seeing for the first time the glistening snail trail of oil. 'Shit!' I exclaimed.

'How many revs were you pulling?' Simon asked with obvious irritation, looking down at his injured 'baby'.

'No more than 8000, honestly.' I said. 'Look for yourself.' I gestured towards the telltale on the rev counter. 'I was just doing what we agreed – a gentle shake down.'

We'd driven the short distance to the Snetterton race track in Norfolk, to run a series of systems tests, prior to leaving the following week for the Le Mans 24 hours. Since the Nürburgring test session, where the Lola had completed just eight laps, it had been completely rebuilt in preparation for the gruelling 24 hour race, with fresh discs and a new, low-drag rear wing. In the last few frantic days, I'd finalised the co-driver deals with François Migault who'd agreed to provide eight thousand pounds and accommodate the team at his ancestral chateau. A further five thousand pounds worth of urgently needed funds were coming from Inmac Plus, the sponsor of an old friend and Formula 3 driver, Steve Kempton. With everything in place, this engine problem was a major setback.

With mounting apprehension, I stepped across the sticky pool of blood red fluid that was slowly spreading from beneath the Lola and helped remove its rear body section. I watched as Simon leaned in, almost tenderly checking the engine.

'What's the problem?' I asked, desperately hoping for some simple solution like a loose hose but instinctively knowing it was serious.

Simon gave an uneasy frown, a deeper crease forming in his brow... 'Well, I reckon the misfire and the loss of power was a valve problem...' he paused as if searching for the words, '... it's almost certainly dropped one, then a piston's punched it out through the side of the block...' another pause. 'Sorry, Will, there's no other way of putting it...this engine's scrap!'

With just four days to go, we now had a car without engine, no tyre deal and had run out of money... there was only one option.

Le Mans, France, June 1984

Every June, the Loire Valley, famed throughout the world as the garden of France for its rolling hillsides, sunflowers, historic châteaux's and vineyards lining the banks of the river, reverberates to the alien roar of more than sixty thousand horsepower, as the famous 24 hour race takes over the historic town of Le Mans. The 1984 event was the fifty-second anniversary, scheduled to take place over the weekend of the sixteenth and seventeenth of June. It was also the third round of the 1984 World Endurance Championship.

We'd arrived at the track five days early in good time to set up camp, complete preparations and ensure the Lola passed scrutineering. This strict process is where the organizers, the Automobile Club de L'Ouest, inspect each car in order to confirm eligibility.

Just the sight of the famous circuit tightened my chest with excitement as our forty foot articulated transporter weaved its way through the restricted paddock and into our allotted space: the *Will Middleton World Championship Racing Team* had arrived, and would be taking on the might of the factory Rothmans Porsches, the Italian Lancia Martini, Aston Martin, Peugeot, Buick, Jaguar, Mazda and Ferrari teams. One thing in my life was totally beyond dispute; in a world of possibilities, I'd somehow been endowed with the perfect combination of optimism and supreme naïvety.

My arrival was however, also tinged with sadness. Following the Snetterton shake down test, I was no longer the number one driver of my own team, and in fact, wouldn't be driving at all. With a replacement engine costing over seventeen thousand pounds, I'd had little option but to sell my drive, my only consolation being that the blown engine, now mounted on a mahogany plinth with a plate glass top, made an attractive coffee table back home.

I stepped down from the truck to be greeted by a smiling François Migault. He offered his hand, '*Bonjour mon ami*,' he said in his familiar French accent.

'Hello François,' I said, smiling.

'This is my friend, François Sérvanin.' He gestured towards his colleague, an older man with thick silver hair swept back from his face. Although in his fifties, the man's physique was lean with the muscular tone of a man half his age. He stepped over, smiling and extended his hand.

'Bonjour, Will.'

We left the mechanics to offload the car and set up camp, whilst François Migault drove the short distance to a tiny crowded local café and ordered three espressos.

Everywhere I looked, the walls were adorned with faded black and white photos and posters from former 24 hour races. As I followed the aged drivers to a quiet table in the corner, it was clear they were both well known to the locals. A few requested autographs; all nodded or tapped foreheads in greeting. There also appeared to have been no charge for the coffees, or the fiery liquor which followed.

We talked for almost an hour before François Sérvanin gave a satisfied nod, and reaching into the inside pocket of his jacket, he removed a thick envelope. He handed it to me. 'Thanks,' I said. 'A pleasure doing business with you,' I lied. I hadn't wanted to do the deal, but it was done; I was no longer driving, but the cost of the replacement engine had been covered.

The summer sun shone down on a quarter of a million spectators, raising temperatures into the mid eighties, as fifty-three starters completed the rolling lap behind the Mercedes pace car.

I watched from the pit wall with Steve Kempton and François Sérvanin, as Migault shot past at the wheel of my Lola, holding forty-eighth place. Up at the front, the two Lancia Martinis stole first and second as the pack made their way beneath the Dunlop Bridge and through the esses for the first time, Paolo Barilla leading with Bob Wollek second in the number five Lancia.

Speeds already exceeded 230 miles per hour on the Mulsanne straight as Roger Dorchy in the Peugeot, bravely out braked Barilla's Lancia at the Mulsanne corner, taking the lead. As the pack streamed through the Porsche curves, on into the right-hand

White House Corner and out of the Ford chicane for the first time, Wollek was in second place, Barilla had dropped to third with Stephan Johansson fourth, Pescarolo fifth, Schuppan sixth and Jonathan Palmer seventh. A sudden flash of movement made me turn... the Lola was being directed by marshals into our pit behind me, its offside gull-wing door partially detached, the wing mirror hanging from its frame.

The pit burst into practiced activity, Simon replacing the mirror in seconds, securing the errant door firmly shut with sticky tape. With most of the twenty-four hour race still to go, Migault had felt it prudent to pit for repairs. The last thing he'd wanted was a repeat of Thursday's qualifying, when the same door, complete with mirror, had detached at over 200 miles per hour, resulting in a collision with the works Lancia Martin! Fortunately, on that occasion, the damage had been relatively minor, but with the Lola stranded on the circuit, we'd missed the rest of qualifying, resulting in our lowly grid position.

The Lola now returned to the race having dropped only one place, thanks to a variety of helpful incidents having occurred on the track including several early retirements. Thirty-four minutes elapsed and Migault was back in the pits for our first planned stop. I helped switch drivers, strapping Sérvanin into the cramped cockpit as our refueling team, swathed in fireproof overalls, pumped one hundred litres of high octane juice into the Lola's fuel cell, overseen by a French refueling steward.

Back on the track, Roger Dorchy had crashed his Peugeot, and Bob Wollek's Lancia was now leading the race.

Steve Kempton's voice suddenly crackled in my headset. 'Will! Something's wrong. Low battery light!'

Just fifteen minutes earlier, we'd switched drivers and Steve was now at the wheel. Minutes after his radio call, the car shot back into the pits and I helped Simon remove the rear engine cover. I stepped back and the mechanics swarmed over the car like a small army of ants, swiftly locating and fixing the problem.

'Alternator belt was broken.' said Simon, as a pair of mechanics lifted the rear body section back into position.

Standing at the front of the car, I signalled to Steve to restart the engine. I could see him repeatedly jabbing the start button. Despite the noise from the track, I could hear the whine of the high pressure pumps but nothing more, other than a click from the starter solenoid.

From behind the Lola's screen, Steve was frantically waving. I clicked the transmit button on my headset. 'Steve, mate, what's up?'

'It won't fire up... fucking batteries are dead.'

I turned to Simon. 'Shit! What do we do? We're not allowed to use the auxiliary starter, or a battery pack.'

He frowned. 'We don't have much choice. The batteries are flat because the alternator drive failed. It just needs to run a few laps and it'll recharge.'

'But if anyone sees, we'll get banned!' I replied.

He shrugged. 'There's no choice.' he repeated. 'We can't bump start it...' he paused, '...and we're losing time.'

Ian discreetly plugged an external power pack into the Lola's electrical system and I signalled again to Steve to fire up the engine. This time it burst into life and he left the pits in a cloud of frustrated tyre smoke. We'd lost almost forty-three precious minutes.

I clicked the transmit button. 'Steve? Is the battery showing a charge now?' I asked.

A few seconds passed, and then amid a storm of static, I heard his voice. 'All okay, Will, everything running fine.'

I breathed a momentary sigh of relief as I turned to see an irate French official urgently waving in my direction. 'Non!' He yelled, wildly gesticulating at me. 'Force auxiliaire!'

At that moment François Migault fortunately wandered back into our pit. Seeing the irate official, he switched instantly into charm mode. As Steve continued to lap the circuit, an ever larger contingent of French officials arrived to join us. I couldn't understand a word that was being said but it was clear, no one was happy! Amid much gesticulating and nodding, François Migault continued to fight our corner. Finally, he stepped over to me and smiled. 'Will, there is a problem.' His voice was suddenly serious. 'They say the car must return to the pits and restart 'under own momentum'...' He paused. '...will it?' I shook my head. 'Steve's only done a couple of laps, François.' I replied. 'And he's just switched on the headlamps, the batteries were completely dead. It'll never restart. It needs at least half an hour of running to recharge.'

He shrugged. 'So... it's over.' He replied despondently.

'Hang on a minute.' I said as an idea suddenly hit me.

I turned to Simon who'd been listening. 'They say it's got to start under its *own* momentum... right?'

Simon nodded. 'Yes...' he cocked his head to one side. 'What are you thinking?'

'Do you think we could use the engines own momentum to restart itself?'

He raised an eyebrow. 'What do you mean?'

The French officials were gesticulating again. 'Will,' interrupted François, urgently, 'You must call the car in immediately, or they'll black flag it and we'll be out for certain.'

'Okay, tell them we're calling it in now. And tell them we'll switch it off on *their* signal and restart it only when *they* say. Is that clear?' François nodded. I turned to Ian. 'Ian, get on the pit blower and tell the signaling crew to put an "IN" on the board.' He nodded and rushed over to the phone.

Turning to Simon, I grinned. 'Let's see if we can restart a Cosworth with its own momentum.'

With the Lola hopefully now in range, I clicked the transmit button and carefully explained the situation to Steve in between bursts of static. 'Remember, Steve,' I reiterated, 'watch me *very, very* carefully and *only* kill the engine when I give you the signal. Is that clear?'

'Yes, but why do you want me to give it so many revs?' He asked.

'Don't query it!' I yelled back. 'Just do it! ...do it *exactly* as I signal, okay?'

Three minutes later, the Lola sped down the pit lane and into our allotted area. As instructed, Steve kept the engine running at around 4000revs. I turned to the assembled French officials with hands raised, as if conducting an orchestra, awaiting their response. The man in charge indicated with a curt nod to kill the engine. I relayed a signal to Steve with an upward swiping digit motion, indicating to switch off the ignition. As instructed, he instantly hit the throttle, sending the revs to around 10,000, and then cut the Lola's electrics. A French official, watching through the side screen, indicated thumbs up. I paused for the merest moment, as if unhurried. Then turning to the French man in charge I gave a querying smile. As hoped, he responded with a courteous nod of approval.

With the engine still revolving under its own centrifugal force, I quickly signaled thumbs up and Steve, with his finger still on the switches, flicked the pumps and management system back on. To the incredulity of the assembled officials, the engine instantly burst into a beautiful symphony of sound, without needing the power-hungry starter motor. I stepped quickly to one side as Steve floored the throttle and exited the pit lane, leaving two long strips of rubber on the French tarmac.

Not wishing for a further reprimand, I headed for the pit wall, leaving the squabbling officials to poor François Migault.

A few minutes passed before a hand appeared on my shoulder. It was François. 'Mon ami,' he said softly in his deep French accent, 'that was clever, très clever!'

It was just before eight. Dusk; one of the most dangerous times at Le Mans. I was sitting in the pits, draining the last dregs of a strong black coffee from my mug. Forty minutes earlier, we'd strapped François Sérvanin back into the Lola for his second stint. He was due to pit on the next lap and the team were busy preparing the refuelling hose and a fresh set of tyres for Steve to take over.

He had just donned his helmet, when my headset exploded with a sudden burst of static and French expletives. 'Shit!' I yelled, jumping to my feet. 'He's off... François' off!' I paused, listening through the static. 'He's off on the Porsche Curves!' I added.

'How bad?' asked Steve gloomily, removing his helmet.

I stepped out and into the pit lane, looking for better reception as John Sheldon in the Aston Martin Nimrod shot by, turning into his pit to refuel.

Cradling the headset to my ears, attempting to block out the noise of the track, I listened through the static as a breathless François Sérvanin explained what had happened.

Turning to the expectant faces of my pit crew, I said, simply. 'Sorry guys. François's okay, but the car's toast. He's hit the Lancia, or the Lancia has hit him, I'm not sure which. Anyway the Lola's being pushed off the track... We're out of the race.'

Despondently I wandered over to the pit wall as John Sheldon hurtled back out of the pit lane and onto the track. We'd lasted just eight hours.

For a few moments I stood in silent shock watching, as a plump full moon disappeared behind a haze of cloud. It was only moments later, as it reappeared, that I became conscious of a menacing plume of black smoke rising on the far side of the track. I felt suddenly cold; there had to have been a massive accident. I called to Simon, pointing in the distant direction of the growing cloud.

'It's got to be around the Mulsanne kink!' He said.

Moments later, we heard via the grapevine that John "Driller" Sheldon, a British dentist by profession, had been approaching the Mulsanne kink at over 190 miles per hour, having just taken on board a hundred litres of fuel. Without warning, a rear tyre had blown and his Aston Martin Nimrod had veered violently left, impacting the guard rail, disintegrating over two hundred yards; the wrecked car spinning back wildly across the track. Moments later, American driver, Drake Olson in the team's second Aston Martin, shot by, straight into the strewn debris.

The explosion and fireball from the first impact was so violent, that the surrounding woods were instantly set ablaze. Olson was mercifully unhurt, but a forty-two year old French marshal, Jacky Loiseau was killed in the initial impact and his colleague, André-Guy Lefebvre, lay seriously injured.

Driller remained fully conscious, strapped in the ensuing inferno of twisted metal as it came to rest on the right side of the track. Badly burnt, he was taken by helicopter to the Trousseau burns unit at Tours.

31

THE PAST YEAR had been a steep learning process. In the national series, with Steve Kempton as my usual co driver, we'd battled our way through the races, and although failing to finish a few times, had moved progressively up the grid. But as the year drew to a close, the old Lola was becoming tired, its chassis losing rigidity, its ill-fitting bodywork regularly detaching during races, altering the aerodynamics. Added to this, it was a complicated and heavy design. Only two such models had ever been built and the manufacturers weren't interested in us running it in the junior C2 category of the World Championship. What I needed was something light, simple and competitive. A car designed specifically for the C2 category.

Robert Arnold had offered me such a car. He was the new owner of Devron, a specialist race car manufacturer, and only last week, I'd arranged for his preparation business to take over the running of the Lola, for the final World Championship race in Australia.

Beth and I had also moved forward with our first little house, which we'd now named "The Burrows". The tiny semi-detached was no longer a building site and after months of painstaking work, the transformation was complete. Our restoration included a new kitchen, bathroom, central heating system, and a small conservatory. All the hard work, combined with the rapid house inflation of the eighties, resulted in it virtually doubling in value in just eighteen months.

Following George's arrival and with the renovation a success, we'd scoured the papers for weeks, peering into estate agents' windows, our enthusiasm driving us to find another project, something bigger and better to renovate. Perhaps a windmill or possibly an old barn, something we could make our own.

It was a late October weekend and I got up, pulled on my jeans and T-shirt, peering from the bedroom window at my pride and joy, my latest 'investment opportunity'. I'd sold the TR7 for a small profit a few months ago after finding the little red Ferrari at the local car auction. It still had a myriad of faults and more than 100,000 miles on the clock, but despite that, its value was rocketing faster than an express elevator. My plan, as with all my past investments, was to fix it up and sell at a profit, and in the case of the Ferrari, when the market peaked.

Looking from the window, the sun was high in the sky, the perfect day for a drive I thought. Beth was already downstairs feeding George. 'Fancy a walk?' I called. 'We could take Cossie and go in the Ferrari,' I said. Cossie was short for Cosworth, another growing investment, our first family pet, my Golden Retriever. From the day we'd picked up the little bundle, he was always by my side, ever hopeful of a little tit-bit, or a run in the Sussex countryside. Anybody who has ever owned a dog knows the endless pleasure gained from watching that sleek coated, graceful little animal bounding ahead, tail wagging happily, sniffing at the wondrous scents left by the local animal community. It was later that morning, at the start of the walk, that we happened upon the ivy covered derelict granary, set in one and three quarter acres of disused farm land, bearing a recently erected sign 'For Sale by Auction'.

It was set back from the road, bordered by a low weathered fence, behind which ponies roamed nonchalantly. 'Oh Will, it's wonderful,' exclaimed Beth, as she stepped from the car.

'It's amazing,' I agreed, 'but it's only a shell. I doubt there's any water or electricity and almost certainly no drainage,' I said. 'What do you think it'll go for?'

'Probably a lot more than we can afford,' she replied ruefully, wandering off towards a gate and patting one of the inquisitive ponies. She turned and smiled back at me, a snapshot that'll remain with me forever. An almost magical expression on her face, she was wearing tapered blue jeans, red and blue plaid shirt and white trainers. Behind her bounded Cossie, coat glistening, tail wagging happily, the nose twitching as he searched out the local wild life.

I lifted George to my hip and joined her at the gate. Looking back, the roof of the barn appeared to be bowing inwards and on the verge of collapse but the brickwork seemed sound enough. Beth pulled at my arm. 'Let's take a look around the back,' she said, rampaging off through the deep grass like an eager child. I smiled, there was little point in asking her impression. I followed her to the back where she reappeared from an opening, partially obscured by tendrils of ivy. 'Will! Come and look, it's incredible inside.' I joined her and was as affected as her. Sunlight shone through the huge gothic arches. 'This would be our lounge, and through there, the dining room.' She mused eagerly.

For more than an hour we sat in the old barn, gazing out at the surrounding Sussex countryside and dreamed...

It was the 1st November 1984 and the auction was due to start at 10.30. I arrived at the offices of Smiths Gore early and made my way up a flight of stairs to a small office, where a young girl with piercing green eyes and shoulder length brown hair was manning the phone system. There was nobody else in sight, so I waited.

'I'm interested in bidding on a property later this morning,' I explained as she put down the phone. I handed over the brochure.

'Oh, yes, that lovely old granary. It was originally built around 1890. It looks beautiful, doesn't it? You'll need to make a sealed bid,' she said. Glancing up at an office clock, she added. 'Not later than 10.30 this morning, I can give you a tender form if you'd like one.'

'I've only ever bid at car auctions,' I explained, 'and I've never made a sealed bid before. Is there anyone I could speak to? I'd just like to know a little more about how it works'.

I was shown to a waiting area and a few minutes later, a tall, distinguished looking man in his fifties, wearing a dark suit arrived. 'Mr Middleton?' he enquired, offering his hand. 'My name is Tom Parminter.'

'I'm interested in this barn,' I explained, 'the old granary. I'd just like to be sure of the rules and the exact sealed bid procedure.'

Parminter couldn't help but smile. 'Well, it's very straight forward,' he began. 'All you have to do is write your bid on the tender form and then seal it in the envelope. The full procedure is explained in our catalogue.' He handed me a glossy brochure. 'I can take your bid now if you like. They'll be opened at 11.00 today and the successful bidder notified immediately. It's very simple, the highest bid wins. Oh yes,' he added, 'the successful bidder must also make a ten percent deposit payment immediately and the full balance has to be paid within one month.'

'Could you tell me who owns the barn?' I asked.

'I can't give you the client's name but I can confirm that it's currently owned by a pension fund.'

'Has there been much interest?' I asked, still fishing.

He smiled, 'Well, I obviously can't say too much but there are one or two property developers that have expressed an interest and also the current tenant farmer, a Mr Adams.'

'Have there been any offers?'

'We have had a number of pre sale offers in the region of £60,000 but they have all been rejected by the vendor.'

I sat back in the chair, studying the bid procedure, the sounds of the busy office fading out of focus. Over the years I'd discovered that the curse of dyslexia brought with it certain benefits, a strange ability occasionally, to see beyond what others saw. It wasn't that I intentionally set out looking for loopholes, more that I sometimes interpreted information differently from non dyslexics. I tended to view things very visually, somehow seeing a wider picture, often calculating intuitively, as if by a higher consciousness, oblivious to how I'd arrived at the correct answer. Yet, inevitably, the solution I'd come up with *was* correct.

At school I'd always found it hard to concentrate, as information from all around me appeared to crash in on my senses from every direction. But as an adult, I was slowly learning to embrace this strange gift. Nurtured, I'd often found that it worked to my advantage; even letting me know what opponents may be thinking. It was the reason I didn't plan what I'd say in a business meeting, I did everything by intuition... and more often than not, it worked. I had no idea *how* I was going to win the auction, when I stepped into the offices of Smiths Gore, but somehow I knew I would win.

I snapped back to reality. 'So, can I be absolutely clear on this?' I finally asked, still pondering some wording I'd just read and reread on the tender form. 'You're saying that so long as I bid the highest amount, we win the auction, no question about it. Is that right?'

'Yes, that's quite correct, Mr Middleton.'

'And nobody sees the bids until they're opened at 11.00?'

'That's right and everyone's welcome to watch the opening of the sealed bids, if they wish. I will be handling the sale myself.'

With a rush of excitement I took the proffered pen and completed the tender form, completely ignoring the box headed "Bid amount"; I simply wrote a line of text in block capitals beneath it, and sealing the form in the envelope, handed it back.

Returning an hour later, I discovered that four bids had been received; two were from property developers, one from the tenant farmer and ours. I was shown into a conference room where a small group was seated on either side of a long table. Parminter was at the head, with the four envelopes stacked neatly before him. An assistant sat by his side ready to record the proceedings. I took one of the remaining seats and scanned the faces of the other bidders. It was immediately obvious who the farmer was; a wiry guy in his late forties with healthy outdoor features and a receding hairline. He coolly held my gaze.

Parminter studied his watch and smiled. 'Well, gentlemen, it's precisely 11.00am,' he began. 'I'll now open the four tenders in no particular order. The highest bidder will be the successful purchaser of the old granary barn. The sale procedure will be as outlined in our sale documentation and tender procedure. The winning bidder will be required to make an immediate, non refundable ten percent deposit payment with the full balance paid by cleared funds within twenty eight days.' He took a few moments opening the first manila envelope before announcing clearly, 'The first bid I have is for a sum of £74500.'

I quickly scanned the faces around the table as one of the group rose and headed grim faced towards the door, the others giving nothing away. The farmer coolly stared back at me. Parminter continued. 'The second bid is the sum of £71500.'

A small flicker of disappointment appeared on one of the two remaining faces. So, I thought, the farmer has bid more. Parminter removed and unfolded the next slip, the farmer's body language instantly giving away that the folded paper was his offering. 'The third bid,' Parminter continued, 'is the sum of £75650.'

The farmer was now watching me intently as the final bid was removed from its envelope. A look of confusion spread across Parminters face, his brow creasing as he read the words: *"Half of one percent above any other bid received."'* His eyes appeared above the paper. 'I'm sorry but this bid is void,' he announced firmly. *'Escalating* bids are not acceptable.'

'Why?' I blurted. 'It doesn't *say* escalating bids *aren't* allowed. Our offer is half a percent above any other bid received; we've therefore tendered the highest bid in accordance with your terms of tender.' I looked around the table, taking in the surprised look on the faces of the two remaining players. Clearly the only person affected was the farmer who was suddenly looking in doubt, having just been technically outbid. He turned, fixing me with a baleful glare. 'This is *bullshit!'* he exclaimed. 'I've bid the highest amount, so I've won!'

'No, you haven't, because I've bid half a percent more!' I insisted.

A commotion quickly ensued when the remaining property developer began arguing that the entire bid process should be void, and the farmer, cheque book in hand, continued to insist he'd already won. I was hurriedly ushered to a side office.

A few moments elapsed before the young girl with the green eyes appeared. 'Would you like a coffee whilst you wait?' She asked smiling.

I nodded back. 'Yes, black please,' I said, 'no sugar. I think I've caused a bit of an upheaval in there.'

She grinned. 'It was a bit different from usual,' she said smiling. 'I don't think anybody has ever done that before.'

In the background I could hear a raised gruff voice. 'Somebody doesn't seem very happy.' I said. 'Any idea what's going on?'

'Well, they've just sent for the company solicitors.'

'Shit… that doesn't sound too good.'

'I wouldn't worry too much. I think they're checking their legal position.'

'Has anyone said anything?'

She glanced back down the corridor, before whispering. 'Don't say I said anything, or I could lose my job, but I think Mr Parminter is on your side. I overheard him arguing that you'd bid the highest amount, so in accordance with the way everything's currently worded, you appear to be the winner.' She shrugged. 'The vendors are obviously happy, they just want the highest bid and the other developer was outbid anyway. I think he's just trying it on in the hope he'll have a chance to put in another bid. Between you and me, I think he's intrigued by your interpretation of the rules. It's the farmer that's kicking up a stink.' She laughed. 'You do realize he'll be your new neighbour if you've won, don't you?'

Another half hour passed before I was shown into Parminter's office. He rose from behind his desk offering a hand. 'Congratulations Mr Middleton, that was quite an unusual morning. I can confirm you are the successful bidder and new owner of the old granary barn!'

I'd done it, the barn was ours! At least it would be, so long as the bank honored the cheque!

Coming up with just the deposit had drained all our spare cash, as well as stretching our overdraft to the limit. I *had* to persuade our bank to increase our lending limit and fast.

Gripping the wheel of the old Ferrari, I turned left onto Kingsway and flicked a look at my watch; we were already late. Since signing the papers, I'd had more than three weeks of sleepless nights, as each mortgage company in turn, had rejected our application for a mortgage. The problem wasn't just my lack of regular income, it was the barn itself. None of them considered it to be a house, so it simply didn't qualify for a mortgage. I now had less than five working days to find the money. My latest idea was to try for a short term bank loan and as soon as the old barn was considered habitable, switch to a more manageable mortgage. I'd already advertised the Ferrari and knew I'd sell it at a profit, but I needed time, and if I couldn't come up with the balance within the next week, we'd lose not only the barn itself but our deposit as well.

'What if we don't get it?' Beth asked nervously.

'We will, 'I replied, 'everything's going to be fine, it's all under control.' I said as positively as I could manage, but in truth I was worried.

She didn't buy it. 'If you don't slow down, we're going to get stopped, and we won't even get to the bank!' she admonished from the passenger seat.

I backed off and perched my right arm on the frame of the open window, glancing out over the sea. The ocean always seemed to have a calming influence on me, reminding me of my childhood, life at the hotel and walks along the promenade with my parents. Looking over at the water, I breathed deeply and told myself to relax *everything was going to work out.*

Moving to the inside lane, I made another turn left into West Street, then floored the throttle. I made another quick left turn and then headed into Kings West multi-storey, the old Ferrari protesting loudly as we grazed the speed bumps. The tyres squealed against the concrete floor as I headed up the ramp to the second level.

'Are you going to come in?' I asked Beth, as we sprinted out of the car park and into North Street.

She smiled nervously. 'I don't think I can face it, Will, 'she said. 'This is our last chance, if he says no...' her words trailed away. 'I think I'll wait outside.'

She straightened my tie and kissed me. 'Do you know what you're going to say?'

'Not the foggiest idea,' I replied with a grin.

'Thank goodness for that!' she replied. 'That's when you're at your best.'

I made my way into the bank and headed over to the enquiries hatch. A few minutes later, a secretary arrived and guided me down a corridor and into a small but business like office on the ground floor. 'Good to see you again,' Jack said, rising from his chair, smiling. 'Now, tell me all about this barn, Will.'

An hour later, I made my way back out onto the street. The tight look on my face told Beth that things hadn't gone well. 'Oh...' she said, trying hard to fake a brave smile. '..that's that then, I suppose.'

'Not quite,' I said, my face breaking into a broad grin, 'they've agreed to give us fifty grand over ten years!'

Beth released a big sigh of relief, thumping me on the chest. 'Don't do that, you rat bag!'

'All I have to do now,' I continued, 'is to find a buyer for the Ferrari, then see if we can borrow the difference from our parents, until we sell The Burrows.'

One week later, indebted up to our eyes, we became the proud owners of one very large gothic Victorian barn, set in one and three quarter acres of Sussex countryside. Four weeks after that, with George only eighteen months old, we moved into the unconverted hay loft, with no running water, no heating and not even a front door or windows. It was paradise, but it would take more than a year before we could persuade a mortgage company to switch our loans to an affordable mortgage. Over the many years that followed, we slowly converted the barn into what would become 'The Old Granary'.

32

---

*"If you can keep your head when all about you are losing
theirs, it's just possible you haven't grasped the situation.*

Jean Kerr

Melbourne, Australia. November 1984

IT WAS SIX THIRTY, Tuesday 27th November 1984 as I turned into the car park of the Melbourne Hilton, feeling an uncomfortable mix of excitement and tense uncertainty. I'd spent the day testing the Lola at the Sandown Park circuit in preparation for the coming weekend's final race of the year. I was tired and apprehensive; this meeting with Robert Arnold, the MD of Devron Racing Cars, could well lead to a winning drive in next year's World Championship. Less than a year ago he'd purchased the assets of the bankrupt race car manufacturer. After the disappointment of Le Mans and the difficulties of the national series, his UK workshops had taken over the preparation of the Lola, his mechanics also running it here in Australia. However the costs had been almost three times his most pessimistic estimates and as the mountain of expenses continued to grow, he'd agreed to offset some of the bills in return for joining me as co-driver in the coming weekend's 1000km race.

Since meeting him, he'd occasionally mentioned the development of a new car, but tonight for the first time, I'd see the actual drawings and we'd talk money, maybe even agree a deal that could propel me up the grid. 'We need to discuss this face to face, well away from prying eyes and somewhere we'll not be overheard by other teams,' he'd said, when I'd picked him up earlier that day from the airport.

I parked the Ford Falcon hire car and made my way through the bright modern hotel atrium and up the smoked glass stairway to the bar.

Robert was sitting in a quiet corner. He jumped up smiling and beckoned me over, 'Good evening, Will. Beer?' he said offering an outstretched hand. He was a tall man of medium build, with penetrating eyes and dark receding wisps of hair carefully combed back over his pink cranium.

I smiled back. 'Thanks, that would be great.'

He made his way to the bar, returning a few minutes later with two pints. With the usual pleasantries out of the way, he looked around the crowded bar as if others might be watching, then unrolled a set of drawings, spreading them out across the table. I leaned in and studied the first image of the car that was destined to become my attack on the 1985 World Championship.

In the racing world there was a general belief that if a car looked right, it most probably *was* right, and this didn't just look right, it looked stunning. The sleek aerodynamic design bore more than a striking resemblance to the earlier classic Devrons of the seventies, the days when Devron was a world class name, but this new design was fresh, clean and uncluttered, with lightweight Kevlar bodywork sloping elegantly from the nose with its flared-in halogen headlights, up over the cockpit and engine bay to a slick full width rear wing. The smooth undulating sides incorporated low drag NASA style air intakes, channelling air to the powerful Cosworth engine. The lightweight Kevlar bodywork rippled in and around elegant eighteen inch aluminium wheels and scoops rammed air, via ducting to hefty ventilated disc brakes.

For the next half-hour I listened intently as Robert talked about his takeover of Devron, its background and how he hoped this new advanced design would come to dominate the junior category of the following year's World Championship.

He spoke passionately of Devron's pedigree, how the company had been formed almost twenty years prior, but then following the founder's death in a flying accident, had floundered and ultimately collapsed. 'The assets were then taken over by a consortium of Scottish racing enthusiasts,' he explained, 'but things didn't work out and they ended up in liquidation. It was then that I and a close friend acquired the assets.'

How secure was the new company now, I wondered as he finished his story. I had always prided myself on my ability to second guess opponents, my knack in anticipating their every move... But what was the old proverb about *pride*? *It cometh before a fall!*

I could already see myself at the wheel of this new car, winning races... maybe even the championship! I desperately wanted this to work, and for the first time in my life, I ignored the warning bell ringing wildly in my ears.

Robert edged forward on his seat, flashing a disconcerting smile, 'So, Will... what do you think?' he asked proudly, like a father showing off a photo of his new baby.

'It looks beautiful,' I said quietly, still thinking, still studying the drawings, convinced, despite the even louder warning bell, that this was the way forward.

'Have you started building it yet?'

'We've completed all the drawings and jigs and the monocoque is currently being built by an outside fabricator. We'll have it by early January and we'll start the actual assembly by the middle of the month.'

'And you're sure you can have it finished in time for the first race at Mugello next April?'

Robert paused, then levelling his penetrating eyes at me answered, 'Yes, providing you can guarantee the money.'

I took a deep swallow of beer and returned his stare, trying to read beyond the penetrating eyes. Unknown to Robert, I had already secured a fifty-thousand pound part sponsorship deal from Diamond Sound for next season's championship. 'Thirty thousand pounds, right?' I asked. It was the figure he'd mentioned several times before.

He nodded, 'Yes, thirty grand, but only to whoever orders the first car. For that price you'd get a rolling chassis with gearbox and one spare set of wheels. You'd provide your choice of engine, I'd suggest a Cosworth DFL, and we'll install it as part of the deal.'

'What about other spares?' I asked.

He cleared his throat, 'For thirty grand, Will, that would be it.... It's a very good deal... You're already saving at least fifty percent on what we'll be selling a second car for.'

'If I go for it, when would you need payment?'

A thin smile, then he replied, 'For that price, we'd need it all up front, at the time you place the order.'

I smiled back into his unnerving eyes, 'You're kidding? I couldn't pay *everything* up front... what guarantee would I have that I'd get it on time once I've parted with all the money?'

He turned his head towards me replying, 'You have my word... It's the only way we can give you that price.'

I paused, thinking about it for a moment, 'We'd actually need it well before Mugello, so we'd have time to test. At that rate you'd have less than three months. Could you definitely build it by then?'

Another pause ensued as Robert's face reflected a moment's uncertainty, then looking up from the drawings, he smiled and replied, 'Sure, that wouldn't be a problem. You'd have it by the first week in April...guaranteed.' He cocked his head to one side, awaiting my response.

I smiled back at him, 'Okay then, thirty grand but it'll have to be in two instalments. Fifteen when we return to the UK, the second fifteen by the first week of February, but I'd want you to include a spare nose and second set of spare wheels.'

There was a sharp intake of breath, his face grimaced theatrically, then a moments pause... 'You drive a hard bargain,' he finally replied, offering his hand, his smile returning. 'Will, you have a deal... a very good deal I might add!'

33

It was the best of times, it was the worst of times, it was the age
of wisdom, it was the age of foolishness, it was the epoch of belief,
it was the epoch of incredulity, it was the season of Light, it was
the season of Darkness, it was the spring of hope, it was the winter
of despair, we had everything before us...

Charles Dickens – A Tale of Two Cities

IT WAS MONDAY morning, two weeks after the Australian race. We'd spent a week in Thailand before returning home and I was still jetlagged, though far less tired. Languidly, I woke from a deep sleep, the kind of sleep I hadn't afforded myself since beginning all the frenetic activity of the past season.

Still half asleep, I reached out across our makeshift bed on the floor of The Old Granary to find Beth. She was fully awake, propped up on pillows, contentedly smiling down on our son George, snuggled in between us. 'Good morning darling,' she said inclining her head towards me. 'You seemed to sleep well.'

Pushing myself up into the arctic chill of the unheated hayloft, I smiled back at them, 'Yes, I think I must have been off the moment my head hit the pillow,' I replied.

Bright winter sun was streaming through gaps in the old dust sheets, tacked over openings we hoped would soon be windows. 'What time is it?' I asked.

'It's past nine, darling ... and it snowed last night,' she beamed excitedly. 'It's still falling and it's started to settle. I think we'll be celebrating George's first ever *white* Christmas!'

For a while I just lay there relaxing, taking in the peaceful scene, thinking of the time we had ahead of us. We had more than eight weeks before testing was due to start with the new Devron, lots of time to enjoy relaxing together over Christmas, and to make a start on some of the building works.

Thinking of next season and the new car, sent a rush of nervous excitement coursing through me. Unlike this year in the old overweight Lola, next year would herald the first ever drivers world championship for my category, and in the new Devron I could dominate, potentially even win. Thinking back to the last race, I considered the team setup. Everything would have to be more professional, I thought. Sandown had been a total disaster; a twenty thousand mile round trip, to finish seventeenth overall.

It had been a difficult race, with the track surface breaking up badly, causing a plague of punctures for everyone. Six times we'd pitted the Lola for fresh Avon slicks, each time falling further and further down the field as Robert Arnold's team of mechanics franticly battled to change wheels in the torrid Australian sun. But the wildly understeering Lola had been a handful from first qualifying. Then, in the race, more problems had occurred with fuel pressure; the failing high pressure injection system losing us precious seconds on every torturous 2.4 mile lap, the engine refusing to run cleanly through the entire tight, slow speed, infield section of track.

If I'd ever needed reassurance of having made the right decision to go ahead with the new Devron, that race had proved it.

Yet, despite the track problems, twenty eight year old Stefan Belloff had dominated Sandown from the first qualifying session in his Rothmans sponsored, works Porsche. The young German ace, famous for setting the fastest ever lap on the Nürburgring, ultimately won the six hour race comfortably, by more than three laps, clinching the 1984 World Endurance Championship.

Ten Days Later

Over the Christmas break, I'd had the chance to relax and think through the decision I'd made. Almost everyone I'd spoken to had agreed that I'd made the right choice to go with the Devron for 1985 and the positive reaction in the racing media had also reassured me. This coming year was going to be my chance to shine in the spotlight. But there was more – unknown to all except Beth and myself, there was also our wedding to arrange. It was early January and we'd just set the date for 23rd March.

With my confidence at an all time high, I quickly set about trying to find the balance of the race budget plus a suitable co-driver. I approached all my old sponsors with a variety of proposals and contra-deals. Diamond Sound had already signed for the full season bringing in a healthy fifty thousand. Aztec Finance had agreed to come back on board and cover the cost of an engine. Saunier Duval had signed a deal for ten thousand. Alan Smith Racing in Derby had offered to build a pair of Cosworth DFL's for the price of just one. DRG Croxley Script had chipped in five thousand and Gareth Hunt had also said he'd help out with promotions again. Everything was going well but I still had to find more. With a commitment to the bank for the barn loan and funds urgently needed to start building works, it was crucial I found a regular source of personal income, a working wage. Applying my usual lateral thinking to the task, I set off back to Goodwood...

The circuit had become a regular testing venue and on my last visit I'd again noticed the little red helicopter parked on the side of the airfield, but this time it had a For Sale sign forlornly attached to its Plexiglas screen. The thought of the helicopter had rekindled an idea from years earlier. It was a quarter past ten in the morning when I made my way into the offices of the flying school, Blades Helicopters, which was made up of three linked portacabins, and asked to speak to the owner.

'That would be me,' replied a man in his late thirties. He was of average build, wearing a smart white pilot shirt with blue and gold epaulettes, his thick dark hair swept back from a tanned face.

'Hi,' I said extending my hand. 'My name's Will, Will Middleton. I noticed the little helicopter over there's for sale,' I said, pointing out of the office window.

'Ah, the Enstrom,' he said, flashing an excited smile. 'Yes, it's an F-28 model, been for sale for over a month.'

Interesting, I thought. Clearly he's no salesman. 'Is it yours?' I enquired, turning back from the window.

'No, but we've been using it for training. We're now selling it on behalf of the owner.'

'Who might that be?' I persisted.

His eyes narrowed a little. 'Belongs to the director of a local construction company,' he replied evasively.

I nodded, not pressing the point further. 'How much does he want for it?'

'Twenty five thousand,' he said.

'Why are they selling it?' I enquired.

'It was really the MD's toy.... he's just bought himself an old fort in middle of the Solent between Portsmouth and the Isle of Wight. He's planning to convert it into a luxury home. I think he's just trying to raise funds.'

Interesting, I thought, as I drove out of the airfield gates half an hour later. *Twenty five grand almost certainly means he'll take twenty, and the flying school will probably be earning around ten percent. That brings it down to nearer seventeen grand.*

An hour's work on the phone found me the name of the construction company that had recently purchased *'No Man's Land*

Fort'. Another phone call to a friend in London provided the name of the managing director and within fifteen minutes a financial report whirred out of my fax machine.

It was clear from the accounts, that despite the building boom of the eighties, this company was strapped for cash. I picked up the phone and dialled the eleven digit number. A few seconds later I was speaking to the director himself. 'I understand you're selling your old Enstrom for seventeen and a half thousand,' I began, 'is that correct?'

'Er...' a moment's pause, '... well yes, that's right. Where did you find out?'

'I've been speaking to Bruce down at the Goodwood flying school,' I explained.

'Are you a pilot?' he asked.

'No, not yet but I'm seriously thinking of learning. I was wondering if you might be interested in a deal.'

'Never any harm in talking,' he replied.

'I have fifteen grand burning a hole in my pocket today,' I said. 'Just wondering if that might buy me the Enstrom?'

There was another pause, then he replied, 'Not quite, but if you could make it seventeen I think we could do a deal'.

'I'd need to get the thing re-sprayed in my company colours and that'd cost me another five hundred. If you could make it sixteen, I'll pop round with a cheque!'

'I'll think about it ... let me have your number.'

I checked the reflection in the full length mirror, not through vanity but objectivity, no different to evaluating the car before a race. I respected the challenge that lay ahead, and with only eight weeks before the first race, my new routine had been in place for the past two weeks: a two hour circuit at the local gym, three mornings each week, then a four mile run on alternate evenings. I was six foot one and now weighed in at just 168lb. At thirty years of age my body was lean, the muscles defined with barely an ounce of fat visible. With ten races ahead of me, I needed to be fit. Each race would last between six and twenty-four hours, with cockpit temperatures exceeding 120° and G forces of over 4G. Every race would be the equivalent of running a marathon in a sauna, wearing three layers of fireproof overalls whilst pumping weights. If anything was going to fail, I was determined it wasn't going to be me.

A little over two hours later I was showered and back at my desk, drinking a strong black coffee, the phone pinned to my ear. I'd been due to drive over to Devron later that day for a fitting in the new car, but Robert Arnold was trying to stop the meeting. 'There's no point in wasting your time driving over,' he breezed. 'The chassis won't even be here until next week.'

'Next week!' I repeated incredulously. 'I thought it was supposed to have arrived early January?'

Robert paused momentarily as if trying to recall. 'There were one or two minor delays,' he finally concluded. 'Mainly due to improvements we've been implementing along the way. But it'll be here next week,' he said confidently, 'and all the component parts are coming together well.'

'But Mugello's only eight weeks away. Is it still going to be ready?'

'That won't be a problem,' he smoothly assured me. 'It won't take more than eight to ten days actually, to assemble the first car!'

I was certain he'd originally told me the assembly had already started, but decided not to confront him. 'You're certain it'll be finished by early March? We must have time to test it thoroughly before we leave.' I said. 'And remember, I've arranged the press day for mid March at Goodwood...'

'Yes! Don't worry, Will! Everything's under control.' he assured me again.

Almost a week had passed when the MD of the construction company finally phoned me back, agreeing to the deal on the Enstrom for sixteen thousand pounds.

It was late afternoon as I made my way towards the offices of Blades Helicopters, noticing that the "For Sale" sign had already been removed. 'Hi Bruce,' I said cheerfully as he offered his hand.

'I understand you've managed to buy the Enstrom,' he replied gloomily.

I flashed a smile. 'Yes, we did the deal this morning.'

He gave a dismissive shrug. 'You got yourself a very good buy, if you don't mind me saying.'

'Well,' I replied, 'I was wondering if you might be interested in a little deal yourself.'

'Oh?'

'You mentioned that you occasionally hired the Enstrom for training. Is that right?'

'Well, yes, that's true. We have a fleet of two, plus two Gazelles, but we often need another.'

'Well, I was wondering if you might be interested in using mine occasionally?'

'Well, it's possible...'he replied hesitantly.

'If you're interested, you could have it for free the first month.'

His eyes lit up 'Oh?'

An hour later, I left the offices with the deal done. It was simple and straightforward. Blades Helicopters would lease the Enstrom from my team for twelve months but during the first month they'd have it rent free whilst they trained me to fly it. As a private pilot I wouldn't be allowed to directly earn income from flying. However, the helicopter would be re-painted in my team colours and at all times carry team sponsor logos. In return, both

Diamond and Croxley had agreed to pay an extra eight and a half thousand each for two years, for additional exposure on the side of the aircraft. The minimum monthly return from Blades, after general maintenance, would be one thousand pounds per month. Not only had I secured an ongoing guaranteed monthly salary, to more than cover the expensive bank loan on the barn, but I'd also become the proud owner of my own helicopter and within weeks I would be a qualified pilot. I'd also have an impressive advantage when trying to entice new sponsors to come onboard. And the bottom line was, it hadn't cost me a penny. In fact I'd already made a thousand pounds profit!

* * *

On the twenty-third of March, Beth made her way slowly down the aisle on the arm of her youngest brother to the organ strains of Jeremiah Clarke's Trumpet Voluntary. She was wearing a beautiful, white, off the shoulder gown, that set off an elegant white and gold filigree bead choker. Behind her, George, twenty months old, followed with a beaming smile on his chubby face. He was smartly dressed in a specially tailored pageboy-blue velvet suit, both hands firmly grasping his mother's dress train, supported on either side by Beth's older sister and my niece.

Almost two years on from my mother's insistence of a *quickie* wedding, and with all with all arrangements secretly in place, we'd deposited fifty- eight wedding invitations into a Gatwick post box, before flying off to Tenerife with George, for a week's holiday in January.

Lying there in the sun, watching Beth and George happily splashing about in the shallow pool, I smiled at the thought of my mother, decapitating her boiled egg, as she discovered their surprise invitation in the morning's post for our nuptials, three months on.

Space Mouse had flown in from Belgium on the morning of the wedding to act as my best man. He handed the vicar a gold band and I slipped it onto Beth's finger.

'I now pronounce you man and wife,' the vicar announced, as I kissed Beth.

The organ burst into Mendelssohn's Wedding March and as we turned to make our way back down the aisle of Climping St Mary Church, Space Mouse stepped smartly forward in his top hat and tails, beaming happily and began leading us out into the sunshine.

'He's not supposed to do that, is he?' whispered Beth, grinning.

'It's okay,' I whispered back, 'he's from Belgium, they do things differently over there!'

Our reception followed at Bailiffs Court nearby and after several hours of eating, photos and speeches, I scooped Beth up in my arms and carried her to the waiting Enstrom, now decked out in Diamond Sound logos. As our family and friends gathered around the perimeter of the helipad to see us off, I cautiously took the controls of the Enstrom helicopter, having only just obtained my flying license the week prior, and lifted the red and black 'bug' into a hover. A few moments later with the guests below waving, we flew off for our honeymoon in the New Forest.

* * *

To compete with the big teams I still needed to find more money. In 1985 a realistic budget for a C2 team competing in the full World Sportscar Championship was around a quarter of a million pounds, excluding the cost of the car and engines. It was whilst pondering where I was going to find the balance of our budget, that I had the most bizarre of breakthroughs.

John Fitzpatrick was a well respected, successful racing driver, winning many titles throughout an illustrious career including the Nürburgring 6 Hours, Bathurst 1000 and the Silverstone 1000 km. He'd established his own team, John Fitzpatrick Racing, and competed regularly in the World Sportscar Championship, running Porsche 956 cars. The team was well funded by long-time US chewing tobacco sponsor, Skoal Bandit. Fitzpatrick was considered to be a front runner with big name Formula One drivers such as Thierry Boutsen, Roberto Moreno and Rupert Keegan driving for him. At the end of the 1984 season, his sponsor Skoal Bandit had shocked everyone by switching allegiance from four to two wheels.

My phone rang and I grabbed it from the cradle. 'I have a call for a Mr William Middleton,' an American twang announced over a crackly line. For the next half hour I simply sat, trying to remain calm, trying to keep my voice steady, every so often answering, 'Yes... absolutely... that won't be a problem... Yes, it's a brand new car... Yes, we have a former Formula One driver in the Le Mans line up... '

Replacing the handset, I ran a hand through my hair and turned to Beth, 'Perhaps that's how it works,' I said, still in shock.

'What? How what works? Who was it?'

'That was US Tobacco and they want to sponsor *me!*'

Beth just raised an eyebrow. 'Yeah, sure...' she regarded me for a long moment. 'You're having me on...'

'I'm serious,' I said, spreading out my hands in an expansive gesture. 'It *was* US Tobacco and they want to sponsor us at Le Mans promoting their Skoal Bandit brand. They've just offered me twelve grand for the one race, but if all goes well, they're seriously talking about carrying on for the full season. It's a massive blue chip sponsor...' I paused, '...and they called me!'

34

"Promises are like the full moon, if they are not
kept at once they diminish day by day."

German Proverb

FOURTEEN WEEKS had now passed, and despite ongoing assurances, countless phone calls and several face to face meetings, the Devron remained unfinished. We'd already missed the first two rounds of the championship, and as the date for the British race loomed ever closer, our concerns continued to grow.

I reluctantly made my way over to the offices of Diamond Sound. Terry Thompson rose from his desk, smiling, as I made my way into his office, passing a large photo of our last year's Lola proudly displayed on his wall. Terry was around fifty years old, stockily built and his six foot frame still topped by a thick mop of dark, wavy hair. He had been the company's Chairman and Chief Executive for the past three years, two of which he'd sponsored me in the lower formulae.

'So ... update me.' he said, 'Are we going to be at Silverstone?'

'I've just come from the workshops,' I replied. 'They're still saying the car will be finished in time.'

He leaned back in his chair, smile fading, marshalling his thoughts. 'And what do *you* think, Will,' he finally asked.

'I think they're still in trouble.'

He frowned, 'Will, this simply isn't good enough. Maybe it's time I visited them myself.'

'I've tried everything, Terry,' I said, 'but nothing I'm ever told happens. If you'd be prepared to give it a shot it might help,' I agreed.

'What's left to do on the thing?'

'Based on what I could see, they're still finalising the body moulds, so they haven't started making any actual bodywork yet. There's a ton of jobs left to do but fitting the first set of bodywork is probably the single biggest job. The chassis is sitting on trestles,' I went on, sliding two photos across his desk. Terry listened attentively as I continued outlining the situation. 'The car's roll cage, suspension, uprights and steering are all fitted and the engine and gearbox are installed but they haven't started to plumb an oil system in or any wiring, and they've still got to fabricate the exhaust system, produce the ground effect tunnels and the rear wing assembly!'

Terry looked up from the photos. 'How long do you reckon that lot will take?'

I shrugged, 'Excluding the bodywork, tunnels and rear wing, I think they *could* get the other bits finished in time.'

Terry sat back, arms folded, his whole attitude saying: *Spell it out, give me the facts.* 'And the rest...' he said, '...what are *your* thoughts?'

'I've only got limited experience on mouldings. When I was in electronics, some of our first equipment cases used custom glass fibre mouldings. My understanding is that the moulds themselves have to cure for quite some time before you can start producing actual mouldings from them. But these are supposed to be light weight Kevlar, *not* glass fibre. I've no idea what other complications may be involved.'

'I don't need to remind you that we have fifty guests invited to the Silverstone race.' He glanced at his calendar, his face pensive.

'That's less than three weeks away. I've just authorised your invoice for almost three thousand pounds worth of hospitality unit and catering for that event! What happens if the car isn't finished?' I could hear the anxiety in his voice.

I rubbed my temples. That was a nightmare scenario and I hated to think of the ramifications. It was bad enough missing the first two races but at least none of my sponsors had guests invited to those events. Silverstone was on home soil, and to my backers it was almost as important as Le Mans. If the car wasn't ready, not only would it look bad with Terry's high profile guests, it would also reflect on his judgement with the rest of his board. 'The only guarantee would be for me to find a backup drive in another car with another team.' I answered.

'Perhaps you should consider finding another team altogether...to finish building the car we've already paid for?' he suggested.

Hmm... I thought... *that's a possibility. I do know the chap who originally owned Devron before it went bust, a short, fiery Scott by the name of Angus Maciver ... I could give him a call.*

I shrugged. 'It'd be a very big step,' I said out loud. 'A huge gamble! We'd have no backup, no access to spare parts and this thing is a total prototype. If we needed mouldings or replacement castings like uprights, it'd be impossible to get them unless we engineered everything ourselves.'

Terry thought about it for a few moments. 'Okay, leave things as they are for the time being but I want you to report back to me regularly.' He paused.. 'And try dropping in on Devron unexpectedly a few more times.'

I left the office with a mounting feeling of dread. This was *not* what I'd planned.

One week later

Seven days after the meeting with Terry, on a bright sunny winter morning, the still unfinished Devron, little more than a mock-up, was finally unveiled to the racing press. *'Yes, it was a beautiful looking car...' 'Yes, it was unfortunate we'd missed the first few races...' 'Yes, we should be at the Silverstone race, and absolutely, definitely we will be at Le Mans for the 24 hours... no question.'*

35

EVERYONE WAS half expecting the call. I grabbed the phone from the cradle on the second ring. 'Robert? What's happening?'

'I'm afraid I have some not so good news.'

My heart sank. 'What is it? Is the car going to be ready?'

'I'm afraid not. There are just too many little jobs left over to get finished.'

'But what about all your guarantees, Robert? What the hell am I going to tell the sponsors? They could all withdraw!'

'That's not my problem, Will. It's your job to find the money and deal with the backers.'

'I'm sorry Robert but it *is* your problem...it was *your* responsibility to provide the damn car *and* in good time for the first race!' I retorted.

'If you'd ordered it a little earlier, Will and not wasted our time with press launches, it may have been ready!'

'I can't believe you're saying this... I agreed to order the car as soon as you put the proposal to me in Australia, and you repeatedly told me it would be built in time!'

'If it's any use, you can have it as a static display up at Silverstone.'

Silverstone Circuit, Northamptonshire. May 1985

It was a cold blustery May morning, more winter than spring, as I drove into the Silverstone paddock and parked. Despite the weather, the race had attracted one of the best entries in years with a record thirty-one cars qualifying for today's 1000km World Championship event, with tens of thousands of spectators eagerly packing the grandstands.

Everything about this year's championship seemed bigger and more glamorous than the last, with more cars and more spectators. With my mind preoccupied, I made my way past the forlorn, statically displayed Devron and into the warmth of Diamond's luxury double decked hospitality unit. I'd arranged to have it carefully positioned on the inside of Copse Corner, affording the guests an excellent view of the pit straight, first corner and next section of track leading into Maggots. I'd been scheduled to drive the Devron with François Migault and Max Oliver, a Moroccan racer from Casablanca but now I was just one of the fifty guests.

Among the invited elite were buyers from the Ford Motor Company – Diamond's biggest client. A gloved hand offered me a flute of chilled champagne as I mingled with the guests that had expected to see the thrill of the team's debut, whilst savouring five-star hospitality.

I wandered about, chatting with each person in turn, lost in my own hideous nightmare. On the far side of the hospitality unit I could see Terry Thompson, his ashen face. Understandably, he looked very annoyed. I slipped back outside as the speaker system announced Riccardo Patrese in the Lancia Martini was leading the race.

For a few moments, I wandered about under the awning, examining the still unfinished Devron. A hand appeared on my shoulder, it was Terry. 'Some of the board are already questioning if there should be a pro rata refund for all the missed races,' he said stone faced.

'I'm sorry, Terry.' I paused. 'What can I say?'

'Give me a cast iron assurance, Will, that it'll be finished and tested in time for Le Mans.'

'I want to believe it will be, Terry,' I replied, 'but I have to say I'm not convinced. There's just so much left to do.'

'Shit... Will, it has to be. Have you thought anymore about taking it away...' he paused. 'Do you know anyone willing to take over the project and finish it?'

I'd visited Angus Maciver, the former owner of Devron only yesterday, taking him photographs of the car in its current state. Early today, he'd driven more than 170 miles from his workshop in Wales to see for himself. 'I'll give you a 100% guarantee', Angus told me. 'We'll get it finished and running in time for Le Mans. I give you a cast iron assurance of that,' he promised.

'I've had a few of those already!' I replied cynically.

'Not from me, you haven't,' he answered sharply. 'We have all the resources, workshop facilities and manpower to take over and get the job done...there's just one thing I want out of the deal,' Angus said. It had been the one thing I didn't want to give.

I turned now to Terry, 'I don't think we have a choice, we're going to have to take it away.' I hesitated. 'The only thing is Terry, he wants my seat at Le Mans.'

Two Days Later

It was 9.45 in the morning when I pulled up outside the workshops of Devron racing and parked the transporter. A few moments later Terry arrived in his company BMW and parked alongside.

The large roller shutter doors of the workshop were open when we reached them, so we made our way directly into the brightly lit interior where groups of mechanics were busy working on rows of immaculate looking race cars. At the back of the shop I noticed the Devron sitting on trestles. 'It's over there Terry,' I said pointing.

'I see nobody's working on it,' he replied drily.

Hearing the sound of our approaching footsteps, a mechanic looked up. 'Can I help you?' he enquired.

'My name is Terry Thompson,' Terry responded. 'I'm the chairman and managing director of Diamond Sound. I think you know Will Middleton,' he added. 'We've come to collect the Devron.'

The mechanic looked slightly taken aback. 'I didn't know it was going anywhere,' he replied raising an eyebrow.

'It's going to Le Mans!' Terry said firmly.

'Are you serious? I'll need to have a word with Robert first,' he replied. 'He's not in yet, I'll have to call him at home.'

'You can speak to him later!' replied Terry with authority. 'I want *our* car in the back of *that* truck in the next five minutes...Is that clear?'

I reversed the transporter into the loading bay. Three mechanics carefully pushed the car into the back and helped to secure it down. At the back of the workshops I could hear a flurry of excited chatter. 'There's supposed to be a spare nose and a couple of sets of wheels,' I said.

The mechanic who appeared in charge, shrugged evasively. 'I don't know anything about that,' he said. 'You'll have to speak to Robert, he's on his way here,' he said as I pulled down the roller shutter and applied a large padlock.

'If he wishes to speak to anyone,' interrupted Terry, 'he can call me on this number.' He handed over a business card. 'But aside from sorting out the missing nose and wheels, this concludes our business!'

36

"The only real failure in life is the failure to try... the measure
of success is how we cope with disappointment."

Unknown

I FLICKED OPEN THE envelope and read the contents open-
mouthed. At that moment something cold shifted in my
stomach. For a few seconds I was too angry to speak. With
mounting horror I re-read the wording of the enclosed injunction,
prohibiting us from taking the Devron out of the country. With
acid boiling in my stomach, I turned to Beth. 'They can't do this,
they'll blow everything!'

'What is it, Will?' she said with concern.

'It's bullshit, a total load of crap!' Any nerves or apprehension
of the race to come left me. In their place came an anger I'd
never known before. It coursed through me in a great burst of
fury, the adrenaline causing my hands to shake as I handed the
court order to Beth.

She read the official looking document, perplexed. 'What does
it mean?'

'It means we can't go to Le Mans!'

I had never been good at leaving anything to others. I'd always
needed to be in control, making things happen, steering the
outcome. But suddenly, everything was out of my hands. I had
little knowledge of legal matters, court procedures or injunctions.

All I knew was that I had both a moral and contractual commitment to my backers to compete in a minimum of ten World Championship races this year. We'd already missed three and now Devron had taken out an injunction preventing us from leaving for Le Mans, the crown jewel in the Championship. If we didn't race there, Diamond, Skoll Bandit and the rest would undoubtedly sue, and that would be the end of everything.

I picked up the phone to my lawyer, Toby Jackson. He was in his early thirties and a partner in a firm based in Southampton. As the family's solicitor, he'd handled all legal matters for us, everything from drafting wills to the recent purchase of the Old Granary. Toby listened intently for the next fifteen minutes as I outlined everything; from the decision to purchase the new Devron, to the delays and problems with the unfinished car, ultimately leading to us having to take it away for completion elsewhere. All the meticulously engineered sponsorship deals now hung precariously on that one major race and were likely to crash and burn if we didn't get there. 'We have to be on the ferry for France tonight!' I finished.

'It sounds as if they're trying to call your bluff,' Toby responded. 'I suspect if you went back to them and let them run it, all this would disappear.'

'Never! I've had enough Toby, no one's holding a gun to *my* head. There has to be a way of getting this overturned!'

'Okay!' he eventually replied. 'This isn't going to be easy. Especially not on a Sunday, but somehow we've got to get it sorted today. What time are you due to leave?'

I flashed a look at my watch. 'We've got less than eight hours! The whole team is booked on the Southampton – le Havre ferry for tonight at eight-thirty.'

'Right, fax everything over to my office. I'll be there within fifteen minutes. Just be prepared to leave for London at a moment's notice. I'm going to pull in a favour from a barrister friend and try to get an emergency hearing this afternoon.'

'Can you do that?' I said impressed, 'On a Sunday?'

'Leave it to me, Will ...just get yourself ready to leave and make sure you fax all the paperwork over to my office immediately. I'm leaving now.' He paused. 'By the way, this isn't going to be cheap! You do realise that, don't you?'

I didn't have a lot of choice, I thought. Lose everything and end up being sued by my sponsors or pay a few grand, overturn the injunction and be free to carry on with what I loved most. 'Please just get the injunction overturned Toby...okay?'

It was three-thirty in the afternoon as my taxi turned into John Street, London, WC1 and pulled up outside an imposing Georgian listed property, just five hours before our ferry was due to depart. Somehow, Toby had managed to persuade a colleague working at the famous London solicitors Nabbaro's, to arrange representation for me, with a hearing at the judge's house.

I stepped from the taxi, made my way up the pathway, rang the door and banged the brass doorknocker. A smartly dressed lady in her forties, presumably the judge's wife, opened the door and led me directly into the dining room. His Lordship was already seated at the head of the table with Toby to his left and another smartly dressed man seated to his right. They all rose as I entered. Toby extended his hand. 'Hello Will,' he said in hushed tones. He turned back to the table. 'This is His Lordship, Humphrey Fotheringham-Brown,' he added more clearly with great reverence, gesturing in the direction of his Lordship, a short, rounded man with stern complexion, grey receding hair and intelligent eyes. Turning his attention to the other man on the opposite side of the table, he added. 'And this is Mr Sebastian Whitcomb, your barrister instructed by Nabarro's'. The barrister, a slim man in his mid thirties with boyish good looks, rose from his seat offering a slight, congenial bow. Toby's words of earlier that day floated into my mind: *this isn't going to be cheap!*

I was offered what was most likely the most expensive cup of coffee in history and directed to sit at the far end of the highly polished table. Devron, undoubtedly caught off guard by the speed of our response, hadn't sent a legal representative. I sat, carefully listening in the strangely informal, yet formal setting, as Sebastian Whitcomb outlined our argument for overturning the injunction.

'The evidence is damning my lord,' continued Sebastian Whitcomb. 'There was clearly a contractual commitment for the car to be completed in good time and well prior to the first round of the championship in Italy last April. It was only after Devron failed to complete the car in time for the first three races that my client decided to remove *his* car and take it to another workshop for completion.'

His Lordship listened intently, his hands placed together to form a steeple, head inclined to one side. Every so often he nodded in thought. 'And you say your client,' he glanced in my direction and smiled, 'Mr Middleton...had paid in full, prior to removing the car from Devron's workshops?' Toby slid copies of the receipted invoice across the table. His Lordship studied the papers before asking. 'And you have a copy of the cheque stubs and bank statement showing both these payments have cleared?'

Toby took a few moments to retrieve the additional papers from his briefcase, before handing them to His Lordship, who nodded approvingly. I furtively glanced at my watch. It was now 4.40, less than four hours before our ferry was due to leave.

Sebastian Whitcomb paused for a few moments before adding, 'My lord, you will also see before you an inventory headed "Unfinished Works". This is a list of work or items which, despite having been already paid for by my client, have ended up having to be completed by the new team of engineers to ensure the car is fit to compete.'

'Yes, I see,' His Lordship replied softly whilst scanning the document.

'You will see item four refers to the Devron's gearbox.' Sebastian continued. 'This is a Hewland FGB model and should clearly have been a new unit. Only after the car was taken away and inspected, was it discovered that the serial number was from a three year old, Formula Two, March race car. We maintain that the Devron should have been equipped with a brand new unit, not somebody's warmed up leftovers!'

'Hmm...I think these latter areas are something to be considered when time is less pressing,' His Lordship concluded.

A few minutes later, we all stood and His Lordship led us from the dining room to the front door. 'Well, Mr Middleton, for the time being, just concentrate on the race,' he smiled, extending a chubby hand. 'I'll be watching for you on television,' he added. I felt a sudden rush of relief and elation; relief that we'd overturned the injunction, and elation that we could leave tonight as planned for Le Mans. Our ferry was now due to depart in little over three hours. For the moment my personal disappointment was forgotten.

37

---

*"My ambition is not to be just a good fighter.
I want to be great, something special."*

Sugar Ray Leonard

THE RELIEF OF finally making it to France was tempered with trepidation. Thanks to Robert Arnold's failed promises, the Devron had barely turned a wheel from design concept to actuality. We now had only two days in which to qualify it for the Le Mans 24 hours, a demandingly competitive endurance race, in the full glare of the world's media, pitted against multimillion pound teams and car manufacturers.

The Devron's arrival created a small ripple of interest through the crowded paddock, as the red and green car was wheeled from the transporter, and I had to admit it looked stunning in its Diamond Sound and Skoal Bandit livery.

One of the first to wander over was team owner, John Fitzpatrick. Only last year he'd lost the US Tobacco marque after years of financial backing. He was silent as he circled the car, solemn faced.

In the week before receiving the court injunction, we'd managed to run a systems test at the Mallory Park track in Leicestershire, but it was little more than a basic shakedown, lapping the 1.4 mile Kirkby circuit at a sedate 80 miles per hour. In the cool of an English summer, all systems had appeared to be working. La Sarthe however would be a very different matter. Here the

Devron would have to run in anger for the first time, reaching speeds of around 200 miles per hour, *averaging* more than 110 miles per hour over a race distance of some 2600miles. If the car failed to qualify, all the months of fighting to bring each of the deals together would be for nothing.'

There were still important technical details to be completed to ensure the car would comply with the stringent scrutineering before qualifying began, and over the next two days, our mechanics set about preparing for the long race. But by this stage, the crew had already been up for most of the forty-eight hours preceding our ferry crossing!

Two days later

Angus was on his first qualifying lap when his voice crackled over my headset. 'Temperatures running high, Will.'

'What's it reading?' I shot back.

A series of clicks, followed by a burst of static ensued before his voice replied, 'Too much vibration on the gauges... everything a blur...' For a moment his voice was lost again in static, but then it cleared. '...looks as though it's into the red, and the car feels like it's lifting on the straight.'

Five minutes later the Devron shot back into the pits in a swirl of dust and I hinged open the door. 'What's happening?'

'It felt okay, other than the vibration and it feels very light on the Mulsanne,' Angus replied as he released the strap under his chin, pulling off his helmet. 'The cooling problem's what worries me.' He peeled off his gloves, unclipped his belts and stepping from the car, tugged off his damp balaclava. Mechanics began removing the rear body section. 'Cooling problem could be something as simple as an air lock...' Angus added, but then his expression switched to a grimace, '...or it could be a fundamental design problem.'

Turning, I stepped across the pool of green coolant that was now spreading beneath the Devron and helped the crew remove the rear engine cover.

Angus unzipped his race suit, pulled his arms from the sleeves and yanked the top half down, so it hung around his waist. Going to the front of the car, he knelt down to examine the splitter, a flat extension protruding from the bottom of the Devron's nose. Running parallel to the ground, the splitter's job was to reduce aerodynamic lift and help channel flow to locations such as radiators and cooling ducts.

'What do you reckon?' I asked, returning to Angus.

'I think the splitter isn't ridged enough,' he said pushing down on the black moulding which clearly flexed far too easily. 'What we want is low pressure, faster-moving air below the car, and the higher pressure, slower moving air above it; that way we reduce lift and gain positive downforce.' He straightened back up, a crease now forming in his brow. 'But this thing is just *far* too flexible,' he tapped the splitter with the toe of his race boot, 'and is resonating, causing the vibration and the lift. I also think there's insufficient airflow to the radiators and engine bay.'

I listened as Angus walked to the back of the car and leaned in, checking the engine.

'So... what's the answer?' I asked, following.

'We can stiffen up the splitter by laminating a plywood panel into it. But I reckon these damn NASA air intakes are the overheating problem,' Angus replied with frustration. 'They look nice but they don't channel enough air through the radiators.'

'I don't suppose you've got anything *good* to say?' I replied with a grin.

'Oh, yes... it might be getting hot, Will, but this thing's got the potential to be quick... very quick!'

Over the next days we struggled to find ways to keep the powerful Cosworth engine from overheating in the ferocious heat of the French summer. On the 15th of June at 3pm the Devron lined up, thirty-third on the grid with a qualifying time of 3.51.77, but as the pace car led the fifty-three starters away in a crescendo of horsepower and cheering, an ominous pool of green coolant was left from beneath the Skoal Bandit Devron...

It had taken me almost eight months of painstaking work to get to this point. We'd barely slept more than half a dozen hours in the past week. Looking out over at the opposite grandstand, I felt a deep sadness as I scanned the excited spectators. The whole stadium was a riot of colour and waving flags. I felt a failure. Not only had I been forced to hand over my drive in return for getting the Devron finished, but an expensive court battle awaited my return; a case which threatened to further derail my career and drain our already restricted budget.

Moments later, the Rothmans Porsches shot past on the pit straight and as the lights turned to green, I watched the blur of the pack disappearing into the first corner. Sighing, I turned to Ian. 'It's only a matter of time before we blow the engine in this heat. Our only hope is to keep the revs down, wait for the night temperature to drop, and pray.' At that moment my headset crackled and amid the static, I heard the words I was dreading. 'Will, the engine temps already into the red!'

Four hours later

Our dishevelled group of ten made our way dishearteningly into the Le Mans 24-hour restaurant. Harry Norfolk, one of the sponsors, had arrived just before the start and following the demise of the Devron, when the engine finally blew just sixty minutes into the race, kindly offered to take us all out for a meal. Harry was the managing director of Saunier Duval and, over the years, had become more of a friend than just a sponsor. He was in his late sixties, medium build with greying hair. He'd first taken me under his wing way back when I was racing the old Delta.

It was just past 8pm and we'd spent the past few hours packing everything into the transporter for the long journey home.

The restaurant was a steaming mass of humanity, well over a hundred packed into the restricted space. Squeezing our way past tables, I beckoned to a waiter and we were shown to one of the long trestles covered with white paper, all ten of us attempting to squash in alongside a group of German Porsche fans.

'It's hopeless,' said Angus, clearly irritated, his Scottish brogue intensifying as his anger rose, 'there's nay enough room man!'

'Look'... I said pointing to a table further down where a few people were just leaving. 'Grab those seats for you, John and Ian. We'll stay up here.'

'Just order whatever you want,' added Harry genially to Angus. 'It's on me... okay?'

Half an hour later, we pinned down a waiter and ordered drinks and the 'plat du jour'. Slowly, with the help of several pints of French beer and the camaraderie of the chatty Germans, our spirits revived a little. I glanced down to Maciver's table. Angus appeared entrenched in an animated discussion of some kind with his group, and I noticed for the first time that the fiery Scot had somehow obtained a large bottle of Bells Whisky which was residing by his elbow, and already half empty. *Oh, well,* I thought, *he's earnt it.*

Finally, after almost two hours, our waiter returned with our plates of fried chicken and cold French fries. We sat eating, sipping a final beer whilst cars thundered past, yards away on the Mulsanne Straight; tormenting sounds and headlamps sending flickering images up and around the walls of the eatery. It was almost midnight but even busier, when Harry tried to grab the attention of our waiter.

After a few attempts, I stood and beckoned pointedly at a passing waiter. 'L'addition, s'il vous plaît.' I called, whilst making a scribbling motion in the palm of my outstretched hand. The waiter nodded back in recognition and I pointed towards Maciver, indicating to include his bill. As I did so, I noticed the whisky brand had changed to Black and White.

Pulling on my distinctive Skoal Bandit jacket, I muttered to Beth. 'Doubt US Tobacco will stick with me after all this.'

An arm wrapped around my shoulder. 'Don't look so down, son,' said Harry. 'You did everything possible to bring this together. It's because of what you do, that people put their trust in you. One day soon... very soon, *you'll* make it big, and when it happens, I for one will be there....'

Suddenly, from the corner of my eye, I saw a trestle table upend on the far side of the restaurant; plates, dishes and glasses smashing to the ground. I swung round to see Angus, on the edge of exhaustion, staggering to his feet in the centre of the uproar; wild eyed, and bellowing at a waiter.

'Whoa! What the hell's he doing?' I exclaimed, as Angus threw himself bodily at the startled French man, who rapidly buckled, sending the unbalanced Scot hurtling over his head into a table laden with chicken and chips. In the ensuing pandemonium, diners surged for exits, overturning more tables in a wave of panic to flee the turmoil. Meanwhile, a crazed Angus caught and wrestled the distressed waiter on the ground, trying to force what looked like a bill into the small mans mouth, the poor man attempting to escape by crawling his way to the sanctuary of the kitchen. Suddenly, in one swift movement, he made it to his feet, wildly lunging through the swing doors to safety. But whatever he'd done, Maciver wasn't letting him get away that easily. Moments later, staggering to *his* feet with a wild, drunken predatory glare on his face, he shot after him.

Ian and John silently appeared as I attempted to shepherd our group towards the nearest exit. 'What the fuck happened Ian?' I asked, as everyone pulled on their Team jackets, exiting through a back door. Behind me, I heard Angus' voice and turning, saw him shoot back out the swing doors, hotly pursued by a stocky French chef, wielding a substantial meat cleaver in one hand and violently gesticulating with the other.

'I think he gave Angus the bill!' Ian replied.

'What?'

'The waiter seemed very insistent that Angus pay for the whole group,' John added, 'but we hadn't even got our food yet!'

Suddenly, in the background, there were voices shouting, 'C'etait Skoal Bandit! Team Skoal Bandit!' accompanied by the wailing of police sirens and blue strobes flashing through the trees. I turned to the group. 'Quick! Lose the jackets and leg it!' Turning to my startled sponsor, I added as we headed for the woods, 'I bet US Tobacco didn't get anything this exciting with John Fitzpatrick!'

Brands Hatch England – 22nd September 1985
Approximately 3 months later

The sun was rising slowly in the east, its late summer rays welcoming and warming the overnight campers, heralding the start of a new race day. The intermittent crackle of race engines, like the call of a morning cockerel, drew the hardened fans from the comfort of their sleeping bags. Around the circuit's camp site, the sounds and smells of the British summer floated, merging with the mouth watering aroma of frying bacon and fresh coffee. A queue of Renault Cleo's were lining up, preparing to enter the main paddock for the first session of the day, as a man of around thirty entered the tunnel ahead of them. Casually dressed, he had a thick mop of brownish hair that was receding slightly at the temples. Reaching the paddock, he made his way past row upon row of glistening race transporters, all neatly aligned behind allocated pit garages. He stopped for a moment by the oldest transporter, as if unsure whether to enter, and for a moment stood peering back through the racetrack fencing at the Renaults as they made their way onto the track to commence their warm up session, the drone of their engines already reverberating around the vast amphitheatre formed by Clearways and Paddock Hill bend.

Inside the tiny living area of the transporter, I'd been locked in a deep discussion for the past half hour with my race engineer, Simon, who'd taken over from Angus Maciver following the le Mans debacle. 'You're still planning on using the old qualifying engine for the race then?' Simon asked, the familiar anxiety in his voice undisguised.

'I don't see that we have any choice,' I replied. 'It's not that I want to, but it's the only way we'll have enough hours left on our main engine for the Selangor race in Malaysia.' I watched him closely for a long moment before adding. 'The litigation with Devron is draining our budget, Simon.'

His frown deepened further. 'As long as you realise it's a gamble, and the odds aren't that good,' the strained impatience was obvious. Simon was a racer; he just wanted the Team to win. He had little interest in the business side and no understanding of outside distractions such as the Devron court case, which still rumbled on in the background like a tropical storm.

'The qualifier's already completed over twelve hours of running,' he went on. 'It needs a complete rebuild, not another thousand kilometres added to it, it could well let go like at Snetterton 84 in the old Lola.' As he stood to leave there was a hesitant knock on the open transporter door and the casually dressed man stepped in, hesitantly.

'Sorry to interrupt,' he said, tentatively offering me his hand. 'My name's Rob, er... Rob Allan and well, ermm... I was just wondering... er, um... well, if it wasn't a bad time... er, well, I was wondering what the cost of a drive might be?'

'Come in Rob, take a seat,' I said offering a hand. 'My name's Will, Will Middleton.' I gestured him to sit, trying hard to remember where I'd seen his face before. 'Would you like a coffee?' I asked, selecting a couple of mugs from the rack, already pouring out the strong dark brew. Simon offered a brief conspiratorial smile before leaving.

'So, what's your background,' I asked, handing Rob a steaming cup of black liquid. 'Have you driven in Group C before?'

He frowned, 'Er, well no... not exactly,' there was a moment's pause, before he added, 'I've driven in Formula Ford and Sports 2000 cars, er... ermm, but nothing bigger.' His Adam's apple bobbed about nervously as he searched for words. 'Nothing at this level,' he finally admitted, 'but I've had some good results... er, in the lower formulae.'

Suddenly I remembered our first meeting all those years ago: *the caravan exhibition!* 'Was that in your Crossley, when you almost got sponsored by a big firm of undertakers?' I asked grinning.

His frown deepened further and he managed a few more "Er's" before his face broke into a broad grin, 'Shit, that was you!' he exclaimed, beaming, the stammer vanishing.

In the months that followed, I fought with every fibre of my being to keep the Team afloat as the lawyers continued to drain our budget, fending off the Devron case until the conclusion of the 85 championship. Following the Brands race, Rob Allan became both Team member and friend, bringing new sponsors with him to replace the lost U S Tobacco. But as the Championship moved east, first to Japan and then on to the final in Malaysia, I knew it was only a matter of time before I'd be back in court. A hearing had been set for mid December and if it went badly, we stood to lose the lot; the car, the Team, our home, everything...

38

London, England – 9th January 1986

Royal Courts of Justice Court 17 – Chancery Court
Devon Racing Cars Limited v William Middleton

FOLLOWING THE Christmas break, we were back in court number seventeen. Humphrey Fotheringham Brown smiled down on the small assembled group. 'Good afternoon gentlemen. I trust you all had an excellent Christmas?' He glanced to the back of the court where I was sitting next to Robert Arnold. Smiling, His Lordship added. 'I see Mr Middleton and Mr Arnold are sitting a little closer today and the latter appears to be smiling. Do I take this to be a good sign?'

I felt like replying *"that's because he's got me by the nuts, My Lord!"*, but I restrained myself.

Glancing at the court clock, the judge continued. 'We are somewhat later than originally listed,' he went on. 'But I understand that there has been some recent progress. Is this correct, gentlemen?'

It had been more than three weeks since our last attendance at court. On that occasion, His Honour had ordered Devron to place ten thousand pounds into court as security against my legal costs.

Acting on behalf of Robert Arnold, Devron's owner, Percival Drummond, had requested my diary for inspection. Clearly whatever they'd been hoping to find hadn't materialised, and the filofax had been returned three days ago, along with a request for a meeting.

Toby, my solicitor, had broken the news excitedly over the phone, 'It appears they haven't managed to pay the money into court. I think they want to settle!'

My barrister, the Honourable Sebastian Whitcomb QC was rising to his feet. 'Yes, My Lord, both sides have now agreed a form of settlement and the document has been signed.' He held aloft a neatly bound agreement which the court usher relayed to His Lordship. 'I would like to submit these documents for approval.' said Sebastian Whitcomb.

Earlier that morning

The settlement agreement appeared straight forward, but neither Beth nor I felt secure. 'Do you trust him to stick to it?' Beth asked uncertainly.

'What choice do we have?' I replied. 'If we turn down their offer, carry on and win in court, they'll simply go bust on us to avoid paying. As a sole trader, that would bankrupt us with crippling legal fees. We'd end up losing the house, the Team, the car, everything. This way there's at least a chance, albeit a slim one!'

Beth paused, then levelling her eyes back at me, reiterated softly. 'But what if they don't honour the agreement?'

I shrugged. 'If they don't stick to what's agreed, at least we'll have a chance to put something else together, and we'll have drawn a line under this mess. In future, we'll operate the race team as a limited company, that way we'll be protected from frivolous and damaging legal actions like this. Toby reckons

Devron only sued because they thought we had money. He's going to set us up a company, called Team Capricorn.'

Beth smiled and with an approving nod, replied. 'As you say, we don't have a lot of choice.'

Leaning forward, I kissed her. 'Remember, Beth, if this works, we'll save more than a hundred grand this season in running costs, and they're not seen to have lost face. That's all they want.'

By midday, the agreement had been signed and everyone including the lawyers, had smiled and shook hands. Devron withdrew their legal challenge and, as the deal stipulated, we both paid our own legal bills.

In return for Devron agreeing to update the car to the latest specification, preparing and running it for the coming season at no charge, I agreed to transfer ownership of the car back to them. Other than engines, which I'd provide, my only running costs for the year ahead would be for accident damage, tyres and fuel. Everything was written down, nothing left to chance...

Le Mans France – 31ˢᵗ May 1986
4 months and 22 days later

The pack of fifty starters thundered through the fourth gear Dunlop Curve, passing beneath the iconic bridge. Charging downhill through the 140 miles per hour esses and channelling into the 120 miles per hour right-hander Tertre Rouge, they scorched down the infamous Mulsanne straight.

On the left, the famous 24-hour restaurant flashed past at over 200 miles per hour as the top C1 cars accelerated on to over 230 miles per hour at the end of the three-mile straight.

At the front, Klaus Ludwig eased ahead of the pack in his Joest Porsche as the field blurred its way through the flat out kink. At Mulsanne corner, Derek Warwick snatched second place in his Silk

Cut Jaguar, accelerating back up through the gears and on towards the right, left, right Indianapolis bends.

Weaving out of the 140 miles per hour Porsche Curves, the pack fought for track position into the right-hand White House Corner. As the fifty cars exited the Ford chicane for the first time, Ludwig was still in the lead with Derrick Warwick holding second place.

Standing in the pit lane, listening through my headset, I breathed a huge sigh of relief. I'd barely slept for the past four weeks, since the final Devron disaster, at Monza. Turning wearily to Simon, I said. 'Thank God... Max is through the first lap and we're running seventh in class. At least that means I'll get paid.'

Just over a month earlier I'd driven despondently from the historic Monza circuit in Northern Italy, where the Devron, back in the hands of Robert Arnold, had failed to qualify after blowing its engine.

'What now?' asked Rob Allen, as we set off down Viale Cesare Battisti in the heavy traffic.

'I haven't the foggiest idea.' I replied glumly. 'When I signed the settlement agreement with Arnold, I hadn't expected a lot,' I said, 'but I certainly didn't anticipate *that* fiasco.'

'You realise Le Mans is just over a month away?' he added softly.

I shook my head, fully aware that the race had been rescheduled two weeks early this year, to avoid a clash with the Canadian Grand Prix. 'There might not be an obvious answer yet, but if you want to make something happen badly enough, there's always a way.' I said. 'I believe if you can dream it, you can make it happen. We'll be at Le Mans, somehow. I guarantee it.'

Rob glanced at his watch. 'There's a little club just out of town,' he said with a grin. 'I'll take you there; it'll take your mind off things.'

As he fought his way through the Italian traffic in the hire car, I sat deep in thought. I suppose with hindsight, the disaster had been predictable. Following the legal settlement, I'd kept in regular contact with Arnold, updating the progress to my sponsor, Terry Thompson. The trouble was, progress was too slow and the promised development simply wasn't happening. It was as if nothing had changed and I was back, locked into the same old nightmare as before. But this time it was worse. There was now no interaction with the Devron management or mechanics; any involvement on my part was greeted with chilled hostility. To them, the car was now owned by Devron and they resented any "outside" interference.

The new deal was supposed to have included a complete update to Devron's latest 1986 specifications, with revised lightweight body work and radically improved air intakes to cool the expensive Cosworth DFL engines. But it turned out that no revisions had even been planned. The car was also supposed to have been finished in time for a full UK testing programme and a press launch. But again Devron missed each and every deadline and when the untested, apparently updated car, finally arrived at Monza, eight hours late after missing the first practice session, nothing had changed. Even more worryingly, the low drag NASA style air intakes, that last year had failed to channel sufficient cooling air into the radiators, remained unaltered. In the fierce heat of Monza, the car managed just a handful of laps of qualifying, before overheating and blowing another eighteen thousand pound engine.

I was two thirds of the way down my fifth beer when the idea hit me. I turned to Rob. 'I know where we can get another car,' I said excitedly, 'and it's less than a mile from my house.' I glanced up at the stage where a naked Italian girl with hairy armpits was performing a bizarre act with a quart bottle of beer. 'Shit!' I exclaimed, momentarily sidetracked. 'I didn't think that was physically possible!'

Rob grinned. 'I certainly wouldn't want to drink from it when she's finished,' he said, matter-of-factly. 'Anyway.' he added, still mesmerized, unable to tear his eyes from the stage. 'What car is it?'

'I think it was called an Arundel. It was built for the Duke of Norfolk's son Edward, but he only raced it a couple of times. I'm pretty sure it crashed at Silverstone. Eddie had a lot of family resistance after that and the project floundered. In his position as heir, I guess they just didn't want him racing.'

For a few minutes we sat watching the ever more bizarre act developing on the stage. 'How the hell did she do that?' I asked. 'She's uncapped the bottle! That's got to be some sort of trick.'

Rob downed the last of his pint. 'I reckon she's got a beak down there.' He turned back to me, still grinning. 'So, do you know him?' he asked.

'Who?'

'The Duke of Norfolk's son of course, who else.'

'Yeah, well sort of, I just knew him as Eddie.' I paused, collecting my thoughts. 'He used to race in the national series. He lives in the castle just up the road from me.'

'Ohh... *that* castle! Does he know it was you that got him evacuated with that "Mystery Whistler" thing?'

'No! And anyway, it wasn't me, it was Des' idea. He brought the thing and built it and dumped it! I just made the electronics for him.'

'So, how do you know this Arundel car's still for sale?'

'I don't... all I know is it was advertised towards the end of last year in *AutoSport*, and I don't think anyone brought it; at least I haven't heard that anyone's got it.'

The following morning I flew directly into Heathrow and made my way down to Sussex and up to the castle.

Six hours later I'd concluded a deal with both Nickleson McLaren for the supply of Cosworth engines, and Eddie for his old car. Unfortunately, given the time restraints, the latter only amounted to several tea chests packed full of parts, plus a monocoque chassis, devoid of engine, and several sections of bodywork. These various Arundel parts were, at that very moment, meandering their way east, through the Norwich countryside, on the back of a low loader, en route to Simon's workshops.

39

"A pessimist sees the difficulty in every opportunity; an optimist sees the opportunity in every difficulty."

Winston Churchill

THE PHONE AT THE back of the pit rang. I sprinted over, grabbing the handset from the cradle. 'Yes?' I yelled, trying to compete with the sound of Ludwig and Warwick, battling for position on the straight behind me. The phone was a direct line to our signalling team, three miles away, on the other side of the track by Mulsanne corner.

'Max is past!' an excited voice yelled over the crackling phone line. 'He's running fine, but it looks like the Lucky Strike Argo is out of the race. Also one of Roy Baker's Tigas is missing. Their signalling team reckon it's lost a wheel.'

Thirty minutes later, Max shot into the pits for the first driver change. Quickly I helped strap Rob in, as our crew plugged the Arundel into the centralised refuelling system. Seventy litres of high octane fuel transferred to the Arundel's fuel cell in just sixty seconds as a steward, provided by the organisers, recorded the time and fuel used. Two Avon technicians moved feverishly around the car, checking tyres, the senior of the two quickly gesturing a thumbs up to Simon. I slammed the door shut and stepped aside as Rob switched in the high pressure fuel pumps, re-igniting the engine with a deafening roar. He floored the accelerator, the car jerking forward several metres, before the engine died.

Rob was gesticulating wildly through the Arundel's screen. I yanked open the door and yelled. 'What's up?'

Rob's crestfallen eyes stared desperately back at me through the window of his visor. 'The fucking throttle cable's snapped!' he shouted.

It was just past six when the Arundel finally rejoined the race. We'd lost seven laps. *At least*, I thought, *we're still running and we're still in the race.* Eight hours earlier, things could have ended very differently. Following a minor royal incident, we'd almost been kicked out of France altogether...

Known as 'Frenchy' behind his back, Pierre Aumonier was not, as his name suggested, French. His descendants had been Huguenots, Calvinist French Protestants, who'd fled France during the religious persecution at the end of the seventeenth century. His mother was English, but Pierre was very proud of his ancestry, and his French name, which came from his father's line. Pierre was sitting at his desk, flanked on either side by officials from the race organisation, the Automobile Club de L' Ouest. He was a heavily built man in his mid-fifties, unmarried and as always, immaculately attired in his trademark blue blazer over grey trousers.

He did not appear amused as he studied me through heavy dark-rimmed spectacles. No attempt was made to introduce the officials that sat on either side, and there was no offer of a seat as I made my way into the tiny office, overlooking the start finish straight. Frenchy was a powerful man: a director of Silverstone circuit and the current British Racing Drivers' Club Secretary. As a steward at world championship events, I'd fallen foul of his authority a few times before, and was concerned to be summoned to his office, under apparent threat of expulsion before the race had even commenced.

Aside from his various other titles, Frenchy was also the president of the FIA Sportscar Commission and it was in that capacity he was now addressing me. 'I take it this was *your* idea Mr Middleton?' he sneered from behind his heavy spectacles.

'I'm sorry?' I replied hesitantly. 'I'm not at all sure what you're referring to.'

He shifted uncomfortably in his chair. 'I'm referring to the little matter of your promotion girls exposing their backsides to the world's media in our pit lane!' he replied with derision.

For the first time, I noticed his colleagues on either side meticulously scrutinising Polaroids of the alleged offence.

'I'm sorry,' I replied. 'I've been totally involved with running the Team and wasn't aware the girls had done anything wrong.'

The incident had occurred earlier that afternoon when Pierre, in his 'presidential' role, had been escorting Prince Michael of Kent around the pits. He had apparently spied a quartet of pert buttocks bending provocatively over our new race car, and whilst royalty was apparently rather amused, Pierre, who was known to have no appreciation of the female form, was most certainly not!

'This type of prank brings this illustrious race into disrepute!' thundered Pierre.

For a moment I considered my response. Not only would it be pointless to argue with Frenchy but I could see no reason to antagonize the situation further and jeopardize our race entry. After all, those girls' bottoms had already served their purpose well; the images set to appear on television screens and in newspapers all around the world, providing hundreds of thousands of pounds worth of free publicity to my sponsor, Diamond Sound.

'May I see the photos?' I asked.

For a few moments I studied the assortment of prints, trying very hard not to smile at the neat Diamond Sound logo that was stretched across each 'pert buttock'. Eventually I replied. 'I have to agree with you Mr Aumonier!' I said, looking utterly shocked. 'This is completely out of place. I will have words with them as soon as I return to the pits. In fact,' I went on, keeping my voice formal, 'I'll tell them to leave immediately!'

My response appeared to take Pierre somewhat off guard. For a few moments, he considered my response, whilst maintaining eye contact. Then, giving a brief nod he added simply. 'Very well, please see to it.'

I had urgently needed additional revenue to buy the Arundel and the idea for raising this, had occurred to me shortly after the abortive Monza race. I'd actually persuaded Eddie to part with the car for just fifteen grand, but I didn't have fifteen grand.

Terry, my sponsor, had been away on holiday and oblivious to the events at Monza until I'd broken the news.

He sat there stony faced as I relayed the end of the sorry saga of the Devron. 'I guess it was all predictable really!' He said. 'So where do we go from here?'

I breathed a silent sigh of relief at his use of the word 'we' and for the next half hour, outlined my past week of frantic activity.

'So...let me get this clear.' Terry said, now smiling. 'We're now going to have a press launch, after all...' he paused for a moment, head tilted to one side. 'But at no extra cost to us whatsoever?'

'That's right,' I agreed. 'It's the least we can do, given the problems of the past year. Everything's set for the twenty-second of May at the Dorchester in Park Lane, as long as that's okay for you?' Terry nodded. 'And the car will then leave for Le Mans immediately after.'

In reality, the Dorchester Hotel had agreed to give me the use of a function room at half price, but only providing I could use that date. My printers produced the glossy invitations for free, Moet et Chandon generously provided all the champagne and unknown to Jean Michel Jarre, he'd provided the evocative launch music, from his album Rendez-Vous, a sound destined to become our anthem for the 1986 season.

I handed Terry a package containing a hundred smart looking invitations, embossed with the Diamond Sound logo. 'Just one thing ...' I added. 'I was wondering if you might consider funding our promotion girls, at the launch and at Le Mans?' I slid over a glossy mock up of four scantily clad girls, in skin tight hot pants, bending provocatively over the side of the new race car!

It was just gone one in the morning and I was lost in my thoughts. Slumped against the pit wall, both mentally and physically exhausted, I was mulling over the past month's feverish activity, when suddenly the pit burst into life all around me. I leapt to my feet as the Arundel swept into the pits in a vortex of dust, having just completed its two hundredth lap.

I hinged open the door. 'What is it?' I yelled to Richard Jones, our number two driver.

'The clutch!' he yelled back, releasing his belts. 'It's fucked... gone completely!'

The Arundel had been running faultlessly, and had, despite losing laps from the broken throttle, been making slow but steady progress back up the field for the past seven hours. A number of retirements had aided its progress, including both ALD's which had been withdrawn hours earlier after losing their rear bodywork, due to aerodynamic problems.

Meanwhile, the pace at the front of the C2 pack continued relentlessly, with many of the cars running faster than last year's C1s, with an average speed of well over 124 miles per hour.

Richard stepped steaming from the car as our mechanics set about removing the Arundel's gearbox and replacing the clutch, a job destined to take over two hours. We were now hopelessly out of contention ... our new goal was simply that of finishing.

It was the early hours of the morning and I was standing in the pit lane as I listened to Rob's haunting words in my headset.

'Shit, Will! It's bad, really bad!'

I rubbed my temples, cursing silently beneath my breath. In the distance I could already see the plume of smoke rising on the far side of the track. 'Not again,' I said, remembering Driller Sheldon's crash a couple of years back in the Aston Martin. I turned to Simon. 'There's been another bad one!'

Clicking the transmit button on my headset, I asked. 'Rob, who is it?'

There was a few moments delay. Then between bursts of static, his sombre voice replied. 'I think it's one of the Kenwood cars, but there's nothing left of it! At least, whatever is left, is upside down and still burning.' For a moment Rob's voice was lost in a mixture of static and emotion, then in a chilling monotone he relayed. 'It's just after Tetre Rouge. It'll be a long pace car session... debris all over the place. Like a war zone out here... at least 100-metres of barriers down, trees burning everywhere.'

The BMW pace cars were sent out to shepherd the remaining field of thirty cars, as an eerie silence blanketed La Sarthe, bringing with it a chill icier than the night. Gradually, word filtered down the stunned pit lane. Jo Gartner, the popular thirty-two year old Austrian, was dead; everyone quietly restrained, the pits a sea of tight-etched faces. The accident stirred up all my unresolved nightmares. It evolved the Porsche's gearbox had seized, propelling the hapless Gartner at close to 200 miles per hour into the barriers, demolishing a concrete telegraph pole, before disintegrating over the next 200-metres, finally landing upside down in a ball of flames.

Haunted by the events of the night we all battled on, as the rising sun revealed a trail of subdued, exhausted teams. Gradually the Arundel was climbing further up the field, but we'd lost too many laps with the breakdowns to be in contention.

With the rays of summer sun warming our backs, I turned wearily to Simon. His face was ashen, his overalls black. 'Just five minutes left to go,' I said. 'We're running in seventh place. We're going to make it!'

As I spoke the fateful words, Rob's voice crackled in my headset. 'Will… I've got a dash full of warning lights! I can smell burning; smoke's filling the cockpit… there are sparks shooting out from under the car!'

'Is the engine running okay?' I yelled back into my mike.

'Yes … but something seriously wrong!'

'Rob, mate, listen to me… You've got one lap left to go! Don't pull off, keep it going!'

In that same instant, the radio died and the pit phone rang. I sprinted over, grabbing it from the cradle. 'Yes?' I shouted.

'The car's just gone past in a shower of sparks!' an anxious voice on the end of the phone yelled back. 'It looks like the battery's hanging out the bottom. It's scraping along the track. Marshals up here are going crazy. They tried to flag him down but he's just kept going!'

'Let's just pray he doesn't pull off,' I said.

Not knowing if he could hear me, I clicked the transmit button. 'Rob, if you can hear me, you've got a couple of miles left to go. We're seventh in our class… whatever you do, *don't* stop!'

The radio clicked. There was no reply, just static.

The whole Team was on the pit wall, eyes searching anxiously in the direction of the chicane.

Suddenly, thousands of spectators began invading the track as Derek Bell's leading Rothmans Porsche came into view.

At that moment I turned and sprinted down the pit lane to find Rob. Ahead, I could see marshals waving flags and spectators cheering, and there in the small group of finishers being shepherded into Parc Ferme, was a bewildered Rob Allen.

I pushed my way through the security cordon, rushed over and hugged him, as we both broke down. 'Well done, mate! We're twenty-second overall and seventh in class!'

Fighting our way back through the crowds, the ethereal amplified sounds of Jean Michel Jarre's *Rendez-Vous*, began echoing around the stadium. 'They're playing our tune, Rob,' I said. 'By the way, you do realize, we're actually the first all-British team to finish!'

'How d' you work that one out?'

'Well... if you exclude the foreign manufacturers, and the foreign drivers... oh, yes, and foreign engines, then we were the first *totally*, all- British team to finish: British car, British engine and British driver line up!' I grinned. 'Not bad, considering the car was just a bunch of bits in some tea chests four weeks ago!'

He smiled, then reaching out, patted my shoulder. 'Will, mate, you're so full of bullshit! Only you could have figured that one out.'

'But it's true!' I insisted.

* * *

The weeks since Monza, had cemented a bond of friendship I hadn't experienced since losing my best mate Des, all those years ago. From this point on, Rob and I became the best of friends, competing as teammates and circling the globe together; racing everywhere from Silverstone to Selangor, Hockenheim to Jerez.

40

"Rules are for the interpretation of wise men and the obedience of fools"

Colin Chapman

THE CONCLUSION OF the Devron court case earlier that year and our latest performance at Le Mans with the new car had returned something that I'd considered lost; a hope for the future. However, the effect of the settlement had also taken away something very precious. After paying the legal bills, buying the replacement Arundel race car, and now having to fund the preparation for all the World Championship races spread around the world, I was having to take ever more unknown rent-a-drivers, just to keep the Team on the road. I was beginning to build a reputation, but sadly not as a race driver, more as a low budget team owner, a manager and fixer; a person that could somehow make the impossible, possible... on very little money. Only occasionally now did I enjoy the battle thrill of racing myself.

Any recognition I did receive wasn't the kind I sought, and running a team definitely wasn't my goal; I wanted to drive, and I knew I could be fast. I'd already proved it. The trouble was, I was now entrenched in all the administration I hated; booking hotels and ferries, organising freighting, handling customs clearance, and all on top of finding the sponsors and organising their hospitality. By the mid eighties, I was typically working an eighteen hour day, seven days a week. For three years now, I'd circled the globe several times, more latterly with Rob, but he was usually the one driving and I was the one making it all happen!

Just finding the time and motivation to keep fit was becoming a challenge.

As each new pay driver arrived, handing over desperately needed funds, he'd then proceed to throw the car at the first barrier he could find. If the car wasn't smashed, a missed gear change would result in yet another blown engine, costing a further eighteen thousand pounds and I'd be back on the treadmill looking for more cash. I had never wanted to simply manage a team or stand around massaging the egos of other drivers. My idea had been that owning my own team would be *my* VIP pass to race in the World Championship, but it wasn't working out that way. It would take the events of the next two races to convince me to make a radical change of course.

It was the 30th July 1986 and following the 1500 mile journey from England, the Will Middleton race transporter weaved its way through palm lined streets in the searing heat of Southern Spain.

Rob and I had flown into De La Frontera airport two hours earlier, collected a Citroën BX hatchback from *Avis Rent a Car* and were now following the race transporter as it passed through the town of Jerez , acclaimed for its sherry, brandy, white horses and flamenco. Our little entourage made its way past the 11th century Moorish fortress and Cathedral del Salvador, directly to the track to prepare for the sixth round of the Championship, a 360km Supersprint.

It was the first time that the World Championship had featured a Spanish race and following our tenth place in the British round and our result at the Le Mans 24 hours, I did my best to hide my despondency at not driving. The truth was, the *Team* was progressing, and on a fraction of the budget of any other team.

Two days later

During first unofficial practice, the Arundel had been progressing well and, despite suffering from over-steer, the tail happy car was already posting very competitive times well into 1.48s. For the first time it looked feasible that we would be one of the top three qualifiers in our class. But then, as so often had been the case, fate intervened.

Simon removed the last bolts holding the gearbox in place and peered down dejectedly. Just half an hour earlier, Rob had rolled the Arundel back into the pits with no drive to the rear wheels.

It was now 3.45pm. 'The gearbox input shaft's shot,' said Simon, holding up a broken end of a steel shaft. 'And I know we definitely haven't got a spare,' he added.

'Do you reckon any of the other teams could be running the same unit?' I asked, already knowing the likely answer.

'It's unique,' he said, shaking his head, 'totally unique. It was designed specifically for the Arundel. I'm afraid this time, Will, we're screwed.'

Sitting at a bench in the pit garage, with both ends of the broken shaft now removed, I downed the last of my iced mineral water and finished tracing an outline with a pen as Simon held the sheared shaft down, forcing the two broken ends together with oily hands. 'There's just no way you'll ever get this done in time, Will,' he said gloomily. 'Official qualifying starts tomorrow at midday.'

I'd always enjoyed a challenge, particularly one that everyone else considered impossible. I took a certain pride in proving the impossible, possible. Anyway, I told myself naïvely, there's no way this was impossible. I'd already spoken with the company in London that had manufactured the shaft and they'd found the original drawings. All the measurements appeared to match up, but we had to be sure, hence the idea to fax over a tracing of the broken shaft. Once confirmed, they could produce a replacement in a couple of hours. The real challenge would be getting the thing to Jerez in time for official qualifying tomorrow morning.

It was just past 9pm when we received confirmation that the new part had been finished and was being couriered to the home of the Prescott family in Croydon, near Gatwick.

For the almost three hours, I'd been frantically phoning every travel company in the South East corner of England, desperate to find a holiday-maker flying on an early flight to anywhere in southern Spain. Finally I'd hit gold. The Prescotts were flying out of Gatwick at 6.40am UK time, and were due to land at Malaga two hours and forty minutes later. For a small incentive, Mr Prescott was happy to add our input shaft to his hand luggage.

Simon removed a map of southern Spain from the cab of the truck and for a moment the two of us studied the squiggly lines. At that time there were no decent roads linking Jerez and Malaga. Finally Simon spoke again. 'That's the route you want to take, Will.' He pointed to a road winding its way lazily up and around the Andalusian Mountains. 'Malaga's the big tourist resort, right over the other side of the range.'

'What about that road,' I said, pointing to an alternate, intermittent line that appeared much straighter, up and over the mountain peak. 'Surely that's a much shorter route?'

He frowned. 'I'm not sure … the dotted line means it's not a good road.'

Turning to Rob Allen, I asked, 'What do you reckon, Rob?'

He shrugged back. 'I don't think we'll make it in time, Will.'

Looking at my watch I replied. 'It's now 9.45. It'll take six, maybe seven hours each way. First qualifying doesn't start until mid day.' I glanced at Simon. 'We've got fourteen hours to get there, pick up the part and get back to the track. Come on Rob, the only limit to what we can do, is what we can physically do... we *can* do this!'

He returned a tight grin. 'Okay, if you reckon we can make it, I'll give it a shot.'

'Thirteen hours,' Simon butted in abruptly. 'We're one hour ahead in Spain. And remember, I also need to fit the thing. That'll take an hour at least, so at best you've got twelve hours.'

'That settles it then.' I replied. 'We'll take the straighter route. If we drive in relays, we'll be back here by 10am, 11 at the very latest.' I grinned, gesticulating with both hands. 'Come on you two ... what can possibly go wrong?'

It was already dark as the street lights vanished and the highway began narrowing to a single tarmac strip. Gradually over the next hour, the surface became increasingly potholed. Soon, the bumpy ribbon of tarmac became little more than a dirt track, as we sped our way further up the mountain. Swaying through ever tighter bends, the Citroën's complex suspension battled to retain control as the four wheel drive system scrappled for grip on the slippery grey shale.

I glanced at my watch, murmuring to Rob. 'We're *not* making good time!'

It was now just past midnight and we were still on the wrong side of the mountain, hurtling uphill at over 80 miles per hour along a rough track, with no safety barrier and a sheer drop-off on our right side plummeting to several hundred metres below. We'd been sharing the driving; doing no more than one hour stints as the paltry headlamps attempted but failed to illuminate whatever obstacles lay ahead. I was at the wheel when suddenly we became airborne. In the gloom of the headlamps I could see nothing, then moments later the Citroën crashed down, its front right wheel impacting with something very solid.

Switching off the ignition, I stepped cautiously from the car, hearing my feet crunching on the potholed ground, but all around was pitch black. I called to Rob to switch the headlights back on.

In the orange glow the damage became clear. The front right hand wheel was buckled, its tyre hanging from the rim. 'Shit!' I exclaimed, glancing at my watch. 'Quick, Rob, grab the spare and jack from the boot,' I said.

Rob's ghostly face looked back sheepishly. 'Err, Will...' he paused for a moment. 'Do you remember the other night?' He finally said. 'Err, you know... when we were mucking about, trying to get this thing to do doughnuts?'

'Shit!' I exclaimed again, as the memory flooded back. Rob opened the boot and I gazed down despondently at the mangled spare wheel. I was angry but not just at Rob. We'd both been equally stupid, hurtling the car around, failing to get the thing to perform doughnuts, sliding it this way, then that. It was then that Rob had hit one of the high curb stones, destroying a wheel. We had fitted the spare, then forgotten about it. Only now, stranded high up in the desolate Andalusian Mountains, looking down at the useless wheel, did the aftermath of our foolishness become clear.

'Well, that really is it,' said Rob. 'Now we *are* screwed... *and* stranded!'

'Hang on a moment...' I paused, trying to collect my thoughts. 'I've got an idea... this thing's a 4 wheel drive! Quick, get the damaged wheel off the hub.'

A few minutes later we were back in the Citroën, Rob in the rear seat, sitting as far to left as he could, in an attempt to counter-balance the weight. I pulled on a lever, and the Citroën rose obediently on its hydro-pneumatic suspension, like a three-wheeler on stilts. Gently I released the clutch, building up speed; 10mph, 20mph, 30mph... 'It doesn't handle badly,' I called optimistically to Rob in the back as we rounded another sharp bend, the three-wheel-drive scrabbling for grip on the unpredictable scree. Suddenly we were airborne again, this time the feeling of weightlessness lasting even longer, but moments later we were again crashing back down onto hard ground.

As we both stepped gingerly from the car, it was obvious this time, that the damage was terminal. Not only was the remaining front wheel hanging from its hub, but its wing was caved in against a large boulder. Even if we had a spare, there was no way of fitting it inside the jagged, crumpled wheel arch.

For a moment we exchanged worried looks. 'Well, at least no one can say we didn't give it a good shot,' I said dejectedly, slumping against the side of the car.

'Doubt *Avis* will see it that way,' added Rob, starring distractedly into the gloom. For a few moments neither of us spoke, then Rob said hesitantly. 'Can you see that? Up there in the distance?' he said, pointing as he stood. 'There's some sort of light!'

Standing up, I strained my eyes to see where Rob was pointing, staring into the blackness. 'Yes, you're right,' I finally said, excited. 'The light keeps disappearing. It must be vanishing behind low clouds. We must be near the top; I think that's got to be some sort of building.' A ten minute sprint in the thin air ensued before arriving at what appeared to be some sort of local hostelry. Crashing through the door, I yelled breathlessly to the small group of stunned locals. 'My name's Will Middleton... We're a world championship racing team, and we need somebody to take us to Malaga. *Now!*'

A withered old man was standing behind the counter. He turned his head slowly towards us, wispy grey strands of hair sprouting from either side of his otherwise bald head. With a mouthful of yellowing teeth, he smiled back knowingly – *Payday!*

* * *

Mr Prescott was a short, rounded man in his late thirties; an accountant by trade. He, his wife and their six year old son,

Marmaduke had never ventured beyond Brighton before and the Malaga customs had already proved to be a step too far. The family had been shocked after being apprehended and separated from each other by Spanish officials, then quizzed for almost an hour for importing an offensive weapon!

'I'm so, so sorry,' I replied, whilst attempting to prise the input shaft from Mr Prescott's trembling, sweaty grip.

'But ... they seemed to think it was a weapon, Mr Middleton!' He insisted, flustered. 'I tried to explain that it was for your racing car but they didn't believe it. Thank goodness you arrived when you did!'

'Just as well we did.' Rob chipped in, turning to Mrs Prescott. 'The next stage was likely to be a full cavity search!'

Her wide eyes registered alarm as I retrieved the shaft and firmly shook Mr Prescott's still shaking hand, at the same time depositing a fifty pound note discretely into his moist palm. 'Thank you and do have a good holiday,' I said sincerely, before sprinting for the exit.

Twenty minutes later, having complained bitterly to *Avis Rent a Car* about the unreliable nature of the Citroën that had stranded us high up in the middle of nowhere, we were again speeding back over the mountain range. It was now 9.50am local time. First official qualifying was due to start in just over two hours.

'We're not going to make it,' said Rob morosely as I crested a ridge at over 90 miles per hour. Half an hour earlier we'd reached the top and were now weaving our way down the eastern slope. On our left was a sheer drop into oblivion.

'We'll miss first qualifying,' I agreed, 'but the second session starts four hours later at 4pm, we'll make it for that.' I said, focussing intently on the rough potholed track, as all four tyres again left the surface.

The final crash happened almost an hour later, when we were less than an hour from our goal. Rob had fallen asleep and I could barely keep my eyes open. I hadn't slept for almost thirty hours. I woke to the now familiar feeling of weightlessness as our new Citroën took to the sky before crashing down heavily into another mound of boulders moments later. Wearily, we eased ourselves from the wreckage. I sighed deeply. 'Just as well we took out the optional excess waiver!'

Rob levelled his weary, bloodshot eyes in my direction. 'That's it, Will, you've tried everything... give up!'

At that moment I turned to see an old school bus slowly cresting the ridge in a cloud of diesel. Most of the windows had been removed, smiling locals clutching baskets of home produce, hens and goats as they protruded from the apertures. With adrenaline still flowing, I snapped out of my paralysis and sprinted over, frantically brandishing the input shaft at the startled driver. Taking a deep breath, I jumped inside and announced, 'My name's Will Middleton, we're a world championship racing team, and we have to get to the track. *Now!*'

Approximately four hours later

It was now just past 6pm and we were sitting in the back of the pit garage downing a welcome cold beer. Four hours earlier, we'd finally made it back to the track and Simon had fitted the part. With just thirty minutes of qualifying to go, Nick Adams had posted a 1.48.98, making us sixth fastest in our class.

Simon handed me the clipboard. I drew in a deep breath, staring at the figures in disbelief. Only now, after the nightmare sprint over the mountains and Nick's gallant flying last laps of qualifying, did reality hit me. 'I reckon we'll be out of fuel and out of the race by two thirds distance,' Simon announced flatly.

'But why is it using so much more than the other engine?' I asked.

'We'd calculated everything based on the newer engine,' he explained, 'fitted with the later spec Lucas injection system. This backup one's only got the old mechanical style metering unit. It's about twenty percent less efficient.' He shrugged, giving me one of his hard, steady looks. 'I know it's not what you want to hear, Will, but if you want us to be there at the end of the race, we'll need a later spec engine, and we need to fit it tonight.'

After blowing our good motor at the Norisring in Germany four weeks back, we'd fitted our old backup and it had run fine at Brands Hatch only a couple of weeks back.

'Can't we just swop the Lucas system over from the blown engine?'

Simon sighed. 'It's not that simple, Will. The newer one has sensors everywhere, and the whole thing was set up by Nickelson McLaren on a test bed. If we try to cobble something up with bits from both engines, it'll never run properly and could use even *more* fuel.'

'There's just no way I can find another engine tonight.' I said. Then a thought hit me: *what about the sponsors*. I shifted uncomfortably as another thought drifted into my head: *the drivers!* Rob and his co-driver, Nick Adams, had just paid – they'd kill me if I suddenly had to admit we'd no chance of finishing, even before we start.

'There has to be another way,' I said my breath now tight in my throat.

Simon gave me a wry smile and gestured with his beer in the direction of our refueling rig. 'You're into electronics, aren't you? Isn't there a way of controlling that damn thing?'

Lost in my thoughts, I strolled out of the garage and over to the pit wall, gazing out at the expanse of tarmac, its surface rippling in the fierce heat of the Spanish sun. *There has to be a way,* I told myself. *There's always a way…* I glanced over at our refueling system, a tall metal tower with a hundred litre safety cell at the top. Beneath was a cutoff valve and flow rate sensor which fed the refueling hose. The latter was linked to a control box with a digital display, indicating the cumulative total of the fuel used. During each pit stop, whilst drivers and tyres were changed, the refueling hose was plugged into the car and seventy litres of high octane fuel transferred in around sixty seconds. Monitoring each refueling stop and recording the output on the counter was an official scrutineer provided by the organizers.

In my mind's eye, I could see how the digital device worked. Fuel running through the refueling line spun an impeller, sending pulses calibrated to the rate of flow to a microchip which counted the signals, presenting the output in litres on the digital display. At that moment an idea hit me. I wandered back to Simon. 'Simon, could you carefully remove one of the magnetic reed sensors from the transporter's alarm system?'

There was no doubt that my idea would circumvent all the fuel regulations, but then everyone bent the rules, didn't they? It happened at the highest level of motorsport: It was generally felt, for instance, that the FIA had always biased rules in favour of Ferrari. And the big F1 teams were always bending the rules – only recently it had become known that Williams had been using a "special" fuel provided by Elf, without which they might never have won the Championship. In a previous year, Ecclestone's Brabham team had developed the illegal "fan car" and Colin Chapman's Lotus team had introduced a blatant cheat to hydraulically lower their car to within a centimetre of the track, increasing ground effect and cornering speed.

Some fans referred to all this as cheating, others that it simply bent rules. Whatever it was, it wasn't allowed and without doubt broke regulations. But then, I told myself, a race on the track wasn't simply a contest between drivers, it was also a competition between teams who constantly strove to outwit each other's ingenuity. With the big teams, finding ways of getting around rules cost millions of pounds and employed the cunning of highly paid designers and engineers. I had no budget left whatsoever, so I needed to be creative – my idea would utilize a *coffee cup* and a few bits of electronics from the trucks alarm system. I justified all this in the belief that nobody liked fuel restrictions, which only served to slow down the racing. And anyway, after forty hours without sleep, I wasn't about to let a stupid fuel economy rule stop us now.

41

"It is the nature of ambition to make men liars and cheats, to hide the truth in their breasts, and show, like jugglers, another thing in their mouths, to cut all friendships and enmities to the measure of their own interest, and to make a good countenance without the help of good will."

Sallust

T HE SEARING HEAT had already pushed temperatures way into the hundreds as the grid formed up behind the pace car for the start of the 360 km Supersprint. We were expecting the run-up to the first corner to be thrilling, especially as a pace car had to pull off just before the pit straight, allowing the entire field an unchecked 500-metre dash to the official green light.

I watched from the pit lane as the pack blasted past, racing well before the official start. Gianfranco Brancatelli in the Brun Porsche and Derek Warwick in the Silk Cut Jaguar went first and then Eddy Cheever in the second Jaguar shot through on the left as Larrauri slew off the track in a cloud of dust. Brancatelli was hugging the inside line into the second gear first corner, as Warwick turned in on the outside line, cutting across the Italians bows, the two cars contacting heavily. Derek, already on the limit, spun off wildly into the gravel trap, as Brancatelli slid directly in front of the remaining pack. As everyone fought for track space, weaving their way through the mêlée, I closed my eyes in silent prayer; *don't throw it away now Nick... please! Not after all this!*

The previous day, in the dying moments of qualifying, Simon had fitted the new input shaft and Nick Adams had qualified us sixth in class, but as a result of the first corner skirmish, he'd moved up two places. As Oscar Larrauri surged into an impressive lead, damaged cars pitted and Nick continued his fight through the field.

We'd planned our first stop for lap twenty, and as Nick shot into the pits, Ian stood by with the refuelling hose as Rob secured the strap under his helmet and prepared to take over. No one, other than Simon and I, knew what was about to happen. Irrespective of the battle on the track, if my coffee cup ploy failed, we'd be out of fuel and out of the race by the three-quarter distance mark.

A bespectacled steward with a clipboard in hand was already standing in place, pen poised, preparing officially to monitor the stop and as the Arundel slewed to a halt in a cloud of brake dust, a choreographed dance began. Ian inserted the refuelling hose into it's coupling, whilst John, simultaneously, plunged the vent bottle into an identical fitting on the opposite side, to collect the expelled volatile vapours from the Arundel's fuel cell. Simon darted around checking tyres whilst Nick secured Rob into the six point safety harness.

Whilst all the frenzied activity continued, I stood next to the refuelling tower, nonchalantly sipping an espresso from a delicate cup, every so often replacing the tiny cup carefully against a minute mark opposite the digital fuel counter. Each time I lowered the cup, Simon, who was scrutinising my every move, yelled a distracting command to our bewildered pit crew, causing the bespectacled steward momentarily to divert his attention.

Inside the cup was a small magnet, borrowed from the rear door of the race transporter, and each time the modified cup was placed in the vicinity of the fuel counter, it activated a hermetically sealed reed switch, which I'd inserted in the counter's circuitry (also taken from the trucks security system). As the reed activated, it changed the pulse multiplication rate, slowing the display and ultimately, the accumulative total of fuel shown on the display.

As Rob exited the pits leaving tramlines of black rubber, the steward returned his attention to the digital display. Pausing only momentarily, his curious brows rose above his spectacles as he noticed the impressive fuel economy of the Arundel. He turned to me as if about to query the figures. There was a moment's hesitation before he shrugged and turning back with an obliging nod of satisfaction; he inscribed the figures into the appropriate column on his clipboard.

Simon furtively followed me to the back of the pit garage. 'Well?' he asked.

'Well ... the official recorded figure was twenty litres,' I said, trying hard to hide the grin that was spreading across my face.

'Yes, yes...' Simon insisted, '...but what actually went in the tank?'

'It's difficult to be exact,' I replied. 'The cup changes the pulse multiplication by a factor of three, but only when it's next to the counter. I think I put the cup down three or four times, so I reckon we got around twenty, maybe thirty, extra litres of unrecorded fuel.'

By the quarter distance point, Gordon Spice in the Listerine sponsored car, had pulled out a full 30 seconds lead in our category, but then, following a pit stop, a severe misfire developed, resulting in an unscheduled return to the pits. During this time, the Arundel continued making good progress through the field.

By three-quarter distance, we'd managed furtively to add around sixty litres of extra fuel without difficulty, the last stop working particularly well. I'd just downed the dregs of my latest espresso and having not slept for almost two days, was buzzing nicely. Carefully placing the cup accurately in place, I watched as Ian inserted the refuelling hose. Suddenly, as if on cue, Roy Baker's Tiga in the adjoining pit obligingly exploded into a ball of flames! With its rear body section engulfed and high octane fuel still pumping into the Arundel, our bespectacled official fled for his life as we surreptitiously added an extra, unsupervised thirty litres, before Nick returned to the track.

Everything had been going so well, when suddenly a blast from the warning siren drew my attention to the pit entrance, where the Arundel was now limping slowly towards us, the camber of its front right wheel wildly askew. Simon directed the car into the pits and Ian and John removed the nose, as Simon bent over the wayward wheel. 'What is it?' I yelled above the cacophony of klaxons, air hammers and Jan Lammers Jaguar powering past on the pit straight .

'Damn pin's sheared off in the top of the upright!' Simon shouted back.

I turned and sprinted to the transporter for a spare, as he quickly removed the broken unit. The repairs were destined to take a full thirty-five minutes, losing us thirty-three laps, dropping us back down the field into last place.

In the dying stages of the race, Nick Adam's frustratedly shot from the pits, desperate to climb as far back up the field as possible. We watched from behind the wall as he set a blistering pace, almost two seconds below his qualifying time, but all to no avail. As the chequered flag fell, Oscar Larrauri secured first place in the C1 category, with Gordon Spice winning our C2 class. Despite all our efforts, and regardless of finally finishing fifth in our class on the track, we were officially unclassified, having lost too many laps in the pits for repairs and fuel stops.

My Jerez fuel trick had been a means to an end, no more. A way of keeping the sponsors and drivers happy, and getting the car on track to the finish line, but it was not the way I wanted *my* Team to race. I wanted to beat everyone on equal terms; with ingenuity perhaps, but definitely *not* by cheating, and I also wanted to be *in* the car, not *behind* the pit wall! Jerez was the only time I'd employed trickery to achieve a result on the track and I hated the way it felt ... dirty and deceitful. I decided that, in future, if I didn't have the equipment or means to compete honestly, I wouldn't compete at all.

If our dance with death over the Andalusian Mountains, and the fuel problems that had ensued hadn't been sufficient incentive to re-valuate my career path, the Fuji race that followed two months later certainly was.

By late September, despite our minuscule budget, we were running 12th in the C2 World Championship. Having spent weeks negotiating with new sponsors, I air freighted the fully rebuilt Arundel race car, now with the engine updated to the latest Lucas specification. Half a ton of spares, including two extra input shafts, and a small army of volunteer mechanics, also flew to the other side of the world, to the Mount Fuji circuit in Japan.

A few days later on 5th October, I helped strap in our paying Japanese superstar. Only days earlier, he'd arrived with six thousand pounds of Japanese Yen in a shiny black briefcase, bowing as he handed over a neatly typed note saying *"I speak no English!"* After three abortive attempts to drive out of the pit lane, each resulting in a stalled engine and the burning smell from a potentially damaged, triple plate carbon clutch, costing over a thousand pounds, I opened the door and pointed at the rev counter.

'More revs!' I shouted, trying to compete with the sounds of the track. *'More! More!'* I repeated, pointing at the 6000 mark, gesticulating upwards with an open palm.

A pair of slanted eyes stared back at me through the narrow slit of his helmet. 'Ah, wakattayo,' his helmet nodded in acknowledgement. 'Liyo, ryokai sitayo,' he replied.

'Yes, more! *Lots* more!' I agreed and clicked shut the door.

'Does he understand?' asked Simon in frustrated alarm, his eyes fixated on his baby.

'Well, he seemed to,' I shrugged, hands outstretched in an expressive gesture. 'At least he nodded in English!'

I signaled for the mechanic at the back of the car to plug in the starter mechanism again, then standing at the front of the Arundel using hand signals, I indicated to our driver to switch back on the high pressure fuel pumps, giving the rear mechanic the thumbs up. Moments later the expensively updated engine roared into life. Again, using hand signals, my index finger sweeping around like a rev counter needle, I indicated more revs to the Japanese driver. Checking the pit exit was clear, I stepped aside and gave a sweeping motion to go.

The engine hit around 14,000 revs before he released the clutch, later verified by a Nickelson McLaren mortician. The car leapfrogged forward leaving intermittent tramlines of molten black rubber. Within metres, the right driveshaft shattered, firing shards of steel through the body work like javelins. A loud bang emanated from the gearbox, indicating the internals had disintegrated in protest. I winced, then turning to Simon, my eyes closed in despondency, said simply, 'Time to go home!'

* * *

A life traveling around the world for this type of fiasco was no longer fun. Had my master plan failed? If it had, it was hard to accept and what's more, I'd already committed with backers to compete in the 1987 World Championship. It would take a last season of rent-a-drivers, gearbox failures and blown engines, before I reluctantly accepted the inevitable.

Finally, following a gearbox failure in the 1987 Le Mans 24 Hours, I made my way despondently into the offices of Diamond Sound, giving my all too familiar update to Terry.

'We're just not getting the results this way,' I said.

'I know,' he replied, 'and we rarely see you in the car, Will,' he added. 'At the end of the day, it's *you* we're backing, *not* some unknown driver on the other side of the world.'

'I'd like to suggest a change of plan for the 88 season, that is, if you're prepared to stick with me for another year.' I said, pulling out an artist's impression of a sparkling new car, decked out in the Diamond Sound livery. 'I know this isn't what we'd originally planned, but with spiralling costs in the World Championship, it would dramatically reduce outlay and mean we'd no longer be reliant on rent-a-drivers to supplement the Teams overheads.' Terry gave an uneasy frown but I continued, 'Without having to provide endorsement space for the driver's sponsors, we could increase your exposure to almost double and at the same time reduce the budget by over half.'

He nodded back, thoughtfully, 'And you'd be driving in *all* the races?' he asked.

'Yes, I'd simply turn up and do what I know I can do; *win!*'

'But I thought you wanted to compete in the world series?'

'I do Terry, and I will, but I don't want to be a bit player any more, I want to be a *big* player. I want to make a name for myself as a driver and to do that we've got to be winning. We'll never win this way, but if I can prove myself as a driver in the national series, I'm certain that with the contacts I now have, I'll get a competitive drive in the following year's World Championship.' I hesitated, as an idea hit me. 'And I'll give you an undertaking to carry your Diamond Sound logos on my overalls for the rest of my career, regardless.'

For the next half hour Terry listened as I outlined my revised plans, the winter sun filtering its way through the big office windows. By the time I left, he'd agreed the deal in principle and a week later it was endorsed by the board. It was simple and straightforward. Diamond Sound would pick up the bills for me to join the David Mercer Harrier Team next year. They'd also cover my travel and living expenses for twelve months. For the first time, all I would have to do was to keep fit, turn up and drive. I was now thirty-one years of age but this shift would form the start of my most ferociously competitive season in racing.

42

---

*"Insurance: An ingenious modern game of chance in
which the player is permitted to enjoy the comfortable conviction
that he is beating the man who keeps the table*

Unknown

THE SOUNDS OF A manoeuvring farm vehicle jolted me
awake. The season had ended a couple of weeks earlier
and the late winter sun was streaming through gaps in the
curtains. Disorientated, I pushed myself up and stared at my
watch: past 10.15, I'd slept late.

Swinging my legs round, I slipped out of bed, found my clothes
and quickly dressed. In the background I could still hear the
nearby rumble of a heavy vehicle moving something on the
roadway. I strolled over to the window and pulled back the
curtain. Just below, I could see our neighbour the farmer,
unhitching a massive articulated farm trailer from his tractor
which was now spanning the entire entrance to our home,
effectively blocking all entry. For more than eighteen months he'd
been a thorn in our side, causing problems wherever and
whenever he could. Regularly he'd block access to lorries that
were attempting to deliver supplies for our building works, and
he'd created months of delay to the laying of water and gas
services, objecting to each and every planning request. He peered
up now from beneath his peaked cap and, seeing me at the
window, he tapped his forehead, then raised a single digit as a
gesture in my direction.

I called out for Beth, at the same time sprinting downstairs to see what he was up to. 'What are you doing?' I asked, reaching the farmer.

'Just parking me grain trailer for the winter,' he replied in a matter-of-fact tone. 'Not a problem to you, is it? Doubt I'll need it for a few months!'

'Obviously it's a problem,' I replied angrily, 'you've completely blocked our driveway! Nobody can get in or out!'

'It's a private roadway, son. And I happen to own the roadway.'

'No you don't,' I replied calmly. 'You are a tenant farmer and have access to your farm building via this roadway in the same way that we have right of way to our home.'

He ignored me and continued unhitching the trailer. 'Farmed this land for twenty years and I always park it up, down here over the winter.' He turned to climb back up into his tractor. 'Have a nice Christmas!' he said.

Seething with irritation, I grabbed the back of his coat, pulling him down. 'Move it!' I said. 'Now!'

'Fuck off! It's a private road.' he replied, pulling himself free. 'I can park it wherever I want on me own land.'

Hearing all the commotion, Beth had arrived. She was heavily pregnant with our second child. 'Will... what's going on?' she called, squeezing through the tiny gap between a gate post and the trailer.

'Our friendly farmer's decided to park this thing across our driveway for the winter,' I replied, barely able to contain my anger.

'But why?'

'Cos I don't need it, missus,' he replied gruffly, 'that's why.'

'But how do we get in and out?' Beth asked, perplexed.

The farmer shrugged theatrically, wiry brows lifting. 'Not my problem missis, is it?' He turned and again attempted to climb back onto his tractor.

I'd already put up with more than one and a half years of this nonsense; at that moment something snapped. Grabbing him by his shoulder, I spun him around and grasped hold of his thick plaid shirt. 'Move it!' I bellowed.

Turning, he pulled my hand from his shoulder.

'Pick on somebody your own size,' a voice hissed from directly behind.

I swivelled round, ducking by pure instinct as a hefty fist missed the side of my head by millimetres, its force rippling the air. It was the farmer's son. Without thought, I unleashed my left fist directly into my attacker's solar plexus, the complex network of abdominal nerves. The effect was instantaneous. He buckled, the air leaving his lungs in a single gasp. With his weight off balance from his initial punch, I grasped his quilted green jacket by its lapels, pulling him forward, and in the same instant spinning around, dropping to the ground with my full weight, everything happening in a blur of movement. At that moment his body lifted, and a split second later, he crashed back down on the hard concrete roadway. He lay immobile, his face drained of colour.

'Whooho,' I exclaimed, straightening back up, barely missing a beat, 'did you see that, Beth... I've still got it!' I said panting from adrenalin. I turned grinning, my face dropping in shock at what I was seeing. 'Beth! I shouted, too stunned to process what was happening. Latched onto the farmer's back, her legs were wrapped around him in a vicelike grip, her hands clasping tufts of hair like reins as she battled to stay on board whilst counterbalancing her bump which was threatening to unseat her.

'What the hell are you doing Beth?' I exclaimed, suddenly noticing that the farmer, who was struggling to retain balance, had a heavy paving slab held above his head.

'He was trying to hit you over the head with it!' she yelled frantically, still clinging on.

Two hours later I was being addressed by a pair of serious faces. 'I'm sorry, sir,' insisted the taller of the two police officers, 'but there's nothing we can do. That is, unless Mr Adams decides to press charges for assault.'

'*Him* press charges against Will!' exploded Beth. 'What about us?'

The shorter officer gave Beth a tired smile. 'Your neighbour has complained that your husband exited this property,' he made a show of flicking a few pages of his notebook, 'at approximately 10.15 this morning,' he went on. 'At which point your husband allegedly made a serious and unprovoked attack on the persons of Mr Adams and his thirty-two year old son, whilst they were going about their daily business.'

'This is utterly crazy.' I said. '*He* barricaded off *our* driveway with a trailer... it's still there! You can't have missed it!' I added sarcastically. 'It's why you couldn't get your police car onto our drive!'

'Yes, sir,' replied the taller officer calmly. 'We have noted the location of the farm vehicle.'

'Look, I may have lost my rag, but I think it's understandable. He's being doing stuff like this ever since we moved in. Anyway, I didn't assault him or his son. It was his son who threw a punch at me. I simply defended myself.'

'I'm afraid that conflicts somewhat with Mr Adams's statement of events, sir,' replied the taller officer.

'I bet it does,' Beth breathed with derision.

The officer turned the might of his full attention to Beth. 'I'm sorry madam, I didn't quite get that,' he replied dryly.

'He was trying to hit my husband over the head with a paving slab!' said Beth firmly. 'He could have killed him. What would you have done then? Argued that it was just a dispute on private land?'

'That would have been a different scenario, madam. I'm not aware that your husband has been injured. As I've explained, we can't become involved in neighbour disputes.'

'We've never been in a dispute with the man!' I insisted. 'He seems to have some sort of issue with us.' I retorted.

'And why might that be, sir?' enquired the shorter officer.

'He thinks I tricked him out of buying this place, about eighteen months back, at an auction.'

'And did you?'

I paused. 'No... No, I didn't. I just bid more than he did... could... more than he could have bid.'

'Well, as I say, this is clearly a neighbour dispute, sir, and we can't get involved.'

'But he's completely blockaded our driveway.' Beth repeated. 'We can't even get our car out of the drive. How does my husband get out to work? And what if there was an emergency? What if there was a fire? The fire brigade wouldn't be able to reach the house!'

'It's a private road, madam, so as I said before, there's nothing we can do.'

'This is ridiculous,' said Beth, her voice serious. 'I'm more than six months pregnant, what if we need to get to hospital in a hurry?'

'In those circumstances, madam, I would suggest you call for an ambulance.' The officer replied pedantically, turning to go.

'But how can they be allowed to barricade our driveway and stop us from getting in and out of our home? That can't be legal!' I retorted.

'That's a matter you'll have to take up in the civil courts sir.'

It was destined to take a further three months of legal wrangling, before our friendly farmer relented and moved his trailer. We now had a court order, preventing him from blocking our right of way, but the process had cost us over one thousand pounds and caused considerable stress and even more bad feeling.

Over the past two years, we'd painstakingly worked to convert the barn into a family home, moving more than a hundred tons of building materials, mostly by hand. Windows, lighting and drainage had all been installed. The property now had heating, a large kitchen and its own purpose built gym, but was still far from finished. Despite all our hard work, the farmer's attitude overcast our happiness, leaving us unsure of where our future lay.

It was May 1987 and a new racing season was about to begin. Eight weeks earlier, Beth had given birth to our second son, Jonathan, who'd entered the world golden-haired and blue eyed with a defiant cry. 'He's the absolute spitting image of you!' Beth had said.

It had been around five years since the crash at Brands Hatch and in my selfish attempt to blank out the memory, I'd never returned to visit Paul at the hospital and, as a result often felt guilty. But my irrational superstition still fed off that crash. Superstition: *a belief that one event could cause another to occur, without any physical process linking them.* It was a curse that had affected me since childhood. My mother had always been a *very* superstitious lady, and would regularly rebuke us: *'Never walk in front of a black cat!'* she'd say, and *'Don't let a black cat cross your path!'* There were a lot of black cats in Cavendish Place, and as a result of my fear of what *might* happen, I'd often arrive home late to further chastisement, having battled to outwit the frightful felines.

'*Never open umbrellas indoors or somebody will die!*' My mother had also warned me, and '*Don't leave a hat on a bed or something terrible will happen!*' ... '*Don't walk under ladders*' ... '*Always knock on wood and cross your fingers*' ... '*If your right hand itches, it means money's coming in, but if it's your left hand it means money will be going out!*' It was all completely irrational and yet despite this, much of my childhood was spent throwing salt over my shoulder to 'undo' bad luck.

Based on this same childhood dread, I'd avoided driving green race cars since the Brands Hatch crash ...as vehemently as I avoided black felines. And there was something else; I'd never walk over or near a disabled parking bay, for fear of ending up in a wheelchair, like Paul.

Now, five years on, only rarely did my reoccurring nightmare return, but my suppressed fears, fed by my superstition lived on. *What if something else happened to me, something worse*, how would Beth cope? Unknown to Beth, in the space of just eight weeks, I'd witnessed the deaths of two top drivers, Manfred Winkelhock at the Mosport race in Canada and then weeks later Stefan Bellof at the Spa race in Belgium.

I was sitting at my desk in the office wading through a pile of post. I'd left the bank statements until last, dreading that the figures would be worse than expected. Finally, I slipped open my WPA bank statements and studied the columns of figures. I was surprised; both accounts were in better shape than expected and one was actually in credit. I was about to bin the two envelopes when I noticed the first circular poking out. Pulling it from the envelope, I studied the bold heading on the glossy sales leaflet: "*Guaranteed acceptance for all WPA card members regardless of occupation!*"

"You never know when the unexpected is going to happen, that's why you need to be covered now and why we'll reward you for acting promptly with one month's free cover if you apply before the end of the month!"

Beth pushed open the office door and placed a fresh pot of coffee on my desk. 'What do you think of this?' I asked, handing her the first leaflet whilst removing and studying the second similar looking flyer. 'It's supposed to pay out in the event of an accident, injury or sickness.' I said. 'It would cover things like the mortgage if anything serious ever happened.'

'Would they cover you?' Beth asked. 'Bearing in mind what you do for a living.'

I shrugged. 'It says acceptance is guaranteed for all card members, regardless of occupation. WPA's a gigantic company, Beth. I certainly think it's worth considering,' I suggested, glancing back at the second WPA policy. 'This one's for legal cover,' I commented looking back up. 'It would cost us another five pounds per month.' I thought about the past years of legal troubles. 'It could have saved us a grand on the hassles with our friendly neighbour. It even says it covers against criminal charges!'

Beth took the leaflet and studied it for a moment, her head cocked to one side as if thinking. She looked up. 'Will, something like this could have saved us *tens* of thousands of pounds on that Devron court case, if we'd had cover at the time.' She took a deep breath as if unsure whether to continue. 'I don't like to think of anything bad happening, but I don't know what I'd do if something did...' She hesitated for a moment, and then added softly. '... and there's also our boys to consider.'

Standing up, I took the two leaflets back and signed the acceptance. 'What's thirty pounds a month,' I said, 'if it gives us peace of mind and security?'

It was a decision made in seconds that would ultimately change our lives forever.

43

"Sometimes opportunities float right past your nose. Work hard, apply yourself, and be ready. When an opportunity comes you can grab it

Julie Andrews

Sunday 24th July 1988

TWO WEEKS EARLIER I'd received an unexpected call from Roy Baker offering me a drive in the World Championship race at Brands Hatch.

The Baker Team were a low budget operation, not dissimilar to my old setup of the previous four years, and for all of thirty seconds I'd been a little hesitant.

The fact was, I'd moved on. And to date, the '88 season had been the most successful of my racing career. From the first moment I'd stepped into the Mercer Teams Group 6 prototype, I'd been riding a wave of adrenalin, winning races and breaking lap records in the National series.

After years of being a nobody, I'd at last found a place to shine. Suddenly everyone was cheering and congratulating me, smiling at me, officials placing garlands round my neck. *'Will, I'd no idea you could drive!'* Roy had exclaimed. *'You're a bit of a dark horse, aren't you?'*

I wanted to return to the World Championship at some point, but only in a team that was capable of running at the front, not another low budget team with an inferior car and unreliable engine, struggling to qualify.

Despite my reservations, the thought of driving a powerful Group C car again, sent a nervous rush of exhilaration pulsing through me, making the hairs on the back of my neck rise in excitement. I also realised, that at my age I was running out of time. This was after all, an opportunity to return to the World Championship, purely as a driver. It didn't take me long to consider the offer.

'So, you're definitely on to drive, Will?'

'Absolutely Roy.' I replied. 'Who's my co-driver?'

'An American chap, his name's Andy. He's driven for us a few times in the States.'

***

The previous day had been official qualifying, and we'd flown the forty minutes from the Old Granary to the track in the helicopter. Unfortunately, Harry, my sponsor, hated flying; so today he'd insisted on driving Beth and me to Brands Hatch in his Citroen. After almost two hours of heavy traffic, we arrived at the rear paddock entrance, still in good time and well ahead of the spectators. It was 8am and the roar of distant racing engines echoed round the amphitheatre in the crisp morning air, beckoning us.

Just ahead, the signs on the chain link fence warned all that entered, of the dangers of motor racing. Ben, the security guard stepped from his hut and waved us through. I made my way to the circuit office and handed over my race licence and FIA Medical to the official for checking. The girl scanned the documents and handed me a track waiver for signing. With the formalities over, I set off down the pit lane to find Roy.

After yesterday's rain drenched qualifying, Sauber Mercedes had taken front row with Mauro Baldi on pole, Jochen Mass lining up alongside in the sister car. The ultra competitive Silk Cut Jaguars had surprisingly been bumped to fourth and sixth.

I donned my red, white and blue Nomex overalls, freshly embroidered with Saunier Duval and Diamond Loudspeaker logos, pulled on my Nomex race boots and made my way to the pits.

I was annoyed that in yesterday's qualifying, Andy had managed to squeeze almost .8 of a second more out of the car than I had, placing us twenty-second on the grid. I reminded myself I had not driven one of Roy's Tigas previously, whereas Andy had been racing it regularly for him in America. It had also been wet during most of my qualifying session.

Roy strolled from the pit garage and extended an oily hand. 'Will, I've been thinking; I'd like Andy to start.'

'But the deal was that I would start!' I replied indignantly.

Roy gave a dismissive shrug. 'I know, but it's going to be a wet race; Andy knows the car. I'd like him to do the first stint and you to do the morning warm up.' Roy was being diplomatic; what he meant was that Andy was paying a lot to drive, and had also been the fastest in qualifying.

Brands Hatch was a difficult home circuit which I knew very well. Roy had reasoned that Andy, who had never seen the track before, should have the bulk of the qualifying time. Trouble was, that left me with only a handful of laps in the wet, to qualify myself in an unfamiliar car.

'Roy that's ridiculous!' I exclaimed. 'Andy's never driven in a World Championship race before. He doesn't know what to expect from the C1 drivers. He's out of his depth to start with.'

He gave an expansive gesture with both hands. 'Then it's up to you to talk to him.'

I felt Roy's decision was wrong, but I was new to the team and there was no point in arguing. Anyway, at least I was going to get a few extra laps in the warm-up session, this time in the dry.

I crawled into the cramped cockpit, snapped into the sixpoint harness and pulled on my helmet. Roy's voice crackled over the headset. 'Just five laps to scrub the new tyres. Then straight in.' His stream of staccato instructions continued in short bursts over the next few minutes interspersed with bouts of static. 'Don't take it above 9000 rpm, watch the top end with the lower ratio.' He concluded.

I flicked on the ignition and pumps, signalling to a watching mechanic. The rev counter flickered as the engine roared into life, sending a tingle of excitement running down my spine.

The Tiga handled like a pig but I kept my foot down, knowing the track adhesion changed halfway through Clearways. As the rev counter climbed to 8500, I snatched fourth gear and the counter registered a drop of 1500 revs. My neck muscles strained to hold my head upright against the invisible forces tearing at my limbs, as the momentum carried me hard through the corner. The tyres suddenly found traction, launching me down the pit straight.

The pit board indicating "L4" flashed past on my right as I began my final lap. Scorching the straight, under the gantry, up and over the brow, 160 miles per hour, 8900 revs. Exploding onto the brakes, I flicked the Tiga at the apex a little later than usual, my front right wheel climbing up over the kerbing, causing the back to step out. Downhill sparking embers exploded from beneath the car, as it bottomed out, wisps of smoke churning through the venturis.

I hit the brakes, into second gear, 7000 rpm. The Tiga drifted out of the 180 degree hairpin downhill, using the downward momentum and shortened gearing to shift straight into fourth gear – damn! The rev drop was too high, a loss of more than 2800 revs. I punched the brakes, into third for Surtees, as the car switched from understeer to power oversteer, twitching wildly. Down the back straight into Hawthorns at 170 miles per hour, the water temperature climbed to 100 degrees; five degrees into the red. *Just three more corners to go*, I told myself. Dingle Dell flashed by as Martin Brundle edged past on the inside in the TWR Silk 'cat'. I glanced at the gauge, where the temperature was now registering one hundred and five. One more corner to go. Third gear into Clearways for the last time, 110 degrees, 8700 rpm. I grabbed fourth at the apex as the impetus carried me wide across the track, past Roy holding the pit board with a bright yellow 'IN' in four-inch letters. I checked the mirrors and lifted immediately, the tell-tale needle registered 9400 rpm. Shit, I'm going to get a rocketing!

The radio crackled in my ear, 'Will, that was a 1.25!'

I knew it was going to be quicker than my previous times, but then my wet qualifying session had been a joke. Anyway, a 1.25 still wasn't quick compared with current times. But for a two-year-old Tiga, fitted with the smaller engine, it wasn't bad. Had I been given a few extra laps in qualifying, we could have moved six places up the grid, just ahead of Rob Allan. I grinned with satisfaction; nine whole seconds quicker than Andy!

Later that same day

The mechanics busied themselves making final adjustments, as Andy, swathed in Nomex, sat at the wheel of the Tiga, sucking a chilled isotonic drink through a tube protruding from his helmet. Roy fastened the safety harness, plugging in the radio link and medical oxygen which would provide twenty seconds of life-conserving air to Andy in the event of a fire.

The grid was lined up ready for the first of the scheduled 240 laps, a distance of 624 miles, equivalent to three Grand Prix. We'd planned for Andy to pit on lap fifteen to refuel and for me take over. The klaxon sounded and more than fifteen thousand horsepower of engines roared into life.

Mauro Baldi led the pack behind the pace car for the rolling start, the entire pack weaving frantically to generate heat into their tyres ready for when the pace car pulled off and the race proper began.

The lights changed to green, Baldi botching the start allowing Mass through into Paddock Bend first, ,with Jelinski second, Baldi now trailing third. By the second lap, Andy had moved up four places and was closing on his next target, but by lap eight, the leaders were poised to lap the back markers.

Mass in the Sauber Mercedes shot through Dingle Dell, down towards Clearways, preparing to lap Andy in the Tiga. Seeing the Sauber Mercedes looming large in his mirrors, Andy moved left to allow Mass through – a serious error and something he should have known. Whilst one should never block the race leader in such a situation, it is *their* responsibility to find a way safely though the pack. Travelling off line at over 80 miles per hour Andy hit the debris scuffed from everyones tyres. The Tiga instantly veered sideways as Andy fought for control and in doing so, inadvertently closed the gap that Mass had already committed to. Bang! The Tiga struck the Sauber's left rear, the car slewing as it turned, scorching molten black strips across the track. The tyre wall exploded as the Sauber hit, the impact tearing out the engine, causing an instant flash fire before pitching the car high into the air and back across the track. An instant later, Mauro Baldi in the sister car arrived on the scene narrowly missing the carnage by throwing his Sauber into an impressive 360 degree spin before stalling in the middle of the track. The Silk Cut Jaguars driven by Niesen and Lammers threaded their way through the mayhem into second and third place.

I turned to Harry, my sponsor, who was standing in the pit lane, waiting expectantly for me to enter the race. 'I think Andy has just lost Mercedes the World Championship. It might be time to make ourselves scarce.'

While the track was cleared, the yellow caution flags were put out. Roy's men collected the Tiga and urgently set about rebuilding the front end, a task destined to lose us more than thirty laps.

Mauro's car was fortunately unscathed but lost two laps as a result, also needing to replace all four flat-spotted tyres. A very shaken Andy appeared in the pit garage, hotly pursued by Jochen Mass. 'What the hell do you think you were doing out there? Are you blind?' A TV crew sensing blood, arrived to film the commotion. I felt sorry for Andy. He looked lost, shaken, embarrassed. 'Don't you have fucking mirrors? You shouldn't be out there if you can't drive! You could have killed me!'

For a minute I thought Mass was going to physically lay into Andy, things were getting out of hand. Roy had clearly been wrong to allow him to take the start but how many times in the past had I allowed myself to be persuaded by a fat wallet...when there are crucial bills to be paid.

Roy ran from the pit garage. 'Will, get your helmet on. We'll be ready for you in five minutes!'

The Tiga had handled badly before, now it was really scary; still capable of nearly 200 miles per hour but with a tendency to 'sledge', as the raised ride height caused by the accident affected the under-body air flow and thus the car's ability to stick to the track.

Gradually, I fought my way back up the field, finally finishing thirteenth despite additional dramas on the last lap. At the approach to Clearways, the scene of Andy's downfall, the right front wheel decided, at around 120 miles per hour, that enough was enough. Detaching itself completely from the still mangled hub, the wheel bounced its way over the pit wall, fortunately missing mechanics and teams. Somehow, perhaps aided by my trial run over the Andalusían Mountains in the Citroen, I managed to retain control, completing the last 500-metres as the fastest three-wheeler in Brands Hatch history. It had not been a good day and despite finishing, the officials decided not to classify the result as the mechanics had pushed the damaged Tiga back to the pits following Andy's accident.

Roy helped me out of the car. 'Will, you drove well today. I want to talk to you about Sandown, the Australian race at the end of the year. I'd like you to drive for us again.'

Wow! I thought. Australia, eh... sun, sea, racing cars and perhaps a stopover in Malaysia for a nice holiday. Perhaps it hadn't been such a bad day after all.

44

"Where there is discord, may we bring harmony.
Where there is error, may we bring truth.
Where there is doubt, may we bring faith.
And where there is despair, may we bring hope.

Margaret Thatcher – Prime Minister
Mandate to reverse the UK's economic decline

Sandown International Race Track, Melbourne, Australia, 4 Months later

A VORTEX OF DUST spun in eddies as I swept into the pits and killed the engine. Unclipping the safety harness, I peeled off my Nomex gloves and unfastened my helmet strap. A mechanic inserted an airline into a socket beneath the Tiga's screen and the car rose up onto its jacks. Roy hinged open the door, and I eased myself from the cockpit into the bright Australian sunshine. 'Seventeenth fastest,' he said, smiling. He handed me a clipboard, 'And sixth in class,' he added.

I briefly studied the time log before handing it back. 'I was around two seconds a lap faster on the stiffer setup,' I said, removing my helmet and balaclava. Beth had been helping Rob with timing my laps and she stepped over, smiling. We kissed and I handed her my helmet.

'It'll be easier to drive in the race, especially in over 30 degrees of heat,' Roy added encouragingly. 'And remember, this is a sprint race, it'll be over two hours of racing.'

The pit tannoy interrupted us, 'All world sports car drivers report immediately to the area beneath control tower.'

'What's all that about,' I asked, as Rob Allan strolled over with his new girl friend, Anna. She was in her late twenties, tanned, slender and very attractive. 'Press and organisers want some promotional piccies,' Rob said. 'It's mandatory, so you'd better get a move on.'

Beth handed me a towel and a bottle of cold water. I downed half the bottle in a single swallow and towelled dry my hair. 'You need to move it darling,' she said, reaching up and sweeping a fringe of hair from my eyes, 'they're been calling everyone for the last five minutes.'

Rob helped Roy and the mechanics push the Tiga backwards into the garage as Beth and I made our way along the pits to where a large, curious throng had assembled. The TWR Jaguar drivers, Jan Lammers, Eddy Cheever and Johnny Dumfries, had all changed into freshly laundered race suits, proudly displaying sponsor's Silk Cut logos. Others, having already changed, simply wore casual street clothes. The picture was to be formally posed and officials were hurriedly directing everyone into position, most of the taller drivers were already standing at the back, the shorter ones seated at the front. Martin Brundle rushed over and slumped down on the ground, directly in front of Jean Louis Schlesser. I was ushered into place in the centre of the back row next to one of my former co-drivers, Nick Adams. Mauro Baldi and Jochen Mass were seated in front on the middle row. I glanced over to Beth, positioned behind the photographers, tightly holding onto the hand of our young son, George. They both smiled back proudly.

Standing there, smiling at my little family, it was impossible to ignore the missing drivers that had so tragically been lost in the past years: Manfred Winkelhock, killed during the Mosport race in Canada, Jo Gartner, killed at the Le Mans 24 hours, and Stefan

Belloff, the driver who'd secured the 84 championship on this very track just four years ago, killed in the Spa race in Belgium.

What is it that makes us do what we do, I thought. *What in our past forges our character, driving us to this point in our journey?* I suppose we all had our own stories of battles occurring along the way. For the next few minutes I just stood there, savouring the moment, halfway between a dream and reality, gazing ahead as the officials finished staging the scene. For a few minutes more we all stood there in silence as the army of photographers clicked away, recording the event for prosperity. I thought of the days to come, tomorrow's race, and then next week's holiday in Malaysia. *Our hotel has stables,* I thought, *I'll be able to ride along the beach* – I could hardly wait!

Click-whirr, click-whirr, click-whirr, click-whirr... the cameras continued recording the scene.

Smiling out at them I was reminded of my old school photos, the memories surfacing in my brain like battle scars. For a moment I reflected on those days, and my old cynical masters, Wickham, Brewer and Jenkins. I thought about the journey that had bound Beth and me together and brought us to this place, a journey that would defy the understanding of most. Watching her and little George smiling back, I knew at that moment that I needed them far more than any fame this uncertain life might bring – family has meaning; it transcends ambition, wealth, and fame, far more enduring than glory, it's the greatest gift on earth.

Thinking back, I remembered my earlier days, the wild nights of boozing with my best mate Des at the Queen Ann and our pranks all those years ago. *Poor old Des, with no family,* I thought, and wild Ching Lan, both long since gone. I thought of the struggles that'd occurred along the way, my businesses, the races and the conflict with Devron that had been instigated here in Australia four years ago, almost bankrupting Beth and me. The crackle of a race engine firing up broke my thoughts. Looking back at the photographers, I could already feel the pull of next season, the lure of a new battle. For that I needed a big team and that meant finding that elusive *big* budget ... but I was already working on that.

Ever since Thatcher's meteoric rise to office almost a decade earlier, releasing the full power of the market economy, British business had fuelled my career and the powerhouse, the financial sector, was my big hope for next year – I was confident I'd get it.

Yet, despite that optimism there was *something* in the air, I could sense it. I'd always been that way, intuitive, somehow able to foresee when something was coming – like a canary sensing bad air in a coal mine. The difficulty though, was knowing when to *trust* those feelings. Whatever the mood I was sensing, it wasn't there all the time, but it *was* tangible, and as the eighties were drawing to a close, I could feel *something* was building... like a pressure cooker about to explode.

Maybe it was just the media creating scare stories, I told myself. With the recent scoop of a major hedge fund losing a massive $1.6 billion, the financial markets, the engine of Thatcher's new economy, were starting to get twitchy.

Looking out at the photographers as they continued clicking away, I dismissed any thoughts of doubt; I had to have complete faith in the future. Tomorrow's race day I reminded myself, then our holiday and then we'll fly home for Christmas with our boys.

Standing there in the back of the line, surrounded by champions and future champions, I had a brief feeling of happiness, daring to dream of what the future would bring...

Also from John Bartlett:
Chequered Justice... the story continues.
It's more than just a novel – I was there...

Praise for Chequered Justice

"A chilling tale set on the twin tracks of motor racing and justice, exposing the hazardous pit stops of one against the systemic pitfalls of the other, in which truth becomes the loser."

Michael Mansfield QC – Barrister for the Birmingham Six miscarriage of justice appeal

"As bold and innovative as its author, Chequered Justice gives the reader a breath-taking guided tour of race-track suspense, lifts the lid off lethal insurance brokers, exposes the bent nature of law enforcement, and dives into the depths of emotional whirlwinds, I loved it"

Howard Marks – aka Mr Nice

"A fantastic read whether you're a racing fan or not – a proper page turner... highly recommended!"

Ed Foster, Associate Editor, MotorSport Magazine

"...a compulsive read... could well have a future on television or ...even a movie."

Leslie Phillips CBE

"Very occasionally a book comes along that is hard to put down, and this is one of those."

Tim Vicary – Author

"Ex-racer John Bartlett's first novel charts the nightmare of wannabe racer Will Middleton as an insurance-indemnity scheme rebounds on him. Sinister high powers seem to be plotting against our hero, as the tale often veers into 'faction'..."

Haymarket Publishing – Autosport

"...Chequered Justice... a chilling Kafka-esque tale that sees the hero, who begins with a confidence in his own innocence and an absolute faith in the fairness of the British justice system, frustrated and defeated at every turn... The dust jacket for Chequered Justice claims the story is "inspired by true events". If even a 10th of this book is true, we should all feel very afraid indeed."

The KM Newspaper Group

"5 Stars... [Chequered Justice] ... exudes conspiracy and corruption, and will do a thoroughly good job of making you lose faith in the system – a system that appears to be controlled by powerful individuals with agendas that most of us could never remotely envisage. ... I can't recommend Chequered Justice enough. It's definitely more reality than fiction... isn't it?"

Motorsport Musings

"I would recommend this book for the plot... be concerned about the corruption that is portrayed in Chequered Justice, be assured it really does go on!"

Inside Time

"A fantastic read whether you're a racing fan or not – a proper page turner... Highly recommended!"

Ed Foster, Associate Editor – MotorSport Magazine

Prologue

Childhood never ends. The games just get bigger.

Old English proverb

THIS WAS THATCHER's 1980s, the era of the young corporate whiz-kid, the yuppie; the time when individual bonuses easily topped a quarter of a million pounds. Companies had been growing exponentially and hostile takeovers abounded. The euphoria had been infectious and it was an incredible time for an up-and-coming racing driver to secure corporate sponsors. Merger mania and leveraged buyouts had generated phenomenal sums as companies raised massive amounts of capital by selling junk bonds with a high risk of loss but also an irresistibly high rate of return for those willing to gamble.

With total disregard of risk, and looking only to satisfy shareholders' hunger for bigger and bigger dividends, the pension and insurance industries had gobbled up their share of junk bonds, the billions of pounds generating further hostile takeovers as the bubble continued to grow. It had been the banner time for the stock market, everyone apparently winning. But if everyone had been winning, it meant nobody was losing . . . so money had been generated from nothing. No one had wanted to consider the obvious, that the bubble might soon burst; logic had spiralled into a black hole of delusion.

Will and Beth had been home almost a week when Ned, Will's broker, arrived at the Old Granary. The bell in the hall rang and Beth opened the door. 'Good morning, Ned,' she said, as she took his coat. 'Will's in the lounge. He's not in a very good state.'

'How did all this happen?' Ned asked with a genuine look of concern.'

'He's done something to his back falling off a damn race horse! We were in Malaysia having a few days' break before returning home after the Australian race.'

Will was wrapped in a blanket, heavily sedated and lying as flat as possible on an old grey recliner. Glancing up, he grimaced as a fresh spasm of pain lanced through him – his lower body felt as though it had been set in a rigid cast. The day was damp and overcast which seemed to only exacerbate the pain. A fire crackled in the grate. In the corner of the room a computer hummed, its screensaver bouncing a multicoloured cube endlessly around the confines of the small silver screen.

Will grinned at Ned but didn't attempt to rise. 'I wasn't even moving when I fell off the bloody thing!' he said, reliving the agonising moment in his mind, with all the locals dashing around the accident scene. It happened in a moment, but those seconds were to run endlessly through his thoughts, like a series of still frames in a movie. Coming directly to the point, he added, 'I suppose I'm insured?'

Ned sat down, flipped open his briefcase and began shuffling pages of small print.

'Oh yes. Comprehensively. It's just that, well . . .' Ned looked past Will and for a moment he seemed distracted. 'You know, "back injuries"'

'You don't say!' Will replied dryly with a lift of one eyebrow.

Ned shrugged. 'Sometimes insurers like this just don't like paying out, and currently the industry is not in good shape.'

For more than fifteen years, Ned had worked extensively in the shadowy world of the exclusion zone, before finally setting up his own brokerage in the sleepy town of Arundel. 'This type of accident policy was devised back in the boom period,' he went on. 'Thatcher's recession was never anticipated and risk to the underwriters was considered to be very small. If I submit a claim that's when we'll find out how good your cover is.'

The door of the lounge swung open and Beth deposited a pot of coffee and plate of shortbread biscuits on the table. Will drew in another uncomfortable breath. 'Ned, I don't have much choice, I can hardly walk, never mind drive a racing car. I'm likely to be out of it for weeks, if not months. I'll have to put in a claim.'

'I'll get onto it first thing tomorrow,' replied Ned, 'but be prepared for delays. The staff in the claims departments are little more than paper pushers, it's their job to review applications and if possible reject them there and then. It may take a lot longer than you think.' He added ominously. 'They're a bit of law unto themselves.'

It would take a further six months before Will was, incorrectly, cleared to race again, but that mistake was just the beginning of the nightmare to come.

It was the end of the 80s and the country's buoyant economy had already turned; the era of the yuppie had come to an end. The Maxwell pension fund reported hundreds of millions of pounds missing and other similar funds were said to be on the verge of collapse. Endowment policies, designed to pay off mortgages and provide lump sums for retirement were found to have been mis-sold and worthless. Likewise, the junk bonds wolfed down by the insurance and financial industries were living up to their name.

The entire British financial system was sliding beneath a sea of debt and appeared set to take everyone down with it. More than fifty thousand businesses a week were now going bust and the insurance industry, with its fingers in many of these financial pies, was even being sued by its own underwriters. Claims were running into hundreds of billions of pounds. In short, this was the start of a massive increase in claims and a dramatic drop in profits, a time of huge redundancies and record unemployment.

Underwriters and shareholders had to be accounted to, very powerful people were due to take hits. Inevitably those making claims would suffer, but it was a sacrifice the industry was willing to make.

1

I read the newspaper avidly. It is my one form of continuous fiction!

(Arthur Christopher Benson, English writer, 1862–1925)

October 1992

THE WAPPING PRESSES never ceased. The press hall occupied an area the size of a football field, housing sixteen massive machines; the noise, heat and smell were oppressive, particularly in summer. The presses were living, breathing monsters, consuming millions of kilowatts of power each day, existing on sensational stories and the misery of others; stories of sex, sleaze, murder, politics and political spin. There was a never ending supply; today was just another edition.

It was the night shift, a balmy October evening, the busiest time; more than three million copies of Britain's favourite tabloid had to be printed, cut, collated and distributed before dawn.

By midnight, front pages would be sent by courier to every 24-hour TV news channel, allowing each to present a quick review of the next day's headlines to an audience greedy for gossip, desperate for sensation and fresh scandal.

The printer's routine had not changed in the past fifteen years. As he'd done countless times before, he flicked a switch on his console. Overhead a conveyer whirred, diverting a finished tabloid from the main belt, a few seconds later it rattled down a chute into his booth. He opened a page at random; it was page 3, it usually was page 3! He scrutinised the colours, the alignment and the curvaceous body of some nubile eighteen year-old with brand new silicon breasts. He felt guilty and quickly scanned the page for something else, something short: *'WPA Bank pays racing driver £4000 for bouncing cheque'*. Huh, he thought, how many of his cheques had his bank bounced, and each time charging him for the privilege. He scanned the short article, checking for print density and quality, ignoring the content.

Lee Burton was twenty-eight, short, trim and ambitious. It was 9.30 am, a little early, but he wanted to be prepared. He slipped on his jacket, straightened his tie, and collected the claimant file and the newspaper he'd purchased that morning. Stepping into the lift, he was whisked up to the executive floor. An hour previously he'd sent a memo to his boss, the head of claims, but within minutes it had been relayed to Alexander P. Finnigan, the Chairman and Chief Executive of the WPA Group.

Nobody liked it when Alex Finnigan (Fin behind his back) got involved, but following the BBC exposé, there was little choice. Fin's reply had bounced back almost instantaneously:

Meeting, my office at 9.45 today. Tell Burton to bring the article and the claimant's file. I need hard evidence that Middleton was working during the currency of the claim; send in surveillance, we will need to attract the interest of the police.

Fin had been chairman of the WPA Group for more than twenty years. At almost seventy, the ravages of a stressful city life were written into every pore of his being. He sat in his darkened office hunched behind his cluttered desk, his face wrinkled like an old leather bag. Behind him, resting on ornate Corinthian columns, perched two globes, one celestial, and the other terrestrial. On the wall hung a portrait of his father, the former chairman.

A visit to Fin's office was not generally considered a pleasurable experience, but following his discovery, Lee relished the thought of making his triumphant entry. He had been working in the banking division of WPA for more than eighteen months but this was his first break. He had been responsible for agreeing the out of court settlement, but after reading that the claimant was a racing driver, out of curiosity he'd punched the claimant's name into WPA's main database. What he found was intriguing. The claimant was supposed to be out of work, and according to the computer he was claiming on a WPA PPI policy, yet the newspaper said he was racing endurance cars.

A secretary showed Lee in and shut the door firmly. Fin worked in the shadows; nobody outranked him. He liked solitude and closed doors, it gave him a sense of security. Myopic eyes and an overbearing glare were augmented by a pair of heavy horn-rimmed spectacles. 'Sit.' He spat the word without lifting his eyes from his desk, as though to a dog. There was no offer of coffee, no good morning and certainly no word of congratulation. So much for the triumphant entry, Lee thought, beginning to feel a little less confident.

'You have the article?' Lee handed over the tabloid, the heading reflected in Fin's thick lenses: *'WPA Bank pays racing driver £4000 for bouncing cheque'*. Fin, his nose only inches from the story, appeared almost to sniff the words from the page.

The WPA Bank yesterday agreed to pay racing driver Will Middleton damages of £4000 for incorrectly bouncing a cheque valued at just £18.00. Will, who lives in a half million pound manor house, complained to the bank when the cheque, payable to his local corner shop, was mistakenly bounced. When a second cheque was also bounced in error within days Will, who races sports prototypes in the World Endurance Championship, threatened legal action. WPA, who claimed it was due to a computer error, settled out of court.

In the brief time since receiving Lee's memo Fin had done his research. The claimant was out of work and WPA's redundancy division was being shafted for the monthly mortgage payments.

They were also picking up the monthly finance on the family's car; the claimant seemed to have too many convenient WPA PPI policies. He was clearly insolvent, no savings and all bank accounts were heavily overdrawn. A quick check showed he'd also had an on/off claim running with WPA's sister company for a back injury. Fin scanned a confidential internal report on the back injury, mumbling to himself as he inhaled the words, 'He's broken his back!' If that was true, the claimant was potentially eligible to claim a hefty lump sum. Fin turned back to the newspaper article. *If his back is broken, and he's out of work, claiming to be redundant, how is he racing at all?* A vicious grin touched his lips. He put the paper down and fixed Lee with a glare, then repositioned his horn-rims for a look of self-importance.

'You signed off on this settlement?' it was a rhetorical question; Fin already knew Lee had authorised the settlement. He went on, 'This claimant is seriously in debt, hanging on by his fingernails. He was close to bankruptcy, he needed a shove, the heat turning up, not a handout! There was no way he could have sued us.'

'But he *was* suing us . . .' Lee responded, 'with a WPA Legal Cost policy.'

Fin's complexion changed from its usual pallor to a fetching crimson, his lips quivered. 'He was suing us using one of our legal costs policies?' he seethed, his words catching in his own saliva.

Lee took a deep breath. 'There was no other option, it was checkmate Sir. Either we settled, or we went to court paying both his and our legal fees. Combined costs would have been four times the settlement figure and we would have lost the case anyway. We have no defence for bouncing his cheques; at the time his accounts were inside approved limits.'

Fin swept away Lee's reply angrily. 'Cases are not won or lost on evidence alone. More that some lawyers are smart, others not. This unknown racing driver is having a laugh at our expense. He's claiming for both injury and redundancy . . . how? He doesn't know his back is broken, only that he has an injury of some kind. Our policies contain wonderfully nebulous words, it's called small print. Use it!'

'But he has a claims negotiator, and they suspect something; they are asking for the report,' Lee insisted.

'An ambulance chaser who thinks he's a lawyer,' Fin replied with a curt wave of his hand, fixing Lee with a cold stare. 'You're confident this Will Middleton is the bastard who set off the BBC Consumer Alert fiasco?'

Lee nodded. 'Absolutely, we know for a fact; he warned us in a letter that he'd written to the programme, there's a copy in the claim file.'

For a long time Fin said nothing. To Lee the darkened room chilled, the walls appearing to close in; even the books, files and very fabric held their breath, waiting for Fin's response.

Over the years Fin had woven his network like strands of an invisible silk web; strands that extended in all directions throughout big business, manufacturing, retail, pharmaceuticals, the City,

the legal system, police, and even a few judges; decent people who could easily be persuaded. Hands could be shaken, backs scratched, words dropped in the ears of willing officials at Lodge dinners.

Fin began softly, as if the room might be bugged, 'Do not release the specialist's report, it's ours. Bury it and find reasons to delay the redundancy payments, turn up the heat and stop paying his bloody car finance.' His voice rose. 'I want that car repossessed, I want him watched, I want to know everything. I want all the dirt, every skeleton, all the background, his family, where his kids go to school, the lot. If he scratches his fucking ass, I want to know!'

2

A police officer who carries out an investigation, invariably and properly, forms a view as to the guilt of the suspect. Having done so, without any kind of improper motive, he may be inclined to shut his mind to the evidence telling against the guilt of the suspect or to overestimate the strength of the evidence he has assembled.

(Sir Cyril Phillips, Professor of Oriental History and architect of the Crown Prosecution Service. Reproduced from *The Case for The Crown* by Joshua Rozenberg)

January 1993

THE HOUSE WAS LARGE and the surveillance had been difficult, at least that's what he'd told Fin. The private detective worked from a small terraced house in Kent and had spent almost three months on the case, hiding in the shadows, rummaging through the rubbish and talking to the locals. He'd even tracked the target's wife each day as she took the kids to school in their bright blue Mitsubishi. It had been a long and profitable job, but costs didn't matter. WPA had deep pockets and their instructions had been clear. 'Get the evidence!'

His close watch team, no more than shadowy shapes unseen by the target, had been called in as a last resort after two months of stake-outs by no fewer than three other surveillance operations, each resulting in assertions that the target appeared completely genuine. It was not what Fin had wanted to hear. WPA was a worldwide organisation, the principal provider of payment protection, the target was simply a claimant and a troublemaker.

The target had appeared a little shorter than the detective had been led to believe during Fin's briefing which was odd. The target's hair was darker, which was also odd but of minor relevance. What was important was that the spooks had secured the evidence that the others had been unable to unearth. Clearly they'd uncovered a nice little fraud. The target was obviously fit despite claiming both injury and redundancy payments from WPA. The report the detective had produced confirmed that the target was out every day exercising horses and mucking out the adjoining stables. For a small additional fee the detective could provide Fin with video evidence of the crime. It was conclusive proof that the target couldn't be injured.

On the 18th of January 1993 the detective faxed his report to Fin's office at WPA and within days edited highlights, prepared by Fin, went to an appropriate contact within the Metropolitan Police. Days later a raid would take place, followed by a trial to determine the guilt or innocence of the target. But well before that, an inconvenient discrepancy would be found in Fin's report... the detective had been watching the wrong family!

Climping, Sussex, approximately 9 months later

Will shivered; it was a cold, dark, unfriendly October night. He wrapped his jacket around him tightly and checked his watch; it was 6.15 pm. His two sons were with the sitter and his wife was working late; he knew he wouldn't be disturbed for at least another hour. He opened the fridge, selected a bottle, discarded the cork and placed the bottle to his lips, downing a quarter of the wine in a single swallow.

In the garage, he collected the garden hose and stuck one end into the exhaust pipe of the Mitsubishi, running the other end through a crack in the rear passenger window. He got into the car, took another deep swallow from the bottle and started the engine.

He felt miserable, yet strangely relaxed, suddenly much calmer, as if all the fears of the past months, the accusations of the private detective, the police taunts and hints, the raid and suspicions, had just been lifted. Soon he would be dead and the physical world with all its pain, would cease to exist. Everything that had been Will Middleton, his thoughts, hopes, dreams, the love of his wife Beth and his children, would simply fade away.

The faces of the detectives flared up in his mind like whispering demons, their sneers and words had haunted him for months: *'You're going down Will, you'll see . . . Admit it Will . . . you're just making it harder on yourself.' 'Perhaps we should take a look at your wife's involvement then . . . If we arrest her as well . . .' 'One might have to consider the custody of your children. Why put them through all that Will? All we want is an admission. Save everyone a lot of heartache! '*

Will had expected the case to be dropped the instant the private detective's mistake had been discovered, his faith in British justice being so strong, but for some reason these officers had decided to run with it and they wanted a result. It was as if he'd slipped through a gap in reality into a nightmare. Suddenly he was the criminal; hearsay, gossip and rumour abounded, endorsed by the very system he had grown up trusting and had always believed in.

Will knew he'd done nothing wrong, but the investigation had been the final straw financially, and had already destroyed the new race team, despite the result at Zolder. More than any of that, his family, totally innocent bystanders, were being threatened, dragged down with him. Perhaps with his death they would avoid the humiliation that would otherwise follow.

His eyes streamed as he wrote his goodbyes to Beth. His writing was scribbled, spidery, barely legible. He loved her so much, oh how he'd loved her; could she ever understand, he thought. He felt so very sad, but he couldn't go on any longer. It seemed that for some reason he'd been singled out as a scapegoat, but to bring him down these officers were prepared to implicate Beth, and even to take away their two sons.

He prayed to God to forgive him and inhaled deeply. Holding in his breath, he exhaled slowly. He wanted to die, to drift slowly to sleep, to see his father again. He gulped another quarter of the wine.

The engine continued humming but nothing seemed to be happening, he just felt slightly drunk. He stumbled to the back of the car. The hose had fallen out and lay coiled in a loop on the ground. He quickly stuffed it back into the exhaust and returned to the driving seat.

At last it was working, he was dying. The agony would soon be over. The pipe behind his head emitted strange bubbling sounds and the windscreen misted over, rivulets of silver condensing, then streaking down like rain. Sparkles of white light flared around him as the noxious fumes permeated his lungs. In his mind, his wife's smiling face appeared and he felt his heart pound. The air was moist with exhaust; the stench of death thickening with each minute, every breath gagging in his throat. He took a last gulp of wine and emptied the bottle.

Suddenly the passenger door opened and Beth jumped in, a big smile on her face. 'Hello, darling! Where are we going?' Her gaze swept around to the hose poking through the rear window. 'Oh my God! Will!'

Will had planned a private suicide, just turn the key and drift off to another, less hostile world, but for some unaccountable reason Beth had decided to finish work more than an hour early that night. He leaned against her shoulder, broke down and wept as they hugged and cried together. He felt embarrassed, like a naughty schoolboy caught raiding the fridge. Later that evening the family doctor prescribed anti-depressants. Together Beth and Will vowed to fight on, to get through the ordeal as a family.

The trial, set for 11 months' time, had proved to be the death knell for the fledgling race team. Over the weeks that followed, all that remained of the ill-fated Trans-Atlantic project was gathered up and meticulously packed away, like discarded toys that had lost their appeal.

Everything was going to have to go and that included the Sierra 4x4 estate car. Will cast an eye over the impressive Trans-Atlantic graphics and the still shiny metallic paintwork. It was worth little more than scrap, he told himself, having been seriously damaged, its back end destroyed when a local farmer accidentally slammed his Land Rover into the parked car one rainy day just a few weeks earlier.

A loving hand touched his shoulder. 'Come on darling, dinner's ready.' Will looked over at the two primary assets of the team, a pair of Lola Indy racing cars, proceeds of the Zolder race.

They had just been returned from workshops in Weybridge where they had sat in storage since Trans-Atlantic's last race just two months earlier. 'It's all going to have to go,' he said in a mournful voice, glancing back to Beth. 'You never know, if we're lucky it might just about clear the team's debts.'

Will went over to the scarlet, day-glo Lola T86 Buicks. One of them still bore his name on its carbon bodywork. They looked as beautiful today as when they'd been collected almost a year earlier, like a pair of Formula One cars that had overdosed on steroids. He lifted the rear body panel and for a moment examined the 3-litre Buick V6 turbo engine, capable of producing more than 800 horsepower on full boost.

Will replaced the engine cover and threw a dust sheet over each car in turn, then tapped a four-digit code into the security pad at the front of the garage. A motor whirred into life and the twin-roller shutter doors descended, curtains closing on a final act.

Coming next: Beth's story – By Mary E Bartlett

A Step Too Far... the story continues.

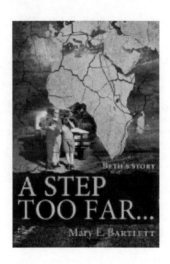

About the Author

JOHN BARTLETT left school at 15, profoundly dyslexic, with an undistinguished academic record, a dream of becoming a racing driver and his headmaster's last salvo: *'You will never amount to anything'* ringing in his ears. At 18 he set up his first business, an electronics company, in a shed on an industrial estate and within 2 years was employing 25 people and driving his first classic Aston Martin. In 1979 he turned his back on security to focus on his childhood dream. From little backing, he rapidly secured major sponsorships propelling him into the World championship. Within four years he'd established his own World Championship Le Mans team and qualified as a helicopter pilot. Six years on, with the country sliding into recession, he suffered a life changing accident, leading to a massive legal battle. Never one to miss an opportunity, he turned tables on the legal system, turning his story into the Number 1 bestselling legal thriller: *Chequered Justice*. When not writing, John, now a Master Scuba Instructor, trains divers near his home in Maidstone, Kent.

Some say, to coin a phrase that *Dark Horse* is the story of John's journey. All we can say is that it's one hundred percent, unadulterated fiction... *honestly!*